C000010112

BORN
DIGITAL

PRAISE FOR BORN DIGITAL

'*Born Digital* covers a lot of ground in reviewing social tech 'weapons of mass distraction'. An important read for parents, caregivers, educators, policymakers and industry. In fact, for anyone concerned about the impact of technology on our children, and in turn, on society.'

Professor Mary Aiken, author, The Cyber Effect

'One of the signature issues of our times. SO much at stake – entirely dystopian scenarios at one end, and yet the potential like never before to nudge society to a better place (but who gets to decide and do the nudging?!). Keen insights. Urgent questions. For friends, parents, colleagues – and indeed for members of the *Born Digital* generation.'

T. S. Anil, CEO, Monzo Bank

'*Born Digital* is brilliant, factual and really reaches deep into the behaviours of Generation Z. From screen time before bed to cyberbullying and mental wellbeing. A must read. Highly recommended.'

Jack Parsons (twenty-five), CEO, The Youth Group

'Technology companies are not neutral and their design choices shape our lives. Starting with this unarguable premise, *Born Digital* raises provocative and interesting questions amidst a hotly contested debate on how we should set new rules of the road.'

Neil Berkett, Chair, NSPCC

'Business leaders seldom reflect on the causes and consequences of social change. *Born Digital* is a searching and critical analysis of the profound impacts of new technologies on business, politics and society.'

Steve Brammer, Dean of Bath University School of Management

'Gen Z have embraced the Smartphone as "their" technology. Robert Wigley's well-researched and timely book highlights the challenges and opportunities for business and government.'

   Roger Parry, Chairman, YouGov PLC

'*Born Digital* holds up a mirror for my generation and calls humanity to reset its relationship with technology. A powerful mission that is both important and overdue.'

   Fritz Lensch (twenty), Founder, G25 and Neonseeds (group of young leaders aiming to create a sustainable and peaceful world)

'A timely contribution to the debate about the role of technology that is overdue. *Born Digital* combines Robert Wigley's experience of leading regulated businesses in rapidly changing environments with that of being a father to teenagers to provide a useful perspective for policy-makers and industry leaders alike.'

   Andrew Griffith MP, former Chief business adviser to the Prime Minister, No. 10 Downing Street and UK's Net Zero Business Champion

'Big Tech has transformed our lives in so many positive ways, but now it must also take responsibility for tackling its negative impacts – or face the consequences. *Born Digital* is a powerful and timely wake-up call for us all.'

   David Grayson CBE, Emeritus Professor of Corporate Responsibility at Cranfield School of Management and Chair of the Institute of Business Ethics

'*Born Digital* is written by a businessman not a neuroscientist, but it accurately describes the way big tech has employed neuroscience to hook its customers. Everyone who wants to understand how their attention is being hijacked should read it.'

Professor Dan V. Nicolau, PhD, author of The Naive and Sentimental Neuroscientist *and co-founder of neuroMONSTER.org*

'Many of us reading *Born Digital* will recognise the traits and behaviours it analyses, but all of us will understand them better when we have read it. Robert Wigley brings a parent's concern and a business leader's experience to this authoritative exploration of one of the defining policy challenges of our time.'

Jeremy Wright MP, Secretary of State Department for Digitial, Culture, Media and Sport, 2018/19

'Tech giants don't just have their fingers on the scales in the battle for our attention. They're sitting on them. This reality is expressed with unusual clarity in *Born Digital*, along with the implications for kids' development and wellbeing in an online ecosystem overwhelmingly focused on extracting monetisable attention at any cost. Robert Wigley has made a timely contribution to a generation-defining debate.'

Oliver Hayes, Policy and Campaigns Lead, Global Action Plan

BORN DIGITAL

The Story of a Distracted Generation

ROBERT WIGLEY

First published in 2021 by whitefox

Copyright © Robert Wigley 2021

The moral right of Robert Wigley to be identified as the
author of this work has been asserted in accordance
with the Copyright, Designs and Patents Act 1988.

ISBN 978-1-913532-45-1

Also available as an ebook
ISBN 978-1-913532-46-8

And as an audiobook
978-1-913532-47-5

Typeset by seagulls.net
Cover design by MECOB
Project management by whitefox
Printed and bound by CPI

Profits from this book will be donated
to charities which promote or support
adolescent digital wellbeing.

*To my three children and the whole of Generation Z:
in the hope that they will mount a revolution against harms
from technology and create the future they deserve.*

CONTENTS

FOREWORD

Society is distracted. Our attention has been hijacked by the tsunami of smart devices and tech companies that provide us with *free* services in return for delivering us, so they say, what we want. As the father of three teenage sons, I observed my children's relationships with their smartphones, gaming consoles and laptops and began to wonder what the implications were for their brains, personalities and lives. I also decided to devote an hour every business day to meeting up with a Generation Z entrepreneur. In the past two years, I have met over 200 young men and women and have been bowled over by their insights, enthusiasm and ambition. But these encounters have also crystallised my views of the effects of technology – and whilst some are good, some are not. My governmental and big-business experience, startup investing and young entrepreneur mentoring have given me a ringside perspective on how differently Generation Z is living its life, sees the world and uses technology.

My aim is to share these insights with you.

Our relationship with tech has far-reaching consequences for all of us, but for Generation Z in particular it is profoundly life-changing. In my view, it represents a new crisis of distraction. I have seen the world sleepwalking into past crises: the dot.com crash, the global financial crisis

(GFC) and the climate crisis. I have also been lucky enough to have led an extraordinarily interesting business life, rising to very senior roles in business and society, many of which involved technology. Unlike Generation Z's, my life started without a mobile phone, so I have observed the effects of this key technology as it has developed.

I was Co-Global Head of the Telecom, Media and Technology team of Merrill Lynch, one of the world's leading investment banks, during the period leading up to, during and after the dot.com boom (1998–2002). This gave me a good understanding of emerging digital technology and an interest in its development. It also taught me how serious the consequences can be when society does not recognise an emerging disaster like the dot.com crash that it should have foreseen.

Later, I was Chairman of Merrill Lynch's EMEA investment banking, global markets and asset management business, with 9,000 employees in twenty-three countries, responsible for a balance sheet of half a trillion dollars in gross assets. Businesses under my leadership managed $50 billion of people's money and $300 billion of institutional money. All used technology extensively in processing millions of transactions for thousands of customers.

In 2006, I was asked to join the board of the Bank of England by the Prime Minister. I sat at the board table as the GFC unfolded, Northern Rock became insolvent, asset prices crashed and a series of banks were bailed out. There is much I could write about that period, but to do so in detail would breach strict confidences and quite literally be treason due to the oath of secrecy I swore. But I can say that in 2006 my appointment followed me telling the Bank of England that there was no time to waste in shouting from the rooftops about the lack of capital and liquidity in banks – calling out the coming crisis.

As the authorities started to deal with the crisis, I was appointed by the then Mayor of London, Boris Johnson (now British Prime

Minister), to form a group of CEOs from London's leading banks, insurance companies, asset managers and venture capital companies. Under my chairmanship, we were asked to look at why London had been so successful over many decades and see what, if anything, given the crisis, it could do to maintain its position as a leading global financial centre. We produced a report called 'London Winning in the Decade Ahead'. TheCityUK was established to scan the horizon for emerging opportunities, including big data and fintech, and to promote UK professional and financial services in the world.

Just before the 2010 election, as *An Inconvenient Truth* was gaining traction and the climate crisis was being recognised as something which needed attention, I was asked by the Chancellor of the Exchequer to lead the Green Investment Bank Commission. I formed a group of knowledgeable people on green finance and technology, and we estimated the shortfall of required investment for the UK to meet its carbon-reduction obligations to be hundreds of billions of pounds. We produced a blueprint for a new Green Investment Bank. The bank ran successfully until 2017, when it was sold to the private sector.

So, throughout my career, I have been close to the development of technology and its effects on society and witnessed three potentially avoidable crises first-hand. Over the last several years, I have made understanding emerging technologies a focus. I chair and invest in some cutting-edge technology businesses.

Right now, in my role as Chairman of UK Finance, I am working with HM Government and closely with the Home Secretary, Chancellor and National Crime Agency as part of the UK's Economic Crime Strategic Board. We have developed world-leading public-private partnerships, engaging AI to combat fraud and other economic crimes and improve counter-terrorism. I also work with leading banks and new fin-tech businesses as they transform the banking industry to a digital one.

Many internet tech developments start in the US and spread across the world from there. Most of the world's leading digital platforms serving the West are based in the US. The US Center for Humane Technology, which is dedicated to reimagining technology for the common good of humanity, now maintains a ledger of harms which it considers to be caused by technology, including harms to: attention (loss of ability to focus), mental health (loneliness, depression, stress, loss of sleep and increased suicide), relationships (less empathy, more confusion and misinterpretation), democracy (propaganda, lies and an unreliable and noisy place to debate), children (new challenges learning and socialising) and 'do unto others' (tech company executives limiting use by their own children in their own homes, whilst encouraging others to use technology more). In October 2020, the Center launched a film in partnership with Netflix highlighting these harms, *The Social Dilemma*. Since the film is inspired by big tech veterans who are in effect, whistleblowers, we should probably pay close attention to the warnings they sound.

As the film makes clear, the cost to society of having almost an entire population distracted by what big tech platforms lure us into doing must be huge. After Covid-19, society will have a massive public debt burden to pay off. By reducing the productivity cost of distraction, we could increase GDP substantially and eliminate this debt faster for our children. So, I believe the world needs to change its relationship with technology to make it serve society, rather than the profit and loss accounts of a relatively few technology businesses. I am not the first to say this, but this book is my attempt to 'shout from the rooftops' again about the need for globally coordinated governance of the internet, better regulation of technology and a radical reset of the relationship between citizens and technology.

Our children deserve better. I want to give Generation Z, with their enthusiasm, open-mindedness, social conscience, aptitude for entrepreneurship and innovation, curiosity and zest for life, the provocation and thinking space needed to lead this reset.

INTRODUCTION

It's Sunday lunchtime and I'm putting the roast lunch on the table for the family. I find my three sons in the TV room, all on their devices. None of them looks up.

'Get off those damn devices. The food will be cold,' I yell at them. Unfortunately, this message does not penetrate their earphones, let alone their consciousness.

How ironic that the device designed to enable us to talk to each other on the move – the smartphone – has resulted in the near-eradication of conversation as my generation knows it. I have spent my business life networking and building relationships. My children's generation seem to prefer remote messaging through a device to face-to-face conversation. And with those devices comes access to the internet, social media and a whole host of positive and negative new influences as well as peer judgement on every aspect of their lives. As Donna Freitas, who has researched university campus life, puts it in her book *The Happiness Effect*, members of Generation Z are, in relation to technology, 'the new explorers, brave and courageous, testing out the unknowns, both the good and the challenging, succeeding and failing and doing their best to at the very least survive'.[1] She adds that neither Generation Z nor we have a precedent 'for a life lived and celebrated and picked apart on a virtual scale'.[2]

My own perspective on Generation Z comes from being a father of three boys aged twenty-one, nineteen and sixteen, observing them and their friends, the children of my friends, and through having met about

200 budding entrepreneurs from Generation Z in London over the last two years. I love Generation Z's positivity, ambition and, in many ways, mature reflection on the society we are delivering them. But I also worry about the effects of technology on Generation Z and think some interventions could improve their lives.

'Come on, guys,' I shout again a little louder. Eventually one of them acknowledges my presence with a look. But not one that suggests it is welcome or that movement to the lunch table is imminent ...

In the hands of Generation Z, the digitally native generation, the smartphone is fundamentally changing children's communication style and brains, perhaps irreversibly. In addition to adopting messaging with the inevitable loss of face-to-face conversation, they are becoming multi-taskers. They snack on multiple information sources and are less likely to engage in a way that would enable them to see physically in their friends' faces the impact of what they have said. Such feedback would enable them to build empathy. As MIT Professor Sherry Turkle notes in *Reclaiming Conversation*, 'We are being silenced by our technologies – in a way "cured of talking".'[3] She argues that 'these silences have led to a crisis of empathy'.[4] Barack Obama famously observed in his 2004 speech that what he coined the *empathy deficit* was a more pressing political problem than the federal deficit. Modern neuroscientists regard empathy as intrinsically pro-social and, in essence, the glue which binds society together. Hannah Arendt, widely recognised as one of the leading political philosophers of the twentieth century, said that 'the death of human empathy is one of the earliest and most telling signs of a culture about to fall into barbarism'. While our society might not be quite at the point of barbarism, it does seem to me more polarised than at any point in modern history. If civilised society survives because we can empathise – that is, enough of us have the ability to stand in another's shoes and care about what it feels like – we should certainly be paying close attention to our loss of empathy. We didn't need a pandemic; we certainly need an 'empidemic'.

Indeed, I think we need to start being more discerning about what we pay attention to generally. Whilst the smartphone brings many positive efficiency and productivity benefits to us all, it also systematically distracts us onto an agenda set for us by the people who design its apps and functionality. The reason that is so important is that it is how we spend our time, or what we focus on, that determines our lives. As the behavioural scientist Winifred Gallagher writes in *Rapt*, 'who you are, what you think, feel and do, what you love, is the sum of what you focus on'.[5]

Generation Z has grown up with the aftermath of the global financial crisis, the war on terrorism, the growing climate crisis and, most recently, Covid-19. All these traumas have shaped this generation's attitudes and approach to life – one aspect of which is a desire to be independent and an incredibly innovative and entrepreneurial spirit. But Generation Z is facing what I term the *fifth trauma*, the so-called 'attention' or perhaps better 'distraction' crisis. This trauma could have the most serious and long-lasting effects of all if we as citizens, and ultimately governments, don't recognise the dangers and take urgent action to restore control of our attention to us, its owners.

A psychological trauma usually includes some or all of the following symptoms: denial, confusion and difficulty concentrating, anger and irritability, anxiety, fear, guilt, self-blame, withdrawing from others, feeling sad and feeling disconnected. We will see how studies show that many of these symptoms can be exacerbated by addiction to, or compulsive use of, technology. Which is not to say that studies suggest there is a direct causality between either high screen time or social media use and rising mental health issues in youngsters. On that the evidence is marginal and inconsistent. What is perhaps of more concern is the effect on those with pre-existing mental health and other vulnerabilities. I believe Generation

Z's constant exposure to negative news, partly reflecting the way social media algorithms amplify bad news and the way Generation Z receives and consumes news, also has an impact. It's perhaps no surprise, then, that a 2019 YouGov survey carried out with the UK charity Barnardo's found that 69 per cent of 16–24-year-old Brits surveyed said that they believed their generation would be worse off in terms of happiness and mental health than preceding generations.[6] The Children's Society's 'Good Childhood Report 2019' concluded that there had been a continuous decline in average happiness among 10–15-year-olds in the UK, happiness *with friends* is in decline and that fifteen-year-olds in the UK were among the saddest and least satisfied with their lives in Europe. And that was before Covid-19, which has brought a new stream of negativity.

I will share the trends in Generation Z behaviours that I think technology has created, accelerated or exacerbated. You may not recognise all the trends I identify; you may not agree with some of them; but if you agree with the general direction of travel these trends collectively represent, the questions about what they mean for the future of society are worth asking. If you are a parent, you may find the book sheds some light on issues you have yourself and with your own children. If you run a business, and you don't understand these trends and how significant they are to reshaping consumer behaviour, your marketing approach and ultimately your business could quickly become obsolete. If you are a media regulator, you may agree that the case for more internet regulation is clear.

The internet (comprising thousands of individual networks, joining millions of computers storing hundreds of thousands of petabytes of data accessed from over a billion websites) is not 'governed' today, but managed, due to its distributed form, by many stakeholders, including governments, private business and civic society, with very different and often incompatible interests. Indeed, in many ways, it is like the great oceans, which have been described as the world's lungs, crucial to the functioning of the planet, but not really owned or managed by anyone individually. The internet could be seen as the central nervous system (CNS) of the world, currently without a suitable brain or conscience to guide it. In this vacuum, should humankind be content with whoever happens to be in charge of Facebook (which owns Instagram and WhatsApp), Snapchat, Amazon, Netflix, Sony, Xbox, Tencent and Alibaba, exploiting the CNS for profit and limited social good? I believe we should be demanding global cooperation to manage the internet and technology to find a better balance towards the good of society.

Treating all digital activity as bad irrespective of the context in which it happens, its content or the connections it affords would be ridiculous, given that digital technologies are no longer optional but necessities of modern life. But recently there has been an increasing debate about the pros and cons of particular aspects of technology amongst citizens and in the media, focusing on 'online harms': addiction, gaming, porn and the effects on well-being. The term 'techlash' has been coined to capture the reaction. I believe Generation Z can and will drive this techlash to restore a better balance between the power of technology and citizens.

Until digital ethics is a more developed academic discipline, and until one of the UN or other initiatives underway to create an internet governance mechanism comes to fruition, we need a combination of better education, voluntary or professional self-regulation, a healthier regard from the boards of big tech companies for how their businesses can become sustainable and some shorter-term regulatory action to address the most egregious harms.

My dad, a wonderful man who was essentially a liberal conservative, used to say that he was up for anything as long as it wasn't illegal, immoral or fattening, and I would say he observed the first two of those principles. I think, as a society, we need to consider how those who dominate the world's CNS might fail his test if it were applied to the internet today. We must call out the most immoral activity and until such time as the scientific research is clearer on the links between screen time, social media use and wellbeing, we should work on the precautionary principle. That says that if an action presents a risk to the public, in the absence of scientific consensus, the burden of proof that it is *not* harmful should fall on those taking the action. This means that in the meantime we should probably move potentially harmful online activity which is capable of regulation into the illegal (or at least regulated) category.

PART 1

BORN WITH A MOBILE

1

MEET GENERATION Z

While there is some disagreement around exact dates (a margin of no more than five years), the general consensus seems to be that those born between the mid-1990s and the early 2010s are Generation Z. The term 'millennial' or 'Gen Y' describes those who reached adulthood in the early twenty-first century, covering the generation born between about 1980 and the mid-1990s. In 2019 Generation Z for the first time outnumbered millennials, making up 32 per cent of the world's 7.8 billion population.[1] What makes Generation Z particularly special is that its members were the first to be born into an age of digital technology. Whereas millennials remember life without at least some of its more recent products (the smartphone, the tablet, the ubiquitous web) and only became fully aware of this technology during their more formative teenage years, Generation Z have no experience of life that did not involve daily interaction with electronic devices. For this generation of so-called digital natives, life has always involved Google, Facebook, YouTube, Instagram, Pinterest, Twitter, Tumblr, WhatsApp, Reddit and, more recently, Snapchat and TikTok. The younger members of Generation Z have always been able to search by voice and ask Alexa or Siri any question they like and get an immediate answer, without even the need to be able to type or use a physical device.

Wi-fi has become an entitlement, and smartphones have become ubiquitous.[2] 'Growing up with a supercomputer in your pocket connected to most of the world's population and knowledge,' writes David Pakman, 'has created an irreversible pattern of behaviour unlikely to revert to the ways of previous generations.'[3]

Generation Z is variously known as the iGeneration, the generation of choice, the hopeful, anxious generation and, based on its propensity to use images embellished with text to share often light-hearted commentary on current events known as memes, the meme generation. Generation Z is the first which regards carrying cash as an option and prefers to pay digitally and for whom cash is a number on a screen, not something physical.

Generation Z has often been ascribed two attributes: being viewed as less resilient and more prone to taking offence than previous generations. It seems likely that this perceived lack of resilience is linked closely to this generation's reliance on technology and may reflect the impact of social media on confidence, self-esteem and sensitivity to, and ability to express, varying points of view. These new norms may, in turn, lead to the particular degrees of happiness or unhappiness we see in the generation.

Whilst Generation Z does not remember 9/11 itself, it has not known a time when the West has not been engaged with the war on terror and global extremism. Understandably, this has resulted in a sense of anxiety and insecurity only compounded by the media coverage of the intergenerational financial effects of the global financial crisis and talk of the likely impacts of the climate crisis and now Covid-19. According to Eddy, nineteen, one of my Generation Z interviewees and an optimistic and ambitious student at the University of Oxford, 'The way tech propagates doom and gloom predictions on current issues and about climate in particular contributes to my generation's existing level of anxiety for sure.'

Generation Z is larger than we might realise, particularly in developing nations. Statistical projections from the UN show that whilst

Generation Z will represent a third of the US population by the end of 2020, it will exceed half in many African countries, resulting in very different healthcare, education and economic needs.[4] Given its propensity to kill older people disproportionately, Covid-19 could accelerate this trend. Generation Z is also anticipated to be the largest generation in China, where there is a severe gender imbalance. When combined with India, these two nations have a combined 50 million surplus of males relative to females under twenty, fuelling loneliness epidemics, human trafficking and prostitution.[5] Much work has been done to examine how the 'missing women' phenomenon has transpired, with sex-selective abortion, infanticide and differential neglect all factors at play. This global youth generation faces a rapidly changing social fabric across much of the world, one that is ageing exponentially. For example, Japan's birth rate has fallen so substantially that its population is estimated to fall 30 per cent by the 2050s. European nations are also experiencing falling fertility rates and an ageing population. Generation Z, in seeing this trend, may not be as conditioned to believe that the nuclear family, large families or families as my generation has experienced them are crucial to fulfilling lives. The decline of religion and marriage, when combined with the advent of the hookup culture, are new phenomena to be carefully examined. And that is before sex robots and virtual reality video become more mainstream. All of these changes may have a major impact on the decline of the traditional nuclear family, the source and nature of human relationships and the existence and form of families in the future.

Generation Y was the first in the Western industrialised world to be worse off than its predecessors in modern history. This leads to Generation Y complaining about their lack of wealth relative to my generation. As my nineteen-year-old son pointed out to me, the fact that this is frequently cited only compounds the problem for Generation Z: they never stop hearing it. As I write this book, the coronavirus is sweeping the world and will no doubt leave an enormous indelible mark on Generation Z, its economic prospects and approach to life. John Goldthorpe, Emeritus Fellow of Nuffield College, Oxford and the UK's leading sociologist on social mobility, believes that for those born since the early 1980s, social mobility is no longer more likely to be upwards due to the halt in the growth of professional and managerial jobs. In fact, it is at least as likely to be down as up, in contrast to most of the postwar period.

The challenges that will be faced by Generation Z are considerable, not least increased academic pressures, unrealistic gender expectations, growing income inequality and now the hangover from Covid-19. I feel my generation was relatively lucky by comparison. I was born in 1961 to middle-class parents and earned a free place in a local independent school. I graduated with a business degree from Bath University and qualified as a chartered accountant. Unlike Generation Z, we had no student loans so left university with no debt. I bought a £13,000 house using a mortgage from my bank and a £3,000 deposit my father gave me and applied for local council grants to improve the property. I let rooms to students to pay the mortgage. In those days, and indeed until the early 1990s, annual inflation often ran in high single figures. Inflation causes house prices to increase whilst the mortgage loan remains the same. So, over our lifetimes, the part of my generation lucky enough to get on the property ladder accumulated wealth from rising property prices. It remains to be seen whether anything other than very low inflation ever returns in developed economies, but it seems unlikely that Generation Z will benefit from the economic conditions we did. I think Generation Z knows it faces a tough economic period, and this partly drives its interest in entrepreneurship as a means of being self-reliant. In their 2017 State of Generation Z study, Jason Dorsey and Denise Villa found that a staggering 12 per cent of the generation, aged fourteen to twenty-two, was already saving for retirement![6]

I have mentored a lot of youngsters during my thirty-five-year career, but as I have met Generation Z over the last two years, the creativity, interest in starting a business and intent on being self-sufficient has been most striking. According to the World Economic Forum, over 20 per cent of Generation Z are interested in attending a trade or technical school instead of college or university.[7] And in response to demand, high schools and colleges across the globe are increasingly including entrepreneurship in their curriculum. A Northeastern University study showed that a 'notable 42 per cent of Generation Z respondents expect to work for themselves during their careers'.[8] The university where I am Adjunct Professor, the University of Queensland, for example, in addition to offering courses in entrepreneurship and innovation, has a Ventures Unit. This offers 'Startup Ventures' – four-week placements to learn alongside tech startups based in Shanghai or Singapore, a short series of four masterclasses on building social enterprises, the 'ilab' accelerator programme to help take student startups to the next level and an annual showcase to learn more about startups who are accelerating ideas to impact. The university also offers its students access tools and spaces in the form of 3D printers, design studios and co-working spaces, hackathons and networking events for entrepreneurial students, and its programmes have already supported over 500 founders across 180 startups.

'China has become the first country to declare internet addiction a clinical disorder, labelling it "the number one public health threat" to its teenage population,' according to Adam Alter, Associate Professor of Marketing at New York University's Stern School of Business, in his book *Irresistible*.[9] Several studies in China have shown that as many as 16 per cent of Chinese male college students suffer from Internet Addiction Disorder, a rate which is even higher than in the US, for example. The psychiatrist spearheading China's attempts to combat internet addiction, Professor Tao Ran, observes that those under his care have a bias towards virtual reality, sometimes spending more than 6 hours a day online gaming. He refers to them as 'the same as heroin addicts – they crave and look forward to playing every day. That's why they call it "electronic heroin".'[10] 'What brings about their undoing isn't that they're suffering from a disease, but that this digital world is so clearly superior to the real world they're supposed to be occupying.'[11]

Perhaps unsurprisingly, there has been a notable rise in short-sightedness, which has doubled in the last fifty years.[12] There is plenty of evidence to suggest a link between the use of handheld devices and eyestrain. International eye doctor professional bodies have rung similar alarm bells, noting that digital eye strain, or computer vision syndrome, is rampant, especially as we move towards smaller devices and the prominence of devices increases in our everyday lives. Other growing issues include the rise of allergies, obesity and diabetes, leading to higher probabilities of heart disease, stroke and osteoarthritis. In this context, the rise in screen time, the prevalence of, and addiction to gaming amongst youngsters and the recent dramatic rise of e-sport (global games played online), making it less likely Generation Z will have time to play physical sport, is something we need to consider carefully. Psychologist Philip Zimbardo and his co-author Nikita Coulombe, in their study of young men in the US, observe that whilst adult obesity rates have doubled over the past thirty years, adolescent obesity rates have tripled.[13]

Generation Z is a more educated, but more stressed and depressed, generation in comparison with its predecessors according to *The Economist*.[14] Recent studies have confirmed that Generation Z has markedly higher rates of anxiety, depression and suicide than previous generations; a 2019 study suggests that, in many areas, rates doubled over the period 2007 to 2018.[15] No doubt some of this is explained by depression being better recognised more recently and being more acceptable to admit, particularly for men. But I believe this trend is partly explained by Generation Z's attachment to what I call 'that bloody device', over-exposure to the toxic effects of some social media platforms, video watching, video gaming, messaging and increasingly virtual reality. Heavy internet use, especially at a young age, is increasingly cited as a serious mental health risk factor. In 2019, the Children's Society warned that children were the unhappiest they had been for almost twenty-five years due to excessive social media use, increasing loneliness and turbulent friendships.[16] Louise Clarkson, head of children and young people at Mind, the mental health charity, recently said 'academic stress, an uncertain jobs market and pressures on appearances can have a real effect on mental health, and for some young people that's compounded by a rise in online bullying and the 24/7 nature of social media'.[17]

Social media pushes current societal issues in front of youngsters and affects their opinions, sometimes with surprising outcomes. The Varkey Foundation and Populus conducted an international study examining the attitudes of 20,000 people between the ages of fifteen and twenty-one across twenty countries in 2016 and found that the support for freedom of speech dwindled if it were deemed offensive to a religion, and, further, that support for legal migration was low.[18] Top concerns about the future included extremism, terrorism, the widening gap between rich and poor and the climate crisis. The same survey found high support for gender equality, abortion, transgender rights, same-sex marriage, albeit with expected national differences reflecting religion and culture.

Young students often seem to exhibit a healthy regard for social issues before they join the workforce. White believes exposure to the GFC directly led to Generation Z embracing socialism even more than younger generations generally tend to.[19] We shall examine the interest of Generation Z in working for what I call 'purposes not businesses', which the failure of the traditional capitalist model has encouraged. The US consultancy sparks & honey's research shows that social entrepreneurship is one of Generation Z's most popular career choices.[20] Certainly, my own experience of Generation Z entrepreneurs is that they are very socially conscious and often wish to start businesses that address social issues and are not just for profit.

2

DEVICE DEVOTION

Perhaps it's no surprise that roughly four decades after mobiles were invented, almost every developed country has at least 90 per cent of its citizens using one. But let's try and figure out why Generation Z are even more devoted to their phones than millennials. GlobalWebIndex.com's 2019 'Audience report on millennials' collected data on 550,000 internet users aged 23 to 36 across 45 markets, and found that 96 per cent of millennials have a smartphone, 69 per cent own a PC or laptop, 38 per cent own a tablet, and 24 per cent have a gaming console.[1] The survey also revealed that millennials spend an average of 3 hours 49 minutes a day on their smartphones *and* an average of 3 hours 37 minutes per day on laptops and tablets. Millennials, the survey suggested, are connected to the digital universe through an average of three devices. Cheetah Digital estimate that eight of every ten digital minutes reside on a mobile.[2]

Generation Z uses mobile even more and spends even more time online, according to the same report: 95 per cent of the generation had visited a social media site in the previous month, 92 per cent chatted or used an instant message app, 91 per cent watched a video clip, and 76 per cent used a mapping product.

Generation Z spent an average of nearly 7 hours a day online overall. Ninety-five per cent said they were using another device the last time they were watching TV, and more than 70 per cent of those said they were social networking or chatting, 14 per cent above the global average for all generations for both of these measures.[3] Similar trends are reported in Asia, with a third of Generation Z spending more than 6 hours a day on their devices by comparison with only 22 per cent of millennials.[4]

The challenge here, then, is to find out *why* this is the case and what it means for this generation of young minds. Is it just because this generation has never known a time without these technologies? We must also find out not just *how much time* they spend on screens, but *when* in the day and *what they are doing* during that time. All screen time is not equal. Screen time immediately before sleep may be worse than during the day. And the very term 'screen time' fails to distinguish between screen time for socialising, surfing, entertainment and education, all of which may have very different benefits and effects.

A survey by TigerMobiles.com said there would be 4.5 billion mobile phones in the world by the end of 2019 and around 63 per cent of people would be using one.[5] The report also uncovered the following data:

1. The average person checks their phone 47 times a day.
2. 80 per cent of people use their phone before they sleep.
3. 61 per cent of people sleep with their phones.
4. 85 per cent of people have no problem using their phone whilst talking to friends.
5. The average user spends nearly 3 hours a day on the phone; 45 per cent of that time is spent on social media.
6. 40 per cent of people had used their phones on the toilet.
7. 20 per cent of people had used their phone during sex.
8. 26 per cent of car accidents are caused by mobile phone use.

Covid-19 lockdown, with us all at home together for three months, has been an interesting window on my kids' own screen time. And it has changed the debate about the effect of technology on kids, as suddenly lockdown boosted the value of technology for children in new ways. My youngster's default activity, absent some seriously better alternative, is gaming, which he argues is not addictive and enables him to interact with his friends despite the lockdown. Fair point, but getting him off the console can be very challenging, and I believe his time gaming increases the likelihood of grumpy and aggressive behaviour afterwards. He would disagree. My middle son has started gaming again since lockdown started and even moved room to get better wi-fi connectivity. All three keep closely in touch with friends on Instagram, Snapchat and Facebook Messenger, and, during lockdown, we have developed a different perspective on the value of these digital connections. Mealtimes are usually interrupted by mobile phone use, although I would freely admit that I have not been the best role model in this regard. And the excuse that in my case 'at least I am working' does not cut it with them for a second.

Social media use is widespread and frequent across Generation Z, but the number of platforms and apps used is small, meaning that Generation Z's screen time is dominated by a few large players.[6] Piper Sandler's spring 2019 survey, 'Taking stock with teens', reports that Facebook and Twitter usage is declining, but Instagram popularity is still rising, and Snapchat's proportion of daily users seems stable.[7] The new entrant TikTok, however, is very much rising, and it remains to be seen what effect President Trump's recent proposed ban on TikTok downloads in the US has. On average, Generation Z uses around eight social networks.

Economists have long studied the market failures which can arise when small numbers of players control a market. The social media market is characterised by a group of monopolies, or more precisely 'monopsonies', who can exert great power since they are a small group of sellers selling to one widely dispersed public which has relatively little power individually.

The Chinese social media landscape, despite its ban on Western platforms, is similarly concentrated at the top end; the most popular messaging, social media and mobile payment app is WeChat, an app introduced in 2011 by Chinese tech behemoth Tencent, which now boasts 1 billion monthly active users.[8] Sina Weibo, on the other hand, is the nation's most widely used microblogging site.[9] With 430 million active users a month (compare this with Twitter's 326 million), Weibo is one of the best ways to amass a following or go viral on social media.[10]

In terms of e-commerce, Alibaba dominates the Chinese landscape, and in 2018 announced a record-setting $30 billion in sales on Singles Day.[11] Introduced originally in 1999, Alibaba now has 552 million active users a month and boasts a wide range of both domestic and international brands.[12] Alibaba has its own widely used messaging service.

For many in my generation, the evening news is still an institution, rounding off the day with a presentation of the world's key events. Some still buy print versions of newspapers to read on the train, or over breakfast. I can rarely tempt my children even to read the sports pages. And whilst many of us now read newspapers online and get news sent directly to our mobiles, Dorsey and Villa found that 24 per cent of Generation Z aged thirteen to seventeen had never read a physical newspaper.[13] Generation Z receives its news from different sources. These sources are overwhelmingly digital and often from media platforms whose primary function isn't news per se, including Facebook, Instagram, Twitter and Snapchat. Take, for example, Facebook. The Facebook News Feed is now *the* primary source of traffic for news websites, giving it enormous potential influence, particularly when combined with the fact that Google and Facebook between them account for 81 per cent of the traffic to online news sites in the UK.[14]

Generation Z is looking for personalised news, not generalised public services. As the Publisher and Vice President of *Wired* magazine Howard Mittman suggests, teen news consumers are looking for 'a level of authenticity that allows you to know that they're speaking to you'.[15] Other teenagers say they get their news from clips of late-night TV hosts, such as Trevor Noah or Stephen Colbert, or from stand-up comedians like Hasan Minhaj, who has a popular show on Netflix. Personalities are replacing news organisations. In Britain, younger teens are far less familiar with the BBC's news brand than they are with those of YouTube or Netflix. According to Ofcom, the public broadcaster will soon 'face a threat to its future sustainability if it cannot engage young people sufficiently'.[16]

These principles hold true around the world, even if the specifics and platforms differ. Between 2009 and 2018, the share of teenagers who read newspapers declined from around 60 per cent to close to 20 per cent, according to the Programme for International Student Assessment (PISA).[17]

Some 80 per cent of Middle Eastern denizens aged 18–24 years old now get their news from social media, up from 25 per cent in 2015.[18] They favour Facebook, though the Gulf states, particularly Saudi Arabia, are captivated by Snapchat. Two-thirds of South Korean teenagers go online to find out what is happening in the world, most of them turning to Naver, a portal and search engine.[19] Consistent with the personalisation need that Mittman identified, a study of American and British teens commissioned by the Reuters Institute for the Study of Journalism in Oxford argues that, when it comes to news, young people are most concerned with 'what it can do for them as individuals – rather than society as a whole'.[20] This may be seen as an inevitable progression of the attitudes of the 'Me' Generation, which preceded Generation Z.

Amongst youngsters, watching traditional broadcast TV channels has been declining, whilst the propensity to watch screen video on demand (SVOD) services like Netflix has been increasing. This is partly fuelled by SVOD enabling you to watch on a device of your choice rather than the TV, watch without ads and watch multiple episodes in one sitting, without having to wait for a scheduled broadcast. While 76 per cent of Generation Z say they still watch live TV on a television channel once a week, 59 per cent now say they watch subscription services such as Netflix, with 24 per cent saying they regularly watch back-to-back episodes from the same series.[21] Interestingly, Generation Z sees SVOD as 'watching TV': 70 per cent of respondents in a recent survey refer to services like Netflix, YouTube and Hulu as 'television'.[22]

Generation Z's top five interests are music, films/cinema, food and drink, gaming and technology.[23] Roughly half of Generation Z say they are interested in sports and being fit. But e-sport, a catch-all term referring to video-game tournaments that are often played globally and have substantial revenue generation potential, is the new rapidly growing phenomenon of the last decade. E-sport has grown fastest in the APAC region, where it has now reached 35 per cent penetration on average amongst Generation Z with a staggering 48 per cent penetration in China. Its popularity is also growing rapidly in other regions and it has perhaps become the most popular sport no one has heard of. New Zoo estimates that revenues from e-sport will exceed $1 billion globally in 2020 from 443 million users.

Twitch, Amazon's video live streaming service, includes broadcasts of e-sports competitions and is rapidly becoming a mainstream competitor to YouTube. It has around 140 million monthly unique viewers and in the first quarter of 2020 was watched for 3.1 billion hours.[24]

Online gaming has become a mainstream pastime for Generation Z. According to the Entertainment Industry Association, 70 per cent of families have one child who games. Limelight Networks' report 'The state of online gaming 2019' surveyed 4,500 game players in France, Germany, India, Italy, Japan, Singapore, South Korea and the UK aged eighteen or older and found that people who play video games spend an average of 7 hours 7 minutes per week playing, an increase of nearly 20 per cent on the previous year.[25] Gamers aged 16–25 play for 8 hours 12 minutes a week. Mobile phones are the most commonly used device for gaming. Casual single-player games like Candy Crush, Angry Birds and Spider Solitaire are the most frequently played, although 18–25-year-olds prefer first-person shooter and battle royale games such as Fortnite, which involve squads of competitors seeking to be the last squad standing. More than 35 per cent of gamers who work also play video games while at work; and 36 per cent of gamers would quit their jobs if they could support themselves as professional video gamers. Being a professional gamer has replaced being a train driver as an aspiration, as more than 57 per cent of male gamers aged 18–35 want to become professional gamers! Today's 18–25-year-olds spend 77 per cent more time watching online gaming than broadcast sports on television, and gamers aged 26–35 spend roughly equal amounts of time watching gaming online and watching broadcast sports on TV.[26]

When it comes to shopping, Generation Z does this increasingly online. Seventy-two per cent of Generation Zers have made an online purchase in the last month, 11 per cent higher than the average of those surveyed.[27] In the US, 44 per cent of those in Generation Z prefer shopping on Amazon, nearly eight times higher than the next retailer.[28] Covid-19 will have brought forward new customers' exposure to online shopping and no doubt converted many who might have otherwise been later adopters.

Children are getting devices at a younger age and spending more time on them. As Sonia Livingstone and Alice Blum-Ross say in *Parenting for a Digital Future*, 'pre-school children have taken to tablets like ducks to water'.[29] Twenty-nine per cent of babies under the age of one watch TV and video content for about ninety minutes a day, while 64 per cent of kids watch a little more than 2 hours of content a day between their first and second birthdays.[30] Forty-two per cent of children under the age of eight have their own tablet, with more than half getting their tablet between the ages of five and eight. Another Common Sense Media study in 2019 found that by age twelve, the penetration of smartphone ownership had increased from 41 per cent in 2015 to 69 per cent in 2019.[31] And more than half of teenagers felt addicted to their devices; 78 per cent check their devices at least hourly.[32] In 2018, two of Apple's largest investors urged the phone manufacturer to take action against smartphone addiction among children amidst growing concerns about the effects of technology and social media on youth.[33]

Even though the average age of owning a phone is becoming younger, the step up to secondary school at the age of eleven is still the point at which many children get a phone and ownership becomes 'almost universal'.[34] Yet, what's commonly reported is that children are bought mobile phones at much earlier ages, with many now having their own phone by the age of seven.[35]

The NSPCC estimates that 62 per cent of children aged 8–11 and 93 per cent of children aged 12–15 regularly use a smartphone.[36] This means they are quite likely to have access to some age-inappropriate content. Since the telecoms companies and tech platforms don't operate *and strictly enforce* age verification policies, the major app stores and the content they facilitate can be accessed by many children. Some platforms, including Facebook, Twitter, Instagram, TikTok and Snapchat, do have minimum age 'policies' (for most major platforms it's currently thirteen), but since they don't typically robustly demand verification, children can simply exaggerate their age or get a parent's permission where this is required. Ninety per cent of those aged 11–16 surveyed said they had at least one social media account, despite the minimum published age policy theoretically ruling out a third of this age group. Children face several risks online – from the production and distribution of child-abuse images to the harmful effect of inappropriate content and the growing scale of grooming being facilitated by social networks.

Live video streaming has thrown up new opportunities for groomers to coerce children into increasingly extreme forms of abuse. One in twenty children who used live streaming had been asked to undress.[37] And of the 40,000 7–16-year-olds surveyed by the NSPCC, 19 per cent of primary-aged children and 29 per cent of secondary-aged children had live-streamed. Twelve per cent of all children had video-chatted with someone they didn't know in person. The platforms which facilitate abuse have shown themselves totally incapable of adequately addressing it, often seeking to address only the most extreme behaviours.

Gaming is an area where particular risks can arise for children. Kaspersky, a major global cyber protection software company, identifies seven dangers specific to children: 1. cyberbullying, where players take advantage of their anonymity online to 'grief' other players by deliberately making the game less enjoyable for them, where 'griefers' deliberately conquer or capture needed quest targets before the child reaches them.[38] Cyber bullies can also be 'whisperers' who send hurtful or harmful messages; 2. abuse of privacy, where criminals piece together information kids reveal about themselves in signing into and participating in the game; 3. stealing information from dead consoles taken to tips without being cleansed of data; 4. hacking of webcams to enable the hacker to see and potentially film the child; 5. typically older gamers posing as younger gamers luring or grooming children; 6. freemium model games charging children fees (the 'free' game market was worth over US$61 billion globally in 2018); and 7. using games to plant malware through Trojans uploading malicious versions of games onto Google Play or other play stores.[39] Because many children don't understand the difference between digital 'play' money and actual money, some children think money within a game is just like monopoly money, free as part of the game.

How much should we worry about the effect of exposing a child's brain to earlier and more screen time? Is this all a rerun of arguments which arose when TV started becoming popular and parents worried about it turning kids into 'couch potatoes', having a detrimental impact on family relationships with the potential to ruin children's eyes and brains? Lynn Spigel, Professor of Screen Cultures at Northwestern University, asked as TV was widely adopted whether TV was a new Frankenstein that threatened to turn against its creator and disrupt traditional patterns of family life. No, digital interaction is different and more concerning. Dr Richard Freed, an eminent child psychologist and author of *The Wired Child*, says, 'the latest brain imaging studies show that young children's interactions with parents and other adult caregivers shape the architecture of the developing mind ... a use it or lose it principle exists'.[40] The American Academy of Paediatrics, whose mission is 'dedication to the health of our children', concurs, noting that 'young children learn best from – and need – interactions with humans, not screens'.[41] We should therefore be especially disquieted by efforts to introduce interactive technologies to the young; the devices' very 'interactivity' may interfere with the human connections young kids must have for optimal brain and emotional development.

Seemiller and Grace found in their study of US college students that more than a third of teens in 2016 were affected by cyberbullying compared to 19 per cent in 2007.[42] Cyberbullying includes unwanted texts, harassing or stalking through social media, sharing insulting and embarrassing pictures and posting on gossip social media sites. When I was talking about the research I was doing for this book to a friend of mine, he froze. We walked around the garden while he confided in me about an experience his fifteen-year-old daughter had on social media. She was 'friended' by someone whose profile suggested he was a boy her age. The friendship grew harmlessly over several weeks until the friend started suggesting they swap pictures of their naked bodies and potentially meet up. Eventually it became clear he was middle-aged, not fifteen. Luckily, at this point, she told her father something was wrong. He intervened, reported the friend to the social media platform, closed her accounts, and they agreed that she would not use social media for a time. He has taken a much closer interest in the online activities of his children since.

I worry more about the effects of technology on their health and wellbeing generally than I do about cyberbullying as a parent of boys. And it starts with a worry about the fact that every day seems to end with a long period of screen time just before sleep, which can go on well into the small hours. I decide to interview one of my research assistants to discover his experience.

Henry, twenty-one, working on his Masters in finance, having graduated from LSE, says, 'During my teenage years, I would stay up late at night on my phone, browsing social media, which had quite a large impact on my sleep, seriously affecting study-work at times.'

'So, how did you stop?' I ask him.

Henry looks embarrassed. 'To be honest, I didn't. I still can't get out of the habit. I end almost every day with what I know is too much screen time.'

My youngest son appears at the table dishevelled for a very late breakfast. 'I know, Dad,' he says as he sees me looking at him. 'I literally fell asleep on my phone.' The World Health Organisation has declared that there is a 'sleep loss epidemic' in industrialised nations and researchers at the University of Michigan looking at global sleep patterns say we have a 'global sleep crisis'.

In his book *Why We Sleep*, neuroscience professor Matthew Walker notes that every major disease in the developed world has very strong causal links to deficient sleep.[43] Generation Z is busy due to its preoccupation with devices and has less sleep as a result. Many youngsters prefer screen time to sleep time. As Walker observes, growing babies and children need even more sleep than adults. Humans are the only species who deliberately deprive themselves of sleep, and no one would accuse a baby of being lazy because they were asleep.

Generation Z spend more time on their devices than sleeping, shocking as it may seem.[44] As any parent can attest, making sure the devices haven't been snuck into a bedroom by younger children at night is nigh on impossible, not least because most of us do it ourselves. In fairness, parents sometimes keep their phones on at night to enable their kids to contact them in an emergency, but more often, probably, just through ill-discipline.

Using a device can subject the brain to the effects of blue light, which suppresses your brain's production of melatonin, a hormone that helps with sleep timing and circadian rhythms. This means that a large proportion of us are effectively 'inducing jet lag at night by telling our bodies that the day is beginning just before we go to bed'.[45] Sleep deprivation is a corollary and secondary effect of addiction to devices.

According to the National Sleep Foundation, the leading expert voice in the world of sleep science, Generation Z is more likely not to be getting good or enough sleep and waking up unrefreshed. Sixty per cent reported getting less than the recommended amount of sleep, requiring daytime naps and weekend catch-ups. Forty per cent of Generation Z report regularly driving drowsy.[46]

Limelight.com's survey of online gamers found that 52 per cent of 18–25-year-old gamers had missed sleep due to gaming.[47]

Marco, a very health-conscious Generation Zer, whom I met when he was briefly my fitness trainer, says, 'Most people aren't aware that simply getting the right amount of sleep isn't enough, but that what happens when we sleep has a significant impact on our lives. It is also not common knowledge that we play an active part in the quality of the sleep produced. As you mentioned, using blue-light-emitting devices just before sleeping impacts the body's ability to generate deep nREM and REM sleep cycles as the body struggles to both get to sleep and stay asleep. This has the same effect as chronic sleep deprivation and therefore damages our bodies in a variety of ways.

'Here's a list of what good quality sleep offers:

1. increases lifespan;
2. enhances memory;
3. improves creativity;
4. makes you look more attractive;
5. makes you slim and helps you lower food cravings;
6. protects you from cancer and dementia;
7. wards off colds and the flu;
8. lowers your risk of heart attacks, strokes and diabetes;
9. makes you feel happier, less depressed and less anxious.

I try to stop using devices at least an hour before going to bed. I've replaced this time with reading a book. I found it very difficult at first, but over time, not only has my reading improved, but so too has my ability to focus. Not to mention how much happier I am receiving all the benefits I have listed as a result of improving my sleep quality.'

Marco is right about the benefits of sleep, but he is a fitness fanatic and he wears a Fitbit, what the tech industry calls a 'wearable'. He goes on to tell me that in pursuit of the ability to post perfect body images on Instagram and improve his attraction rate on Tinder, he had become addicted to his Fitbit and the encouragement it gives him to get better and better abs. The wearable device market is growing rapidly, fuelled by consumers' preferences for connected devices and the increasing number of internet-connected devices which wearables can monitor and control ('the internet of things' or 'IoT'). Smartwatches represent the largest segment, driven by increasing demand for wireless health and fitness monitoring devices. In November 2019, eMarketer.com reported that 15 per cent of 12–17-year-olds and 36 per cent of 18–24-year-olds in the US claim to use smart wearables.[48] It has been postulated that the only real brake on demand for wearables, other than the cost, is consumer concern over the privacy of the data it collects on users, which is obviously quite personal.

Fitness trackers are reported to have the potential to encourage addictive or compulsive traits. They have no doubt spurred many consumers to be more aware of their fitness levels and to improve them; used sensibly, they are a good thing. But '10,000 steps a day' has become a global target following the Tokyo Olympics, and many fitness apps encourage you to constantly run faster, run longer, lift more weight, do more reps, lose more weight, put on more muscle or swim more lengths. And in the wrong hands, this can lead to obsession, guilt and low self-esteem. Dopamine generated by app usage, alongside endorphins, which can help reduce the perception of pain and give us the second wind for our exercise, can be a dangerous cocktail when it comes to creating obsessive behaviour. Marco, so wise about the importance of sleep, attested to precisely this. Marco became addicted to the rewards from his Fitbit and the exercise itself, constantly trying to beat his 'previous score'. He then suffered from an unrelated freak illness which hospitalised and nearly killed him. When he recovered, he had lost his very muscled fitness-model body and returned to just looking seriously fit. What surprised him, he told me, was that his closest friends told him he had never looked better.

3

DIGITAL BEES

As I walk into the lounge, I see my son watching his favourite team playing football on TV. But he also has the laptop open with a YouTube clip running and messages from friends popping up constantly on one side of the screen on Facebook Messenger. His mobile is in his hand, where I can see he has new Snapchat notifications. My question about whether he is hungry is ignored as he taps away rapidly to answer a message on his phone, hardly looking away from the football on the TV. Note to self – don't immediately get cross when kids ignore you in this way. It is how they communicate. Generation Z doesn't experience interruptions as disruptions. They are just one of many different forms of competing incoming information.

Generation Z comprises professional *multitaskers* who, from an earlier and earlier age, spend more and more time dropping in and out of different apps like manic bees grazing on multiple honeypots. The consequence is that they are spending less time doing anything with focus or face-to-face with their families and friends. These changes are gradually and, indeed, insidiously baked into the way their brains develop because of the way the devices, apps and platforms to which they become attached are designed. I believe this is taking a toll on the mental health of our children in a way we should not ignore. It is likely that depression is now more recognised and more socially acceptable to admit and talk about than when I was a teenager. But I rarely go a week without talking to another parent whose child is suffering from anxiety, and very often more serious issues, including, sadly, self-harming and suicidal tendencies. I talk here of relatively high-achieving, physically healthy, good-looking kids with apparently everything going for them and everything to go for. So what on earth is happening?

Generation Z does not distinguish between the online and offline worlds in the same way as millennials, because they have grown up with technology. Millennials, for whom technology arrived part way through their lives, see a distinct difference. To Generation Z, a 'conversation' is most likely a text or messaging exchange. Adam Alter tells the story of a psychologist reacting to one of his internet addiction patients: 'This person doesn't differentiate various modes of communication the way I do – the result is a landscape filled with disconnection and addiction.'[1]

Generation Z cannot be separated from their devices without consequences; as Alter points out, 'This sort of overuse is so prevalent that researchers have coined the term 'nomophobia' to describe the fear of being without phone contact (an abbreviation of 'no-mobile-phobia').[2] Turkle coins the term 'disconnection anxiety' to describe the real angst that grows when youngsters are denied access to their smartphones. A common term used by Generation Z themselves is FOMO – fear of missing out. I have come to recognise one of Generation Z's common refrains – 'Wait! What?' – in my own sons, as they look up from finishing a text or instant message (IM) to ask me to repeat what I have said when their attention was not fully focused.

In his book *The Attention Merchants: The Epic Struggle to Get Inside Our Heads*, Columbia Law School professor Tim Wu, widely known for championing equal access to the internet, and who writes and teaches about private power, free speech and information warfare, describes us as *homo distractus*, suffering an 'attentional crisis'.[3] It is clear that what he calls the 'attention industry', that which drives digital platforms and digital content, has in just a few years come to dominate the waking lives of not just our children, but all of us – in messaging, engaging in social media, getting the news, watching film and video, listening to music, gaming, e-sport, engaging in fitness and online shopping. The question I want to address is whether the benefits of these new technologies outweigh the issues they have created for our mental and physical wellbeing – or are we, as T. S. Eliot once said, 'just distracted from distraction by distraction'.

Wu argues that the tech industry has 'come to exert a more ambiguous though profound influence on how we live'. Whereas we were previously able to set boundaries and keep ourselves safe from the encroachment of consumption-driving companies, the majority of us now 'carry devices on our bodies that constantly find ways to commercialise the smallest particles of our time and attention'.[4]

Shoshana Zuboff, faculty at the Berkman Centre for the Internet and Society, says in her book *The Age of Surveillance Capitalism* that the internet's central role in our lives is 'so profound … that one can say without exaggeration that the individual as the author of his or her own life, is the protagonist of our age, whether we experience this fact as emancipation or affliction'.[5]

The digital revolution has changed the way we converse from talking to messaging. The telephone call, for Generation Z, is to be made in distress only, not for mainstream communication. If your child or friend has lost their debit card, is locked out, is ill or needs immediate assistance, you might get a call. Otherwise, you are likely to get a text, WhatsApp or IM.

Sam, twenty-three, with a Masters in African Studies and working for the Organisation for World Peace, says, 'I had a missed call yesterday from a friend while I was out for a run. My heart rate probably tripled when I saw it. Messaging has become such a throw-away most of the time, but phone calls retain a sense of imminence and importance.'

Use of the fixed landline for voice calls has been in decline for years, but in 2019, Ofcom's third-quarter telecommunications study reported that outgoing calls from mobiles dropped in volume for the first time.[6]

Seemiller and Grace in *Generation Z* observe that 'if they had to make a choice between only having a messaging app or a voice calling app on their phone, 73 per cent of Generation Z and Millennials in the US would get rid of voice calling'.[7] Further, the authors note that 'nearly half of Generation Z teens note that texting is their first platform of choice to reach their closest friends'.[8]

Of course, text chat and messaging is more convenient. You don't have to both be available at the same time, you can deal with it when you want, partially draft an answer, park it and come back to it after consideration. You can also sustain multiple conversations and indeed group chat at the same time. But human interaction through physical meeting and discussion declines as a result. It seems that this leads to more difficulty in holding conversation and relating to other people when the face-to-face moment comes. It could also lead to behaviours that would be much less likely to occur in a face-to-face discussion, including misunderstandings and perceived (or misperceived) aggression.

Martha, a bubbly and bright sixteen-year-old, says, 'In terms of our generation texting instead of calling, personally if I receive a call from someone without them saying they'll call or knowing why they are, my initial instinct is that I'm in trouble or have done something wrong. It is a more formal way of getting in contact with someone and sometimes feels more confrontational than a text message.'

Molly, sixteen, studying for her GCSEs, says, 'Phoning is rarely ever how I chat to friends. A Snapchat seems so much less hassle. My mum is always so insistent I call people if I have an issue or something important to say. She says you can deliver the emotions more clearly if you speak and will end up saying things in a message you would never say in real life. Although I hate it, I have learned that talking to someone face-to-face is so much better for a good stable friendship. I have been in situations where people have said stuff they would never say to my face, and all it does is cause great hurt and misunderstanding. I think our generation's lack of real-life communications will have a detrimental impact on our future lives.'

Henry, twenty-one, an LSE graduate who is a budding entrepreneur, says, 'I have sometimes held thoughts back during face-to-face interactions, but then expressed them later over messages, perhaps because it was easier.'

Baptiste, twenty-one, who works for Nannybag (a Generation Z company which holds your bag between your airport arrival and arrival at your Airbnb), says, 'I have certainly noticed a trend of "offence" increase. But also, a trend of not confronting issues head on; rather turning to your phone to "vent". I remember a friend who got upset over something said by another friend, but instead of turning to him to explain why he was annoyed at the time, he later turned to his phone and began tweeting his annoyance, tagging the "offender" in the posts, rather than simply confronting him at the time and explaining what pissed him off.'

By opting for messaging rather than talking, Gen Z has the opportunity to choose very carefully what to say and how much to reveal and can avoid having to engage immediately in a flowing back-and-forth dialogue. They can hide behind a delayed reply and 'curate' the response so that it conveys exactly what they want to impart. This mode of digital interaction couldn't be more different to the complexity and immediacy of conversation in a bar or sitting with a group of friends in the park, with its visual clues to friends' thinking and reactions.

Indeed, hiding behind the device seems to have become a way of Generation Z keeping friends at the distance of their choice. In *Alone Together*, Turkle develops an explanation as to why Generation Z finds messaging so attractive over conversation.[9] She calls it the Goldilocks effect. Of a particular youngster she says, 'She is a modern Goldilocks; for her texting puts people not too close, not too far, but at just the right distance.' But it seems that today's world 'is now full of modern Goldilockses, people who take comfort in being in touch with a lot of people whom they also keep at bay.'[10] Of course, any face-to-face conversation can involve lying, misleading or simply putting an inauthentic gloss on things. But when it is face-to-face, most people give away their real feelings.

Digital messaging reduces conversation, and many believe it attacks the heart of human interaction with a potentially dangerous loss of empathy. Turkle observed that 'from the early days, I saw that computers offer the illusion of companionship without the demands of friendship, without the demands of intimacy'.[11] This is because humans have needs and make demands that computers simply do not. Turkle continued, 'Most sips of connection don't add up to a gulp of conversation. Connecting in sips works for gathering discrete bits of information or for saying "I was thinking about you" or even for saying "I love you." But connecting in sips doesn't work so well for an apology. It doesn't work so well when we are called upon to see things from another's point of view.'[12] Of course, for some children who are shy, withdrawn or have special educational needs, online social network platforms can be an important way to take advantage of online disinhibition and establish new friendship groups in a way they might struggle to achieve in person, so it's important not to over-generalise.

Ping – goes my phone.

Funny how the incoming message has to be looked at immediately, right now, despite your being with other people, isn't it? It is strange that it has become acceptable to put face-to-face contact on hold in order to address a text message from a virtual presence, without any advance knowledge of how trivial the message may be. This lack of prioritisation has resulted in constant interruptions.

University of Oxford philosopher James Williams, in *Stand Out of Our Light*, compares the idea of the GPS in our car deciding to take us on wild goose chases rather than direct us straight to our destinations with social media interruptions. 'No one would put up with this kind of distraction from a technology that directs them through physical space. Yet we do precisely this on a daily basis, when it comes to the technologies that direct us through informational space.'[13]

Being interrupted has almost become a sign of popularity and is a source of constant stimulation. As Nicholas Carr, who has written extensively on the effects of technology, notes in *The Shallows*, 'We want to be interrupted, because each interruption brings us a valuable piece of information.'[14] As a result, sheltering ourselves from these alerts could lead to 'feeling out of touch or even socially isolated'. This leads to a constant desire for new information, no matter how trivial it may be. Indeed, Carr suggests, 'We willingly accept the loss of concentration and focus, in return for the wealth of compelling or at least diverting information we receive. Tuning out is not an option many of us would consider.'[15] Generation Z must multitask so as not miss out.

My youngest says to me, 'Dad, even something as niche as how many snaps you get compared with your friends in a certain time can measure popularity. It's ironic that those deemed most popular often find it hardest to socialise on their phones, because they have way too much going on with multiple social messaging services and they can't hold proper conversations with anyone because they are juggling too many at once.'

Giovanni, twenty, an Oxford undergraduate and social entrepreneur, says, 'We always check the phone if it vibrates, despite the fact that notifications are seldom urgent to address. I have often noticed this when I am in a group of friends. If one person constantly checks their phone, the question lingering in the air is often not "Why are they being so rude", but rather "Why do you have nothing to check on your phone?" Fear of missing out has given way to fear of having nothing to miss out on!'

Turkle concludes, 'We want more from technology but less from each other. It used to be that we imagined our mobile phones were there so we could talk to each other. Now we want our mobile phones to talk to us.'[16]

The problem with dealing with the incoming interruption regardless of what you are doing is that you have no idea until you look at it whether it deserves the priority you have just given it. The risk is that, as intensive multitaskers, Generation Z's brains are trained to become addicted to what is often spam, in the sense that it isn't at all urgent or even important. Nicholas Carr, author and formerly Executive Editor of the *Harvard Business Review*, believes the consequences for our intellectual lives could be enormous. We get hooked on wanting more and more online communication, much of which may be rubbish, to the detriment of the quality of what we focus on and face-to-face communication. 'As we ramp up the volume and velocity of our online connections, we want immediate answers,' Turkle asserts. 'In order to get them, we ask simpler questions, we dumb down our communications, even on the most important matters. And we become accustomed to a life of constant interruption.'[17]

Today's kids expect an immediate response. Even a short delay in receiving a reply from a friend can lead to a sense of rejection. Paranoia sets in. *He is up to something. He doesn't fancy me any more.* Meet Mariana. She texted her boyfriend Rishi, with whom she had been in an exciting relationship for months. She adored him. Rishi was normally pretty quick to respond to her texts. His phone had run out of battery that evening and he had fallen asleep, so it was the next morning before he responded. In the meantime, she told me, she had convinced herself he had gone off her or, worse, might have gone off with someone else. She wasn't totally convinced by the whole dead battery explanation, so when he texted back in the morning, she left it several hours before she replied in order to punish him.

Text messages are much easier to misunderstand than face-to-face conversation, because they are not accompanied by visual clues. I texted a CEO I work closely with the other morning and started a reply to a message from him with the words 'Read this carefully.' I meant that *I* had carefully *read* an incoming message from a third party that he had forwarded to me, and my subsequent text represented my views on that message. However, he interpreted my message as a directive for him to 'read this carefully', implying he had failed to do so, and so he answered testily that he *had* read it carefully. Luckily we know each other well, and the confusion was quickly resolved with no consequences, but this is not always the case with teenagers. Misunderstandings can lead to what is known as 'escalation' into conflict. Practitioners observe that this potential for misunderstanding and, relatedly, stunted empathy can have serious consequences for the social lives of Generation Z. Dr Hilarie Cash, the leader of reSTART, an internet addiction clinic, notes that she 'has seen dozens of adolescents, mainly boys, but also girls, who have no problem interacting with peers online, but can't carry a conversation with someone sitting across from them'.[18]

Skype, Facetime, WhatsApp video and even Snapchat, all of which involve visual elements, looked like partial solutions to the lack of face-to-face physical contact for a while. They do provide opportunities for quick 'live' reactions. Houseparty and Fam are new apps which facilitate live group video conversations and may also play their part as they become more popular. Such visual communications platforms have very much come into their own during the Covid-19 crisis, with tools like Zoom, Google Hangouts and Microsoft Teams enjoying a massive boost in usage numbers. But there are two issues with these apps in relation to Generation Z's interaction. Many don't like using them because they require focus and inhibit multitasking. This may explain why some prefer to leave a voice message via an instant messaging system, which is efficient, involves just speaking *at* their phone, involves no typing and enables them to continue to avoid an engaged two-way live dialogue and continue multitasking. And very often, the camera on a laptop is situated in such a way that the participants in a video call are not actually making eye contact with one another when conversing. Because they are looking at their counterparty on the screen, they appear to be looking down.

The ubiquity of social media platforms has also changed the way Generation Z interacts with friends. Teens don't engage in face-to-face communication with friends as much as we used to. A Common Sense Media survey in 2018 revealed that the percentage of teens preferring in-person communication had dropped from 49 to 32 per cent in 2018, while social media, texting and video-chatting had all increased.[19] They are much more casual about making arrangements to meet up and about cancelling them at short notice. Social media offers instant 'friends' on tap and facilitates relatively last-minute arrangements. I ask my son who is going to London for the day (an hour and a half away) who he is going to meet there. He says, 'I don't know yet, got a few messages out, but plenty of people around.'

For a book that raises questions about the harms potentially being done by devices and technological hyperconnectivity, I feel it is important to say that social media is by no means all bad and can provide support to Generation Z as they grow up. In a study of Generation Z teens, the Pew Research Center found that nearly 70 per cent had received support on social media while dealing with a challenge or going through a tough time.[20] In polling for a Girl Scout Institute report in 2019, 68 per cent of girls and 59 per cent of boys said they supported the statement 'I have discovered a new talent or interest by exploring online', with 60 per cent of girls and 51 per cent of boys agreeing that they are 'more connected to social issues and causes because of the internet'.[21] During Covid-19, social media has become a crucial lifeline for many, providing connectivity to friends and information at a time when it was otherwise not available.

Rather than, as some suggest, social media promoting negativity, perhaps social media is an amplifier of your underlying mental state. Eddy, nineteen, an Oxford undergraduate and budding TV actor, says, 'I have certainly found social media a very supportive place recently – people posting pictures to raise awareness of mental health and raising money. That said, girls' supportive comments on their friends' profile pictures on FB and Insta are so supportive, they can often seem sycophantic to me. But it has only seemed this way when I'm in a mood that isn't seeing the best in everyone, myself included. I went through a rough period settling/fitting into uni in the first months and spent hours down black holes on social media platforms. Despite the time I spent looking at social media, I didn't post at all and found it hard to reply to messages, probably because I had low self-esteem. Forcing myself to spend less time on social media certainly helped rebuild confidence quickly and get back to making the most out of uni. Now that I am much happier and loving life again, I seem to see the best of social media and how it can be supportive. But equally, I reflect on my rough patch and view it as having been a more insidious presence in my life than I realised at the time. It seems to me it is at its worst when people are at/near their worst and its best when people are at/near their best.'

How Facebook became a global phenomenon with its business model makes much more sense when you know that Mark Zuckerberg, its founder, took a combined degree in psychology and computer science. Facebook's stated mission is to bring people together. But Wu notes that Facebook offered something much more compelling: 'an augmented representation of themselves ... at their contrived best, with hundreds of friends (before success became equated with thousands) and others still in the queue awaiting "approval".'[22] The earliest pitches to advertisers in 2004 touted the platform's 'addicted' users and the potential for 'nanotargeting', harnessing the power of networks and the madness of crowds.[23]

Despite some of the tangible benefits of sites like Facebook, there do seem to be substantial downsides. Alter says 'up to 59 per cent of people say they're dependent on social media sites and that their reliance on these sites ultimately makes them unhappy'.[24] He adds that social media addicts report needing to check sites at least once an hour, after which they report feeling anxious, agitated and distracted. And Alter's research showed that as long ago as 2015, there were 280 million smartphone addicts. As the author notes, 'If they banded together to form the "United States of Nomophobia", it would be the fourth largest most populous country in the world, after China, India and the United States.'[25]

Adolescent children, in particular, have a habit of choosing to compare themselves with people who are superior to them when thinking about a particular physical or mental attributes. As Alter notes, 'Humans are inherently aspirational; we look forward rather than backward, so no matter where we stand, we'll tend to focus on people who have more.'[26] However, the problem with social media is that it conveys a picture of a *perfect* life. Consequently, much of Generation Z feels inferior on some metric at least some of the time. The carefully curated images shown on social media are, however, fake news in the ultimate sense. The real world is unlike the seemingly perfect social media world. As young people continually experience this façade, it is natural for them to feel inadequate and confused, creating ideal conditions for low self-esteem and more serious mental health issues.

So, do these perfectly designed sites make Generation Z unhappy? Could it be that images of happiness engender feelings of inadequacy in those for whom happiness is not their everyday experience? That in our unending quest to appear perfect, 'we often neglect the very parts of ourselves that bring us true happiness, joy, connection, love and pleasure'?

According to Freitas, humans become adept at hiding and putting up façades for an anonymised audience.[27]

Molly says, 'Whilst social media has certainly brought important social issues to light recently, as a sixteen-year-old girl I feel there are too many negative impacts. What I have to keep reminding myself is that all these gorgeous, perfect people blasted all over Instagram and TikTok are only showing their perfect selves. I forget they all have their own lives and issues going on. I do feel that social media has impacted my view of myself, and I definitely have many insecurities that I believe stem from social media. While social media can be brilliant, I think apps like Instagram, in my eyes, do more harm than good. The tragic thing is that I don't really want to use Instagram that much, but feel the social pressure to have an account in order to seem "in" with everyone my age. I have spoken with friends about this and was amazed how many of them agreed.'

Astrid, twenty, a Lululemon marketing officer and model, says, 'My friends are in constant conversation – "Have you seen X's last IG post?" or "Did you see how pretty X is? I wish I could look/be like her" – and coping with feelings of inadequacy when spending long periods of time scrolling through social media. The ideals and perceived expectations set on Gen Z women in this day and age have been crafted by social media and, whilst everyone is aware of the editing that goes into "plandid" (planned-candid) posts, it still creates an expectation of a perfect image, leaving many of us feeling not quite good enough most of the time.'

Personal content on social media is largely user-created and generally not verified by either the platform or anyone else. Wu asserts that Facebook has created what he calls 'another realm of unreality, one that, on account of looking real, was more misleading'. But it is not only in the proliferation of fake news that unreality takes place, but also in the veneer of manufactured happiness. This, Wu claims, hides 'the reality of life with its ups and its downs'.[28]

Ultimately, when it comes to social media, the connections made, whatever they may be called, are often not really 'friends'. Having more followers, connections, likes and comments may lead to more of a sense of support, but doesn't generally lead to the development of deep and meaningful friendships. Turkle echoes this sentiment, noting that 'the ties we form through the internet are not, in the end, the ties that bind. But they are the ties that preoccupy'.[29] As a friend of mine said to me, 'Facebook is where you lie to your friends and Twitter is where you tell the truth to strangers'.

Let's consider the role of the all-important 'selfie' in all of this. You are excited to be at Iguazu falls, one of the world's largest waterfalls and most beautiful natural sites. You have travelled a long way to get there and, once on the viewing platform, you stand, stare at the incredible view and take in the experience for ages, listening to the extraordinary sound of tonnes of water crashing down. Time passes as you try to take in the awesome scenery. But you are struck by the younger travellers who, presumably, have also travelled a long way: they walk up, take a selfie, create some short video clips and then pretty much leave. I call this living 'life through the lens'. Reality doesn't exist unless it's instantly captured on a phone and immediately posted on social media for the benefit of friends. As the poet W. H. Davies famously wrote, 'What is this life, if full of care, we have no time to stand and stare?'

Baptiste says, 'I have found myself multiple times, when leaving on my annual trips, facing the dilemma of whether to take the iPhone or not. It is the best way to bring back memories, but it also quickly means you to live every moment through it. So how to balance the willingness to document and share while enjoying the moment?'

'Selfies are a big part of the happiness effect. They are the product of the need, even the perceived requirement among college students, for self-promotion online. And this in turn takes away from the real joys and happiness of living with someone without worrying about having to promote it on social media,' says Freitas.[30]

And 'many argued selfies were "not good for people's self-esteem" or body image and they contribute to the very problematic trend of "everyone constantly comparing themselves to everyone else" and driving people to compete against each other'. 'A number of students chose this topic to express complaints about how, because of selfies, "we're no longer living in the moment", and this is a tragic loss.'[31]

When you think back to the best moments of your life, it has been sharing special moments with those around you, your close friends, family, travel companions, that made it so special. Now, it seems, this sharing has moved into a virtual world, and I find it hard to believe that any number of subsequent likes or 'awesome' comments on a social media site are as good as sharing the experience live with human beings on the spot. And of course you could have both, much like we used to enjoy the moment and then shared a photo album. And 'with the pressure to post photos to prove that their lives are great comes a further intrusion into time spent alone, with friends, and participating in the activities they enjoy. Whatever else selfies are, they are a particularly immediate and egregious case of the happiness effect.'[32]

Eddy says, 'In Paxos in the summer, we went to a bar to watch the sunset, and there was a balcony where people were queuing up for five to ten minutes just to stand in the best spot to get a selfie. My family spent more time watching this fascinating new species – the selfie animal – than we did taking in the scenery. But I guess we're not completely innocent either!' Freitas says of selfies, 'the quality of experience is beginning to take second place to the quantity of proof we collect'.[33]

Alberto, twenty-one, says, 'I remember going to a concert with my best friend when I was thirteen. We sang and savoured new freedoms for the first time, and it was one of the best experiences of my life. Two years ago, I went to a concert in Milan and was speechless at the number of people who seemed there just to Instagram the event and spent their entire time taking pictures. I also remember my ex-girlfriend being mad at me because I didn't want to take pictures everywhere we went and her being offended if I didn't immediately like her selfies on Instagram. The most unsettling thing, though, was that these absurd quarrels ultimately led to bigger problems in our relationship.'

More worrying is the gender stereotype issue that selfies may reinforce and the need for perfection – the whitest teeth, best eyelashes, most perfect abs, ripped chest. It's not so much an issue between the genders, but one which reinforces the stereotypical view, reinforced daily by social media, of what a perfect (presented as typical) man or woman looks like – leaving the impression that everyone wants to look like a Love Island contestant. Certainly, the numbers of school-age boys undertaking serious body-shaping exercise programmes, drinking protein powders and taking steroids should cause us all concern. Recent studies have shown increased rates of eating disorders in young people, and that most eating disorders develop during adolescence. It's not just a girl problem, as over 25 per cent of cases involve boys. Eating disorders also cause the highest mortality rate among psychiatric disorders. This suggests that the need for the perfect gym body and to look buff in the social media mirror can be dangerous. Dr Terence Larkin, a consultant psychiatrist in Dublin, observes kids are exercising to be big, not fit. 'Men are beginning to go down the route of overvaluing physical appearance, and self-esteem is becoming more dependent on that.'[34] He observes that, as boys don't fit the normal stereotype of those suffering from eating disorders (because it's more prevalent in girls), the stigma is even greater and the likelihood of them seeking help is even lower.

For most Generation Z, a carefully 'curated' post on social media is an art form, not just some random selfie with an idle comment. Curation is the process of selecting, preparing and presenting online content. The practice varies by social group, gender and location, as well as by medium. The text is probably more important than the picture on Twitter, whereas on Instagram it may be the other way round. Freitas speaks of the three c's when it comes to social media posting – craft, cultivate and curate. 'To live up to this pressure and constant expectation infects every dimension of his or her online experience,' she notes. 'It influences a person's vulnerability ... their sense of future, how they feel about the "real them", and how they find authenticity (or don't) in their relationships with others, the ways in which they compare themselves to their peers, and whether or not they feel accepted or isolated socially.'[35]

As a result of the curation, the authenticity level is low. Turkle says 'we hide from each other even as we're constantly connected to each other. For on our screens, we are tempted to present ourselves as we would like to be. Of course, performance is part of any meeting, anywhere, but online and at our leisure, it is easy to compose, edit, improve and revise. The concept is of our better self.'[36] Is it knowing that this better self does not reflect reality that can make Generation Z unhappy? Alter observes that the vast majority of young people always try to *appear* happy, a phenomenon that Freitas calls the happiness effect in her book of that title. 'Simply put, because young people feel so pressured to post happy things on social media, most of what everyone sees on social media from their peers are happy things; as a result they often feel inferior because they aren't actually happy all the time.'[37] Having read the book, I wonder whether a better title would not have been 'The *Unhappiness* Effect'.

Henry, twenty-one, says, 'I deleted my FB, IG and any other social media platforms I was using because I realised it took up far too much of my time – during exams at school, I took the decision to ignore the noise of constant notifications and the need to always check my phone. I stepped back and realised that people used FB / IG to present a certain version of themselves, and at times I fell victim to the age-old psychological issue of comparing myself with my peers – seeing their great holidays, smiling photos, etc. often made me question why I wasn't like that the whole time.'

What started as a different form of communication to conversation becomes addictive self-promotion. Wu goes so far to say that Facebook has created a 'virtual attention plantation' by way of 'attention arbitrage', comparing users to 'renters willingly making extensive improvements to their landlord's property, even as they were made to look at advertisements'.[38] Many teenagers edit texts quite carefully to convey a crafted message. The same applies in spades to images. Sending images is seen as safer than sending edited texts. They can be cropped and passed through a perfect filter.

Generation Z sometimes goes so far as to create multiple Instagram accounts; there is a 'rinsta', or 'real' Instagram profile, where they maintain a public persona of curated images, and a 'finsta', or 'fake' Instagram presence or more unfiltered content for closer friends only. Generation Z finds this completely natural as it doesn't distinguish the online and offline worlds and the real and fake as we might. Eduardo, nineteen, an ambitious Bath University undergraduate from Portugal, says, 'I hadn't thought about it until now, but isn't it bizarre that we call the account with the perfect self, curated images the *real* profile and the other one, with the more authentic personal images, *fake!*'

Baptiste, the upbeat Nannybag worker, told me he was aware his ex-girlfriend had two Instagram accounts. 'Looking back, it doesn't surprise me now that even reaching some kind of celebrification didn't bring her happiness, but the opposite. The more followers, the higher the expectations, the easier to suffer low self-esteem.'

My youngest says, 'Dad, people are so used to people posting the best of themselves now that they see through the façade. It's so easy to tell when someone is catfishing that their perfect/best self pics create a negative sphere around them. Those who post what people can tell are very genuine and natural photos are starting to become the best looked-at – like it's become reputable to do so. The original rose-tinted-glass outlook of social media has started to crack.'

Freitas calls today's social media platforms 'the grand new boulevards of still nascent modern cities', comparing them to 'public spaces for everyone to stroll in their fashionable best, to parade their romances and their families and their finest, to display with pride their riches and achievements, to inspect and acknowledge the similarly garbed and lucky, as well as look down their noses at the less fortunate and even turn their backs on those they simply don't want to see'.[39]

Facebook, Twitter and then Instagram paved the way for what Wu has called the 'celebrification' of everyday life and everyday people. Before social media sites existed, millennials hero-worshipped film and TV celebrities. Sites like Facebook and Instagram have now democratised fame, providing platforms where anyone can market themselves. As Zuckerberg himself notes, Facebook users are 'building an image and identity for themselves, which in a sense is their brand. They're connecting with the audience that they want to connect to … as celebrities had become, the ordinary individual was now more of a business proposition.'[40]

Rex Sorgatz of *New York Magazine* coined the term 'microfame' to describe the phenomenon.[41] Wu observes that 'Twitter … sparked microfame, measured it, and threw fuel on the fire'. Indeed, he observes that the twenty-first century has given rise to a 'rapt audience that is willing to idolise these so-called influencers and give them licence to monetise our attention'.[42]

The search for microfame is a common social craving that is facilitated by a combination of social media platforms and the smartphone. In effect, this combination puts a film studio in the hands of every consumer. I wasn't remotely a social media junkie until I discovered what

I call 'the nice platform', LinkedIn. I call it nice because, so far, it has not attracted the kind of negative people and comments that other platforms like Twitter, Facebook and Instagram have. I waste as much time maintaining my profile there as my wife does trying to get a five-star rating from Uber drivers!

Williams suggests that fame is the main value held up by children's TV shows as being most worth pursuing. In an age of information abundance and attention scarcity, Williams argues, this means fame is a facet of life meriting attention.[43]

The search for fame can become all-consuming. Some are concerned it is leading to a rise in narcissism. In their book *The Narcissism Epidemic*, Jean Twenge and Keith Campbell suggest that 'Generation Z is more generation *me* than generation *we*.' The authors suggest that there is a 'rise in self focus among American young people, including narcissism, high expectations, self-esteem, thinking one is above average, and focusing on personal (vs global) fears'.[44] Freed bolsters this thesis, noting that 'those who spend greater amounts of time social networking tend to be more narcissistic than those who spend less … [and] such focus on self-promotion can encourage teens' self-absorption at the expense of empathy for the needs of their families and others'.[45]

As Wu points out, the problem with the democratisation of fame through social media is that it 'legitimises the self-aggrandisement as an objective for ever more of us'. This, in turn, 'warps our understanding of our own existence and its relation to others', creating what is 'surely the definitive dystopian vision of late modernity'.[46]

Social media has become the conduit for widely and rapidly spreading bad news, delivering it to many who might otherwise have remained blissfully unaware. Williams notes that, 'According to a study in the US and Canada, less than 5 per cent of the population will ever personally experience a truly moral misdeed in real life. However, in the era of smartphones, if anyone experiences a misdeed, then everyone potentially experiences it.'[47] It's not just about the wide dissemination of bad news. There is also a ramping-up of the volume, so to speak. Williams identifies this heightened level of anxiety as 'cyberchondria' – which is defined as the 'unfounded escalation of concerns about common symptomatology, based on the review of search results and literature on the web'.[48] Certainly the constant stream of social media suggesting that due to Covid-19, the end of the world is nigh would support this idea!

The neuroscientists working for the tech companies have worked out that negative emotions are more engaging than positive ones. Their aim, of course, is to keep your attention focused on their platform or app. Jaron Lanier, computer philosophy writer and a key founder of the world of virtual reality, observes that 'negative emotions such as fear and anger well up more easily and dwell in us longer than positive ones … this is true in real life, but it is even more true in the flattened light of algorithms … engagement is not meant to serve any particular purpose other than its own enhancement, and yet as a result it is an unnatural global amplification of the "easy" emotions, which happen to be the negative ones'.[49] James Haig, in *Notes on a Nervous Planet*, says 'Of course, news is almost designed to stress us out. If it was designed to keep us calm, it wouldn't be news. It would be yoga. Or a puppy.'[50] This is why 'watching news can feel like a continuous metaphor for generalised anxiety order'.[51]

The concept of 'liking' bad news postings also seems a strange phenomenon. My wife was very struck when a goddaughter made a Facebook post about her grandmother dying, in which she was very open about her feelings and how much she would miss her. My wife was completely bemused that a post about something so personal and sad got 'liked' by so many 'friends'.

Social media negativity isn't like being hurt by a real person, though, is it? Is it a good thing that youngsters air their feelings on social media or can it be damaging like a face-to-face argument? Alter expresses concern that 'Online interactions aren't just different from real world interactions; they're immeasurably worse. Humans learn empathy and understanding by watching how their actions affect other people. Empathy can't flourish without immediate feedback, and it's a very slow developing skill.'[52] Lanier similarly worries that there is an 'inability to carve out a space in which to invest oneself without constant judgement; that is what makes me unhappy. How can you have self-esteem, when that's not the kind of esteem that matters most anymore?'[53]

Does social media and the need to be seen on it create some kind of Hobson's choice for Generation Z? Catherine Steiner-Adair's study of girls' online use found that they learned and encountered cruelty, oversexualisation and social turmoil. And Nancy Jo Sales, a journalist who interviewed 13–18-year-olds to understand how they interacted with social media, concluded that 'As addictive contexts go, this was the perfect storm; almost every teenage girl was using one or more social platforms, so they were forced to choose between social isolation or compulsive overuse.'[54]

Freddie Pearson, a twenty-one-year-old teenage mental health campaigner, fitness model and influencer, had enormous early success on social media. He then suffered mental health issues from the pressure it put him under, and he told me, 'Social media status has created a new valuation system among young people. The more followers and numbers associated with your name, the higher you appear in a social hierarchy. Followers are the attraction, likes the currency, and young people have fallen into a terrible mindset of valuing themselves based on likes and attention. Constantly comparing themselves to other people, wishing they looked like someone else, living the life of another – social media's addictive yet dishonest nature takes advantage of human nature. The greatest threat that social media poses is the lack of real social interaction. Despite being called "social media", we are getting less face-to-face time, which is detrimental to wellbeing, as we are social creatures. "Anti-social" media is redefining what it is to have friends – are they people we actually see, or just random people we speak to online? People are living their lives through social media to the point where we are not using social media, social media is using us.' His Ted talk on this is very moving.

A rational person would compare their real self with the average self seen on social media. Freitas makes a chilling observation. Generation Z posts the best of itself on social media but then compares what it sees generally on social media not with its own posted best self, but with its worst self, driving inevitable low self-esteem. This seems to create a sort of clinical online bipolarity: presenting a brave face on social media, whilst internally being sad, feeling low self-esteem and potentially becoming depressed. Haig says, 'our bodies will never be as firm and symmetrical and ageless as those of bionic sex robots, so we need quite quickly to learn how to be happy with not having society's unrealistic version of the "best" body ... not least because being unhappy with our body doesn't make us look any better. It just makes us feel a lot worse.'[55]

The dopamine hit from expected approbation for posting the perfect self seems to drive compulsion to post more. Freitas suggests that, while approval for posts was once a by-product of online activity, it is now instead the case that 'the anticipated approval is what's driving the behaviour'.[56] The problem, Freitas suggests, is that this constant approval-seeking mechanism – which poses as socialising – only makes users feel lonelier.

Compulsive use of social media in a never-ending frenzy of approbation-seeking carries not just the risk or real loneliness, however. Freitas suggests that unless users 'have rock solid self-esteem, are impervious to jealousy, or have an extraordinarily rational capacity to remind yourself exactly what everyone is doing when they post their glories on social media, it's difficult not to care'.[57]

Social media encourages the pursuit of 'junk' values, not healthy values, says the charity Global Action Plan. In their recent report on children's use of social media, they looked at the effects of social media in encouraging children to focus on *extrinsic* goals rather than *intrinsic* goals of mental wellbeing. Extrinsic goals include those such as achieving financial success, having an attractive appearance and social recognition, whilst intrinsic goals include self-acceptance, affiliation and community feeling. The report notes that decades of research demonstrate that prioritising intrinsic goals is associated with higher wellbeing and prioritising extrinsic goals is associated with lower wellbeing, and that generational increases in psychological ill-health among young people have been attributed to a cultural shift towards extrinsic goals. The report notes that the focus on extrinsic goals reflects the fact that youngsters' self-esteem is reliant on others' approval, their feeling of self-worth is fragile, and that even when youngsters are successful in meeting their goals, the buzz they get is short-lived, and a lack of external validation from others can quickly deflate them again. Extrinsic goals also encourage upward social comparison, which leaves children feeling worse about themselves.[58]

In an article in the *Huffington Post*, Dr Richard Freed advances the theory that 'entrusting our kids' wellbeing to the capricious and drama-filled world of peer relationships – made even harsher and more swiftly viral online – is a mistake of grand proportions'.[59] The Cyberbullying Research Center has found that nearly a third of Generation Z middle- and high-school students have experienced cyberbullying at some point in their lives.[60] And whereas previous generations were more likely to escape school bullies upon leaving school, Generation Z's bullies follow them around on the internet.

Whilst each online relationship is, in reality, relatively unimportant in the grand scheme of life, they can take on a much higher degree of importance than they deserve. Freed says, 'all too often preteens or teens

I work with go to bed believing they have a best friend, only to find out when they arrive at school that late night online drama has destroyed this relationship forever. Not surprisingly, as these kids watch the peer contact they so deeply depend on suddenly collapse, they can fall into depression and even consider suicide.'[61]

Discussing inadequacy – or feelings of inadequacy – in a carefully curated social media world is next to impossible. Freitas notes that 'many young adults experience some kind of alienation because of social media, but they feel further alienated because they don't see a thriving public discussion about the struggles they are experiencing'.[62]

Marco says, 'I'm glad to see you mention the impact that technology has had on the resilience of Generation Z. In this section you remind me of my little brother, who is looking for his first job after graduating. He had to take a week off to recover because he has received his first few rejections from employers. He won't even pick up the phone to me for fear that I'll mention how he needs to improve his CV. He's been surrounded by instant gratification for years, and I fear there's a chance that he'll just check out when he sees that the world is not as it was at university.'

Some say social media is the digital equivalent of the photo albums my generation created. Freitas disagrees, noting that our social networks comprise 'a 24/7 performance that requires everyone to take acting lessons'. The only thing worse than getting bad reviews on these performances is getting no reviews at all. As a result, 'there comes a point at which it is no longer fun to memorialise our activities and our time with friends, when the documentation begins to detract from and even destroy our time together'.[63]

Social media engagement for Generation Z, seemingly harmless, actually carries much more downside that it might at first seem to. Indeed, it has led to a far-reaching phenomenon of young adults conceiving of themselves as brands and marketable commodities.[64]

In a recent interview in the *New York Magazine*, Kevin Systrom, founder of Instagram, was asked about the human costs of the product he had invented and the pressures it puts Generation Z under. He said, 'the people I have talked to, they typically express the pressure to feel like they have to put on the idea that they're living this perfect life, that they go out every night, that they spend a ton of money, that they're with fancy people, that they're skinny, the list goes on ... and the more interesting life you have, the more jealous others might become'. He identified the shift which Instagram made as it scaled to rank the feed, prioritising the inclusion in other people's feeds of those who posted regularly, putting users under pressure to post more and more. He went on to observe that, having looked at his feed the previous day, he could no longer find posts of his friends, only brands. 'That's a transition that happened at Instagram. It became a marketing tool for a lot of people.'[65]

Alberto, twenty-one, an Italian graduate working in a startup accelerator, says, 'The echo chambers generated by the ubiquity of technology and the messages that continually filter from social media are like a million voices whispering all day long, "You are not at the top of the food chain, you are a failure." One can try to resist such emotional stress, but sooner or later the strain will take its toll on your system. For many it is subtle and gradual. For some unlucky individuals, it can have devastating effects on psyche and body.'

Generation Z finds it difficult to express even slightly controversial or non-politically correct religious or political views on mainstream social media in their own names. Many have found they have been attacked on those same platforms for posting views that are either not the majority view or not deemed socially acceptable views. This has led to a new range of platforms such as Tumblr and Reddit, where Generation Z can create anonymous profiles using nicknames or even just avatars – here they can say what they like without fear of attribution and targeted retribution.[66]

Freitas says, 'They are learning that true authenticity requires anonymity, or at least impermanence, because they are afraid to be honest and truthful on the platforms attached to their names. Standing up for who we are and what we believe in is something that young adults are learning is best done anonymously ... We all become excellent people-pleasers, without concern or worry about the effect such constant people-pleasing might have on self-development and happiness.'[67]

Alberto says, 'The textbook rule is to camouflage with the mass and do not say anything outside the choir, or at least to be part of a faction big enough that no direct responsibility can be attributed to oneself. For many of my generation, the discrepancy between one's true beliefs and those actually shown on social media is hardly perceived as an issue – this applies to relationships, politics, academia and work. This is worryingly reminiscent of the Victorian Compromise vividly depicted in Oscar Wilde's literature.'

Eduardo says, 'I feel that being anonymous on politics is paramount. I thoroughly enjoy politics, although I am very moderate. Seeing controversial politicians like Trump and Boris – especially among Gen Z – no matter what they say or do, you are not allowed to praise them. It seems like I am forced to accept this assertion that they are absolutely evil, when this is not the case. Sometimes I agree with their actions. It's not always bad.'

This inability to express non-mainstream views or be an outlier online has spread into the offline world. Emery White talks of the culture of offence now found on some university campuses where students demand protection from words and ideas they don't like and seek to have those that promote them punished, even if the offence was accidental. He talks of 'microaggressions' – actions with no malicious intent but which might be thought of as a kind of violence, nevertheless – and the need for 'trigger warnings', like you get before potentially disturbing TV programmes or news items, where professors might be required to say if something in the course might evoke a strong emotional reaction.[68] Greg Lukianoff and Jonathan Haidt say that 'A moment is arising … to scrub campuses clean of words, ideas and subjects that might cause discomfort or give offense.'[69]

The increasing pace of technological change when it comes to what's trendy creates new communication gaps. Professor Daniel Zizzo, my mentor where I am an adjunct professor at the University of Queensland, tells me there isn't just a communication gap between my generation and my kids', but that students in successive cohorts say they have problems understanding students who joined ahead of them by only a couple of years due to the rapidity of technological change and its effect on social media communication patterns. A Student Union leader complained to him about the increasing difficulty of communicating effectively with union members who are only a year or two behind at the same university.

4

THE BATTLE ROYALE
FOR YOUR ATTENTION

YouTube is now the second most visited site in the world after Google, and its users are a mix of individuals, hobbyists, professional YouTubers, businesses and brands. It has 1.9 billion logged-in users each month. Every day, people watch over a billion hours of video. Some users just wish to share their content, many use it for education and news, others use it to promote themselves, their businesses or their brands. Roughly half say they use it to express their creativity and half to promote themself or their business. YouTube has in part been responsible for the growth of influencers who make a living by promoting their views on products and services for reward on YouTube and elsewhere, e.g. Instagram. YouTube has arguably democratised stardom, from personal trainers, to make-up artists, to chefs – anyone who can demonstrate their skills in a video can use it to create a business. A study by Google and Ipsos found that 70 per cent of teens who subscribe to YouTube relate more to everyday YouTube content creators than traditional celebrities. YouTube is now a big business owned by Google and it uses its search algorithm to promote its own revenues. Users say this forces them to make more and more videos, potentially daily, to remain seen. The average YouTube video is only about twelve minutes long.

In their 'Generation Z goes to college' study, Seemiller and Grace found that two in three of those in Generation Z utilise YouTube as a way to learn and further that half of them 'couldn't live' without YouTube. They cite a Google study in which more than 70 per cent of Generation Z teens (between thirteen and seventeen) reported watching three or more hours of videos a day for entertainment *on their smartphones alone*.[1]

YouTube has been found to have addictive attractions, just like other aspects of the internet. Williams notes that 'one of the first projects that Google's DeepMind division put their "AlphaGo" system to work on was enhancing YouTube's video recommendation algorithm. In other words … the same system that defeated the human world champion at the game Go is sitting the other side of your screen and showing you videos that it thinks will keep you using YouTube for as long as possible'.[2]

Molly says, 'I can easily watch YouTube for hours and not notice the time slip away. I also frequently watch it while doing other activities, because I like there to be lots going on.'

The Viaccess-Orca blog in 2018 reported that binge watching increased dramatically in the younger generations with 91 per cent of Gen Z watching six or more consecutive episodes in one sitting, up from only 80 per cent of baby boomers watching on average around four.[3] Chris Stokel-Walker explains in his book *YouTubers* how YouTube's algorithm is designed to prioritise and lengthen watch time and to keep people watching for as long as possible.[4] The *Economist* and *Wired* reporter found that children as young as four were spending more than an hour on the website each time they visited it. That steadily increases, almost without exception to the age of eighteen, when 36 per cent of people watch videos for more than sixty minutes at a time. This is more striking than it may at first seem, given the average video length of around twelve minutes – meaning viewers who search on one subject and stay for over an hour are watching on average more than five videos before leaving.

The data was compiled by Kids Insights and looked at the online habits of 20,000 young people.

And it seems watching video is not necessarily an end in itself. Seemiller and Grace cite a study by Hulu which found that 43 per cent of those in Generation Z watch shows so that they can talk about them with their friends, 32 per cent watch just to impress others, and 23 per cent watch to look smart. They say that 'video consumption has become such a form of social currency that one in five members of Generation Z have posted online about a show they haven't even seen'.[5]

Generation Z loves gaming. It is arguably the area where designers have perfected their techniques to lure players into spending more and more time. The video game industry claims some benefits of gaming for children – notably the ability to socialise with peers during the game (something which lockdown for Covid-19 brought to the fore), somewhat reduced reaction times and somewhat improved visual attention (meaning faster processing time for new visual stimuli). UKIE, which represents the UK gaming and interactive entertainment industry, says that games provide rich story worlds, creative canvases, entertaining learning environments, pure entertainment and ways to understand difficult topics such as civil rights and historical topics. They observe that games are a form of play, and play is an activity that is crucial to human development. They also say that games can play a significant part in students achieving learning objectives. Finally, that good game design instils systems thinking, computational thinking and an understanding of good design principles and can be applied across the entire education system. Some of these claims are borne out by science. But Freed points out these are different skills from focus and maintaining attention – the latter being much more important to a child. And time spent on games takes away from family time and study time. A study by University of Michigan and University of Texas researchers show children aged ten to nineteen who played video games spent 30 per cent less time reading compared to non-gamers.[6]

Family doctor and psychologist Leonard Sax, in his book *Boys Adrift*, says 'a series of studies over the past seven years has demonstrated clearly and unambiguously that the more time our child spends playing video games, the less likely he is to do well in school'.[7]

Have the best neuroscientists in the world been employed to make video games addictive? Alter says of gaming, 'As with Tetris and 2048, humans find the sweet spot between "too easy" and "too difficult" irresistible. It's the land of the just-challenging-enough computer games, financial targets, work ambitions, social media objectives, and fitness goals. Addictive experiences live in this sweet spot, where stopping rules crumble before obsessive goal-setting. Tech mavens, game developers, and product designers tweak their wares to ensure their complexity scales as users gain insight and competence.'[8]

Psychology Today cites a report by Doctors Edward Deci and Richard Ryan which identifies that games are specifically designed to provide the three things children need to flourish: competence – the need for mastery, progression, achievement and growth; autonomy – the need for volition and freedom of control over choice; and relatedness – the need to feel like we matter to others and that others matter to us. They argue kids do not feel competence, autonomy and relatedness in school enough. They are told what to do, their timing is controlled, teachers opine on subjects they are not interested in, if they are bored they are punished and if they want to explore something else they are prodded back on track. In gaming, they call the shots, do what they want and experiment with creative strategies to solve problems. They are connected to their fellow gamers or 'friends'. But as Deci and Ryan observe, while a well-designed game attempts to satisfy these needs, it can't come close to the deep satisfaction that real life and real human connection can provide.[9]

Most games are designed with levels that get harder the better at the game you become. As Oliver Burkeman, writing in the *Guardian*, put it, 'When you approach life as a sequence of milestones to be achieved, you exist "in a state of near continuous failure".'[10] This is just like the comparison against perfection problem in social media I identified earlier except with an additional twist. Burkeman goes on, 'almost all the time, by definition, you're not at the place you've defined as embodying accomplishment or success. And should you get there, you'll find you've lost the very thing that gave you a sense of purpose – so you'll formulate a new goal and start again.'[11]

Some researchers have claimed that video gaming can help kids deal with their natural feelings of stress and aggression. But many also say that it makes kids more aggressive after they play. Alter observes that 'one study found that gamers aged between ten and fifteen years old who played more than 3 hours a day were less satisfied with their lives, less likely to feel empathy towards other people, and less likely to know how to deal with their emotions appropriately'.[12]

'The change toward a more aggressive disposition as a result of video games does seem to be a definite global phenomenon across different cultures,' concludes Susan Greenfield, perhaps the UK's best-known neuroscientist and author of *Mind Change: How Digital Technologies Are Leaving Their Mark on Our Brains*, having reviewed all the studies.[13] The problem is worsened by the fact that many video games involve serious violence, including most of the top-selling games. 'The violent content of computer games could have a sensitising effect to violent behaviour towards others, in part by lowering the threshold of response to provocation and through a dwindling in empathy with other people.' A Kaiser Family Foundation study notes that heavy media users are also more likely to say they get into trouble a lot, are often sad or unhappy and are often bored'.[14] And violent video game studies have shown that kids can become tolerant to violence – the more times they see blood and gore, the less they find it distressing, so they become desensitised. In their book *Born for*

Love: Why Empathy Is Essential and Endangered, Bruce Perry, senior fellow of the ChildTrauma Academy and Maia Szalavitz, senior fellow at the media watchdog STATS.org, cite studies which show that people who are less emotionally affected by seeing violence are more likely to be violent themselves.[15]

We have all observed children hooked on games on their mobiles in the car, or on consoles or laptops at home. The draw of the game and extent of the inability to withdraw is, however, quite striking. Limelight.com's survey of online gamers found that amongst 18–25-year-olds, 15 per cent had self-reported missing work due to gaming, 31 per cent felt they had missed time to socialise, 35 per cent had missed a shower, 39 per cent a meal, and 52 per cent sleep. Perhaps this isn't surprising, since, as Freed says, 'Imaging studies show that video gaming triggers the release of dopamine at levels comparable to an intravenous injection of amphetamine, a powerful and addictive psychostimulant.'[16]

One of my godchildren, now eighteen, wrote, 'I was given a PS4 by my parents when I was twelve. Prior to this, I had the previous generation of PlayStation, which I would use maybe for a couple hours on the weekend. However, given the new PlayStation and some games, I began to play a lot with my friends from school. This soon turned into gaming from the minute I got home from school until I went to bed. So perhaps four or five hours a day. And on weekends, if I had no family commitments, I would sit on my PlayStation all day and often late into the night. Every hour of free time I had would spend on my PlayStation. Every day at school became a chore and was just time I had to wait through until I could go home and play more. Although I mainly spent time playing with people I knew personally from school, I did make some friends online. We would also play with people who were completely unknown to me and I would talk to them on a regular basis without even knowing what their face looked like. It would affect my relationship with family members especially my parents, as I would eat dinner in front of my PlayStation and spend a lot of time in my bedroom playing games. I became quite distanced from my parents, which at such a young age could have potentially developed into worse problems. As we often played games in which we would race against each other, or have free-for-all gunfights, there would be arguments. The hard feelings would usually only last until the end of the game. This did normalise calling each other offensive names, which, if you were having a difficult time anyway, may have affected some members of the group seriously. To some extent, the period in which I spent large amounts of time on my PlayStation was enjoyable, because games are really fun; hence why they are so addictive. I would say it also enhanced my friendships at school as I was spending vast periods of time talking to my friends, but this was at sacrifice to relationships with my parents and sister, and further at sacrifice to my school work, both of which are plenty more important. When I was about fifteen, I stopped playing so much, mainly because I had by now moved school and I wasn't so close with my friends from the previous school. At this point, I started to go out and meet my friends, thus escaping the need to game. In hindsight, I would say there is a link between when I began to socially mature and the end of my phase of constant gaming. As soon as I stopped playing as much, I began to get much closer to my parents and this in turn helped me as I became more socially confident.'

UKIE, on behalf of the UK gaming and entertainment industry, objects to careless use of addiction terminology, which it says downplays very real consequences while overstating the risk of harm for those who don't engage in harmful behaviour. The World Health Organisation (WHO) announced that it was planning to include Gaming Disorder (GD) in the International Classification of Diseases as long ago as 2017, based on reviews of available evidence and a consensus of experts from different disciplines and geographies. They do recognise, however, that it affects only a relatively small proportion of those who engage in digital or video gaming.

A study of third-, fourth-, seventh- and eighth-graders published in the journal *Paediatrics* found that symptoms of obsessive gaming often came before signs of anxiety or depression. Freed says, 'this evidence, along with other research, suggests that tech addiction is its own disorder and that other psychiatric problems are often the result of the addiction. This is what I frequently see in my practice: previously high-functioning kids who first become addicted to technology and then develop anger, defiance, and/or depression.'[17]

Greenfield, having reviewed numerous studies on the effects of video gaming, says that 'children who spent more time video gaming had more attention problems, even when earlier attention problems, sex, age, race and socio-economic status were statistically controlled for'.[18] Indeed, she believes that whilst there are many causes of ADHD, 'there is still persuasive evidence that excessive amounts of video gaming can indeed be associated with these disorders'.[19] She also believes that kids with ADHD could be particularly prone to gaming addiction.

Video gaming addiction does seem to be more a young male trend. Dorsey and Villa found that 68 per cent of Generation Z males said gaming was an important part of their male identity.[20] Freed says, 'male college students also videogame at significantly higher rates that their female peers'. He explains that this is partly because latest brain imaging techniques show that video games activate the mesocorticolimbic center more in boys than in girls. 'Unfortunately, evidence shows that their greater gaming time hurts college academic performance and is likely a reason college age women earn higher grade point averages and more college honors and graduate at higher rates than men.'[21] This obviously has implications for jobs and lifetime earnings.

The way games are designed to be fun, engaging and totally absorbing can result in the real world being disappointing by comparison. Freed says he often sees male teenage patients much more concerned about their Halo score than their Spanish grade. 'The video game world is more real to them than the world of homework and grades and college applications … the disadvantage of playing video games especially a lot of exciting video games, is that it can make other people and real life seem boring and not worthwhile in comparison.'[22] Freed says a lot of the negative effects of video gaming on his teen patients can't be undone, that addicted kids obviously don't ask for help or understand why they need it, and that as a form of addiction it is particularly hard to treat and often leads to other damaging behaviours.

The Computer Professionals for Social Responsibility, an independent organisation, published an interesting paper entitled 'Socially responsible video games'. It says 'Video games are frequently violent, sexually explicit, and exploitative and commercialistic. Whether their use leads inexorably to social exclusion or antisocial behaviour and attitudes, the fact that their use occupies the minds of millions of people for billions of hours in a given year might make anybody question whether this is wise.'[23] In the final chapter, I look at suggestions for the creation of responsible gaming and at whether society shouldn't establish child rights in relation to gaming as suggested by UNICEF.

I do acknowledge, however, that in a book of this sort it is not possible to do justice to the plurality of the gaming sector, that some gaming environments are immersive, carefully designed and beneficial and that parts of the gaming sector are more attuned to safer and responsible design than many social networks may ever be.

I grew up reading books avidly and read every night before bed. Kids now often spend time on their devices before sleep and in some cases late into the night, causing the issues with sleep deprivation I have already covered. But they are very much less likely to be reading a book – more likely to be catching up with social media and messaging.

Martha, sixteen, says, 'I agree that instead of reading books before bed like we may have done in the early years of our childhood, it is more common to now find us on our phones. My parents still tell me that when I was younger, I used to be a "bookworm" and loved reading. However, since I have got a phone that has gradually changed. I believe there are many reasons for this, such as wanting to keep up and not miss out on anything that happens, commonly known as FOMO. More people are on their phones in the evenings and into the night as we think of them as quieter hours with less going on, consequently causing more conversations to happen. We want to be in touch for as long as possible.'

Could the advent of new technologies be like the development of books when they were first invented? Carr says, 'The growing availability of books fired the public's desire for literacy, and the expansion of literacy further stimulated the demand for books.' He notes that 'along with the high minded came the low minded. Tawdry novels, quack theories, gutter journalism, propaganda, and of course, reams of pornography.' 'But the froth itself was vital. Far from dampening the intellectual transformation wrought by the printed book, it magnified it. By accelerating the spread of books into popular culture and making them the mainstay of leisure time, the cruder, crasser, and more trifling works also helped spread the book's ethic of deep, attentive reading.'[24] Just as the cost of books falling from an initially high level to a very low level encouraged reading, so the increasingly free and now hyper-personalised nature of social media has had a similar effect on the propensity of people to interact with it.

Are e-books just digital books? A senior executive at Harperstudio says, 'e-books should not just be seen as print books delivered electronically'.[25] The e-book publishers are looking at new ways to addict us to e-books in the same way social media platforms have made their offerings more compelling and addictive. 'We need to take advantage of the medium and create something dynamic to enhance the experience. I want links and behind the scenes extras and narration and videos and conversations. As soon as you inject a book with links and connect it to the Web – as soon as you "extend" and "enhance" it and make it "dynamic" – you change what it is and you change as well the experience of reading it. An e-book is no more a book than an online newspaper is a newspaper.'[26]

The term 'vook' has been coined to describe future e-books, which will contain embedded video clips and hyperlinks, offering you deeper insights into the subjects explored in the book. Seemiller and Grace say, 'rather than publishing e-books, which are essentially books to be read, Pearson has recently released choose your own adventure education subscriptions, mirroring a Netflix-type approach to digitised content, putting information, videos, and animation in a manner to be "consumed" rather than "read".'[27]

I decide to conduct a quick survey of how many books my kids have read in the last four months while we have been locked down (excluding any they had to read for school or university). Two of them are undergraduates, and one studying for his A levels. One says he has read half a book, but is intending to finish it. 'Well, I studied it. I didn't read it as such!' Neither of the others has read a book. None of them has read a newspaper, getting their news from the BBC and Sky News apps, a news aggregator called News.com, Facebook and Instagram. Two have frequently listened to podcasts – sports and comedy mainly. All three love memes and follow meme aggregator sites. The youngest says, 'I do listen to audio books occasionally.' My eldest says, 'I have browsed the links in e-books for university study but have never read one from start to finish.'

Molly says, 'I actually love reading but I rarely do any more. Since the beginning of lockdown, four months, I have read one book. I just can't find a time when I want to sit down and read without having my phone nearby for distraction. On holiday, when my parents don't let me have my phone so much, I remember how much I enjoy reading, but straight after the holiday, I don't read for ages.'

Carr says, 'no doubt the connectivity and other features of e-books will bring new delights and diversions. We may even, as Kelly suggests, "come to see digitization as a liberating act, a way of freeing text from the page". But the cost will be the further reduction, if not the complete loss, of the close direct relationship between the lone writer and the lone reader. The practice of deep reading ... will continue to fade.'[28] He also says of hyperlinks 'that they not only distract us from reading the text in whole, but require us to make judgements and this has been shown to impede our ability to comprehend and retain'.[29]

Certainly, research suggests that if learning and retaining knowledge are two of the principal reasons for reading books, e-books are not going to help. Freed notes that a recent study by the Joan Ganz Cooney Center examines how print books vs e-books compare in terms of parent-child interactions while reading print books, basic e-books (without interactive features) and enhanced e-books (with interactive features). The study finds that 'children's use of both types of e-books, but especially the enhanced e-books, led parent child pairs to have more non content related (i.e. distracting) actions as compared to print books', and 'kids who use an enhanced e-book recall fewer story details than kids who read print or basic e-books'.[30]

I know I find it difficult now to read a book from cover to cover like I used to. 'A search engine often draws our attention to a particular snippet of text, a few words or sentences that have strong relevance to whatever we're searching for at that moment, while providing little incentive for taking in the work as a whole. We don't see the forest when we search the web. We don't even see the trees. We see twigs and leaves.'[31] And the inclusion of hyperlinks in e-books will only exacerbate this.

'I worry that the level of interrupt, the sort of overwhelming rapidity of information ... is in fact affecting cognition,' said Eric Schmidt, the

Chairman of Google, in what I find an interesting but ironic comment, given who he is. 'It is affecting deeper thinking. I still believe that sitting down and reading a book is the best way to really learn something. And I worry we are losing that.'[32]

Greenfield says that spending a growing amount of time reading electronic documents leads to more time 'browsing and scanning, keyword spotting, one-time reading, non-linear reading and reading more selectively, while less time is spent on in-depth reading and concentrated reading'.[33]

One of the benefits of reading a book is to be engaged in the story and empathise with the characters in it. Greenfield says that 'while empathy may be developed from reading books, it may not be automatically guaranteed in a cyber lifestyle that favours the rushed, the shallow and the disconnected'.[34]

Even those who study literature for a living seem not to be exempt. Carr says that even some academics have lost the ability to read properly. He believes we are all developing a new way of reading – he calls it 'power browsing, skimming'.

We recently had a President of the United States who, unlike his predecessor (a bestselling author), boasted of never reading books! The National Literacy Trust, which works with schools and communities to give disadvantaged children the literacy skills to succeed in life, found in 2019 that children and young people's daily reading levels were the lowest they had ever recorded. They say that this a continuing trend and is all the more worrying since reading for pleasure is the single biggest indicator of a child's future success, more so than their family circumstances, parents' educational background or income.[35]

If Generation Z isn't reading, what else is it doing other than social media and gaming? Watching Netflix or binging on box sets, perhaps. According to the Business of Apps, 59 per cent of US 16–34-year-olds describe Netflix as 'indispensable'. Netflix says average users watch for 2 hours a day.

Netflix, of course, was a departure from most of the other platforms, being subscription-based and therefore not needing advertising to make its business model work. As Wu says, 'Netflix rediscovered a lost trove of human attention; not the splintered and fleeting kind being plundered by the web and cable TV, but deeper sustained attention.'[36] Of course, that is true for Netflix itself. In the hands of Generation Zers, however, given their propensity to multitask, the likelihood is that they will be simultaneously messaging their friends using Netflix chat function or on another device. Netflix also developed the concept of hyperserials – long-running programmes requiring constant attention to keep up with developments. *House of Cards* was a massive hit for Netflix and with the release of its second series came the next trend.

In August 2014, the term 'binge-watch' entered the *Oxford English Dictionary*. It means to watch multiple episodes of the same series in rapid succession and has become a widespread phenomenon. As addictionhelper.com says, 'Five years on, in 2019, the binge-watch generation shows no sign of slowing down. Netflix, YouTube, Amazon Prime, iTunes, Hulu, HBO and countless other platforms offer up fast, exciting, and often big-budget entertainment. Global audiences have round-the-clock, affordable, multilingual, and mobile access. One episode rolls into another: each video leads to the next – algorithms get to know our preferences, in order to suggest even more.'[37] In October, 2017 Netflix said that 5 million members that year had 'binge-raced' through an entire series in under 24 hours as compared to 200,000 users in 2013.[38] Covid-19 has certainly accelerated this trend.

Future films will be made to be interactive, with online chat rooms and 'pre-organised backchannelling' so you can 'enhance' your film-watching experience with other online content as you watch it. This will make them all the more compelling and reduce your propensity to deep watch a film from start to finish without interruption, much in line with the trends I have noted relating to e-books and video generally.

Beyond video on demand and gaming, what will distract Generation Z next? Mixed reality is the next version of virtual reality ('VR'), where not everything in the real world is hidden from your view and you see virtual things placed into the real world. It follows from the virtual reality video which is watched through glasses integrated with headphones, which enable you to feel as if you are in a different 3D environment from your actual location. VR as a medium is growing rapidly. Mark Zuckerberg has said Facebook intends to expand VR to sport, education, medicine: 'one day we believe this kind of immersive, augmented reality will become a part of daily life for billions of people'. And 'if you can't think of a way your reality can't be better, you are not thinking hard enough'.[39]

Like all new technology, it may have great utility. Jaron Lanier says, 'maybe VR can give us a hint about what we should want in the future as technology ramps up and people gain more and more options. We can simulate living in a Jetsons world today. Let's try and see if we really want it.'[40] Certainly during Covid-19, demand for VR has skyrocketed as people have sought an escape from the misery of lockdown to a better world.

Many of us have played games which use VR and they are incredibly realistic, but cutting-edge VR fools most brains, so that you can easily feel that not only are you in the location you are watching and listening to, but also that you are a participant in what you are watching. The arm that appears to the lower left of your screen feels like your arm. When someone walks towards you in the video and hands you something, you find yourself putting your hand out to accept it.

The proponents of VR say that it lets you indulge your imagination and experience new things without any impact on the physical world. And that is true. Used harmlessly, as Lanier (who has been at the forefront of VR development since its inception) says, 'it weds the nerdy thing with the hippie thing; it's high-tech and like a dream or an elixir of unbounded experience all at the same time'.[41] In the design and education worlds,

VR is also used for many good purposes, and many doctors and surgeons now train on VR-based simulators. As Lanier says, it allows you to try out potential changes to the real world without having to actually make those changes, e.g. planning a new kitchen, designing a new building, designing whole smart cities, flight simulator pilot training, simulating the interiors and ride experiences of new cars, illustrating what the effects of drugs might be as experienced by a patient and learning to drive a tank and numerous other military applications. My eldest son has just returned from working for a leading-edge VR company, Impersive, in Milan – he was putting music to VR videos which would enable ladies who wanted to try a Prada dress on not just to see it on, but to wear it as if they were one of the models on the catwalk at the launch and feel the crowd's reaction.

Eduardo says, 'What you say about what VR facilitates is kind of what the book and film *Ready Player One* predicted could happen. This is the way we could achieve immortality. It's much more resource-efficient to achieve it though VR than in real life. One second in VR could be ten years of earth time. So in a few hours, you could live longer in VR than any human has ever lived. Plus you could personalise every universe you visited to your liking and have whatever you wanted. You could experience more, develop more and never suffer.'

But there are also those like me who worry about the potentially negative effects of VR. In *The Trust Manifesto*, Damien Bradfield, British businessman and founding shareholder of technology company WeTransfer, examines the potential for VR to assist with the empathy deficit. 'I've seen VR and technology also be really powerful tools for empathy, because you can see right there what's happening to someone and give live reactions.'[42] But he asks, ultimately, is it really possible for a computer to display any sort of empathy? 'I can totally envision again how that experience would be phenomenal, but the empathy side is going to be predetermined by a machine, and predetermined by developers who are … not generally always the most empathetic people.'[43] In a 2018 Common Sense Media survey of parents' views on VR for kids, 72 per cent of parents disagreed with the statement that virtual reality will help children empathise with people different from them, and 60 per cent were somewhat or very concerned about VR's impacts on their child's health.[44]

It seems that whether VR is a good thing or not is all about how we set it up to be used and what content and functionality we put into it. Lanier says the 'set and setting' principle applies to VR at least as well. 'VR can either be beautiful art and sympathy or terrible spying and manipulation. We set its meaning.'[45] But depending on who is choosing the set and settings, I am concerned that VR is the next, and I would argue potentially most dangerous, phase of social media; mixing the potential for escapism, perfection and Freitas's happiness effect all in one and allowing a 'hyper-real' blurring of the human and physical worlds. Alter says, 'VR will allow us to spend time with anyone in any location doing whatever we like for as long as we like. That sort of boundless pleasure sounds wonderful, but it has the capacity to render face-to-face interactions obsolete. Why live in the real world with real, flawed people when you can live in a perfect world that feels just as real?'[46]

Certainly, Lanier says, 'it's one of the only ways, for the moment, to raise billions fleetly in Silicon Valley without *necessarily* promising to spy on everybody', but 'never has a medium been so potent for beauty and so vulnerable to creepiness. Virtual reality will test us. It will amplify our character more than any other media before.'[47]

'I worry when a violent video game feels like a murder,' says Alter.[48] More particularly, in your mind, you will have been holding the gun in the video and therefore will feel like you committed the murder. In pornography, it will seem as if you were having the sex, not watching two or more other parties doing so. Eddy, nineteen, says, 'Yes, there is an infamous episode of *Black Mirror*, available on Netflix, which seeks to warn against VR sexual pleasures becoming more intense and enjoyable than real life, consequently robbing humanity of genuine intimacy.'

Interestingly, while the earliest VR machines worked from gloves with sensors in them which were connected to a headset, and eye tracking is a current driver in some VR, tongue agility may be the way forward. Lanier says, 'most tongues can morph enough that they might someday be the best way to guide the process of geometric design in virtual worlds. It's also easy to learn to use teeth as buttons, if one really wants buttons.'[49] I guess the idea here is that buttons may be made obsolete by some future capacity to connect the VR headset directly to your brain.

It is easy to see a smartphone as a distinct physical object that is separate from us. But put on your virtual reality glasses, immerse yourself in what you see and hear, and it might be different. Wu says, 'it seems only natural that the closer a technology feels to being part of us, the more important we trust it; the same goes for someone who is creating a virtual reality video for you to inhabit. And so, in the coming decade, the attention merchants will need to tread very lightly as they come as close as they can to the human body,' but history dictates that 'what seems shocking to one generation is soon taken for granted by the next'.[50]

Increasingly, smart domestic devices are connected to the internet, including power meters, heating and air-conditioning systems, security cameras and sound systems. Alexa, the voice-activated device, has become a trusted friend and servant in many homes. In a Common Sense Media survey in 2019, 44 per cent of those surveyed said that they or family members were using a voice-activated assistant on a smart speaker (such as Amazon Echo, Google Home or Apple Homepod). Whilst 77 per cent of those surveyed said that it was very important to know when their family's voices were being recorded, 29 per cent had taken no steps to limit data collected by voice-activated assistants, and a further 33 per cent said they would like to but didn't know how.[51] Facebook has recently introduced its portal product incorporating Alexa voice technology, which will increase penetration further. Zuboff notes that 'the personal digital assistant is revealed as a market avatar, another Trojan horse in which the determination to render and monetize your life is secreted under the veil of "assistance" and embellished with the poetry of "personalisation".'[52]

These devices will help improve home safety and security, and reduce power bills and many aspects of our lives. But they will also increase the opportunity for big-tech companies to collect data about us, including in the most intimate moments of our home lives. Zuboff brings the issue of monitoring our most intimate moments to life with the example of the Sleep Number Bed and its related SleepIQ app.[53] The bed has sensors and a microphone, to enable it to make suggestions about how to improve your sleeping habits. And whilst I am not suggesting the manufacturers would do so, the potential for misuse of the data and audio collected in such products is obvious – imagine it being used to monitor the night-time activities of a celebrity or politician. The terms and conditions which accompany the bed, whilst apparently offering the option to turn off some of the data-collection processes, point out that if this option is activated, the app will not function effectively. Zuboff describes the forthcoming IoT revolution as another opportunity for what she terms 'Surveillance as a Service', where devices apparently bringing you benefit simply repre-sent the next opportunity for what she calls the 'rendition' of your data. She says that we should not be fooled by the 'euphemism' of being asked for consent: 'under surveillance capitalism, rendition is typically unautho-rized, unilateral, glutinous, secret and brazen'.[54]

Some believe that the combined surveillance opportunity IoT devices represent is a matter of national security. Williams says, 'fierce competi-tion for human attention is creating new problems of kind, not merely of degree. Via ubiquitous and always connected interfaces to users, as well as sophisticated infrastructure of measurement, experimentation, targeting, and analytics, this global project of industrialised persuasion is now the dominant business model and design logic of the internet.'[55] In *Look Who's Watching*, Fen Osler Hampson and Eric Jardine observe that, as the IoT grows, and we are constantly monitored, 'our virtual tracks will bear an even closer resemblance to our physical ones, to the point where they are indistinguishable'. They cite a survey in which 79 per cent of IoT users said they were kept up at night by the privacy implications of IoT.[56] McKinsey estimate that the IoT could add $11 trillion to the world economy by 2025.[57]

Domestic robots often connected to home wi-fi networks are a rapidly growing phenomenon, particularly in lawnmowing, indoor domestic cleaning, cooking, pool cleaning, gutter cleaning, window cleaning and security – with around 20 million already in service around the world. Humanised robots are now used by some elderly, immobilised residents and even younger people to keep them company. Robots can be used to give physical therapy.

But shouldn't we worry about where our reliance on technology and lack of demand for each other might lead? 'If convenience and control continue to be our priorities, we shall be tempted by the sociable robots, where like gamblers at their slot machines, we are promised excitement programmed in, just enough to keep us in the game. At the robotic moment, we have to be concerned that the simplification and reduction of relationship is no longer something we complain about. It may be something we desire,'[58] says Turkle.

A recent YouGov survey found that 20 per cent of 18–24-year-olds questioned said that they could imagine themselves forming a friendship with a robot, and one in twenty said they could imagine having a romantic relationship with one. Thirty-three per cent of men would not rule out getting amorous with a robot. A third of those 18–24-year-olds said they would be comfortable with a robot colleague at work.[59]

This idea of robots replacing humans as friends and colleagues troubles some. Turkle is concerned that Generation Z will 'become confused about companionship… Their digitised friendships – played out with emoticon emotions, so often predicated on rapid response rather than reflections – may prepare them, at times, through nothing more than their superficiality, for relationships that could bring superficiality to a higher power, that is for relationships with the inanimate.'[60]

Having become used to chatting to their connected devices to get information and control their environments through Alexa or Siri, Generation Z might find it easier to talk to companion robots about personal matters – the robot will not judge or criticise them. Similarly, they could sound off to a robot without fear of the kind of reaction they might get on social media. Turkle found that some of her survey cadre preferred talking to robots and found it made them less anxious. But she objects to the idea of them being called 'caring machines'. Caring, she says, is a behaviour. It is a feeling not a function.[61]

Robots could also be programmed not to react to criticism like humans might. A third of those Brits surveyed by YouGov said they would be ruder to a robot giving them poor service than they would to a human, even if the robot were programmed to respond to the emotion and tone in a human's voice. This reminds me somewhat of the behaviour we have seen in texting and social media, where distance from a human being's reaction fosters less tolerant and more aggressive behaviour, and one wonders whether those behaving rudely to robots would switch back into 'human' behaviour when dealing with a real person, or whether we might not have just found another way to train people out of empathy. As Turkle says, 'in all of this there is a nagging question; does virtual intimacy degrade our experience of the other kind and, indeed, of all encounters, of any kind?'[62]

In Japan, there is a product called LovePlus, a video game which offers a choice of three different female dating simulators – female

Japanese imaginary but visual characters – which has attracted hundreds of thousands of users since launch. Users find these characters attractive and date them through the game, preferring the sweet, acquiescent and obliging virtual characters to more complex human beings. Government surveys in Japan have revealed that 40 per cent of men and women in their twenties and thirties are single, not actively in a relationship and not really interested in finding a romantic partner either. Furthermore, over one-quarter of men in their thirties were virgins – all the more remarkable in a largely non-religious society. But given the population shrinkage this has led to, these trends deserve attention, not least for where they could lead Western economies.

Sex robots are a logical extension of both video dating simulators and other robotic devices and the smartphone, in particular, in many ways. If you are accustomed to talking to and giving instructions to your TV, mobile phone, sound system and vacuum cleaner, why would you find it odd to talk to a physical robot that resembles a human being, or animatronic figure, as they are known? The robot manufacturers point out you don't need to be so sensitive with the robot as it doesn't have feelings, won't get offended and won't judge you or your body or sexual performance, unless it is programmed to. Matt McMullen, CEO of Realbotix, is quoted in *Forbes* as taking issue with the notion that human–human relationships are inherently superior to human–machine. 'There are probably a ton of real-world relationships where one partner feels very much in love and the other does not, or the other partner maybe deceives and lies and so you are not getting the real deal anyway. The thing about AI and robots is they're not deceptive. They're not lying. They are what they are. If the AI is programmed to love you, at least you know that it's programmed to do that. It's not going to deviate from that goal.'[63]

A sex robot doesn't need to be a bad idea – it could be useful. They could be taken by one member of a parted couple and operated remotely by the other partner. They are a potential partial answer to some of the large gender imbalance demographics we saw in Chapter 1. Some think over time they could reduce the need for human trafficking. It is reported that some brothels already offer sex robots as an alternative to sex workers. They could be used for sex education and for those who struggle with real human bonding. But activists against sex robots worry that they are a further development in humans neglecting personal human connection or could lead to partners treating their real partner like they can treat a robot. Whatever their good and bad points, their numbers will certainly grow alongside the growth in virtual reality video.

In this chapter, we have examined how technology distracts us and showers us with new 'friends' and diversions. Some words from Marco after he started to get his social media and online dating habits under control really struck me: 'I'm so much happier now because of the few really good friends I have that I physically speak and spend time with.'

PART 2

FOLLOW THE SCIENCE

5

NOBODY GETS ME

'Come on, Ruben, come on, Ruben, fire you idiot! RUBEN!' shouts my youngest son, who is engrossed in a video game in the family room, wearing headphones, at the top of his voice. Given how the noise permeates the house, we might as well all be playing the game. I appeal for some quiet whilst on a Zoom call with 10 Downing Street. Later I am told, 'Nobody gets me. I can't see my friends due to lockdown. At least this way I get to play with them.' 'Why don't you call or better Facetime them if you want to see them and have a proper conversation?' I suggest, digging myself deeper into the hole and displaying a lack of parental empathy with the sixteen-year-old mind.

Baptiste says, 'There is a misconception that phones and their ability to allow communication prevent people from being lonely and it is a particularly important point now at the height of the Covid-19 crisis. In my experience, the ability to communicate to anyone at any time over your phone does not prevent loneliness, rather it facilitates it. By relying on your smartphone to stay in contact with friends/family etc., you are reducing face-to-face contact with people. This is so important, as it allows that human connection to be understood in a conversation. If you can't see someone's face or hear their voice when communicating, it reduces the ability to gauge the situation, empathise or react accordingly. Instead we are now reduced to showing our emotions through emojis, "haha" or, worse, "LOL". This lack of face-to-face contact makes it really hard to fully involve yourself in a conversation.'

Cigna, the health service company, found that loneliness had already reached 'epidemic levels' in a pre-Covid-19 study, with 48 per cent of Generation Z (aged eighteen to twenty-two) reporting experiencing loneliness, higher than any other generation included in the study. Sixty per cent of those surveyed reported feeling shy and isolated from others, noting that no one really knew them, and that whilst there were people around them, there was no one really *with* them. Those who reported higher rates of in-person interactions reported the lowest loneliness.[1] The Children's Society's 'Good Childhood Report 2019' revealed 132,000 children aged ten to fifteen in the UK had *no* close friends.

Longer screen times and increasing loneliness – exacerbated by our recent Covid-19 lockdown – have in my opinion contributed to a rise in social anxiety. In *Social Chemistry*, Yale professor Marissa King, who has studied how people's social networks affect their personal relationships, says the fear of strangers and social anxiety are common. 'As social animals, we are wired to want to be accepted,' she notes. 'The fear of not being accepted, which is heightened when interacting with strangers, is at the core of social anxiety.'[2] King observes that 13 per cent of people suffer from clinically diagnosable social anxiety, making it the third-largest mental health problem in the US.[3]

Szalavitz and Perry suggest 'that concurrent advances in technology, the high mobility of our populations, ongoing instability of families and communities, and compartmentalisation of educational, work, and living environments have contributed to a reduction in the number and quality of human interactions below that which is necessary for the full development of our capacity for compassion'.[4]

More connection generated by technology does not automatically mean good connection, nor does it cure the lack of direct human interaction.

Social health writer Julia Hobsbawm notes in *Fully Connected* that 'we do not yet have a system of any meaningful kind around good connectedness, and nor are we yet acknowledging the scale of the problem of what happens to the health of a society when overload is unchecked'.[5]

King observes that the internet may encourage the pursuit of *popularity* (a large network, visibility and status) at the expense of *likeability*.[6] She observes that likeable people are good listeners, aren't the first to jump into conversation and tend to make other people feel valued, all of which sound like empathetic behaviours. Interesting, then, that studies over many years show that the most likeable kids seem to turn into the most successful adults 'even after one takes into account cognitive ability, socioeconomic status, parental mental health, misconduct, and a host of other factors that one would think would matter for long term success'.[7] Likeable kids are also less likely to struggle with depression, anxiety and addiction. As King says, most of the time likeability isn't related to popularity or network size as 'only about 30 per cent of people with high network-based status are also likeable'.[8]

This brings us back to the role of empathy and, as Szalavitz and Perry identify, 'how it underpins virtually everything that makes society work – trust, altruism, collaboration, love and charity. Failure to empathise is a key part of most social problems – crime, violence, war, racism, child abuse and inequity'.[9] Without dealing with what in 2004 Barack Obama famously coined our *empathy deficit*, our very survival as a decent society must be at risk. Why? Because empathy underlies just about everything that makes humans different from the rest of nature: that we can love, put ourselves in the minds of others and care about how that feels.

The list of recent books on our empathy deficit is long and wide ranging. One of the most persuasive is by Simon Baron-Cohen, the Cambridge clinical psychologist specialising in autism and its link with lack of empathy, who argues in *Zero Degrees of Empathy* that empathy is a universal solvent. 'It is effective as a way of anticipating and resolving interpersonal problems, whether this is marital conflict, an international conflict, a problem at work, difficulties in friendships, political dead-locks, a family dispute or a problem with a neighbour.'[10] In other words, empathy is our glue. It binds us together.

Social interaction with parents or other caregivers is crucial to devel-oping empathy as a baby, child and adolescent. Screen time threatens opportunities for face-to-face interaction and bonding, which are required for our brains to develop properly. Turkle notes that no matter how evolved we may be as a species, the need to develop empathetic skills is no less present today than in previous generations. She notes that today's youth 'need time to discover themselves, time to think. But technology, put in the service of always-on communication and telegraphic speed and brevity, has changed the rules of engagement with all of this.'[11]

Positive social interaction is good for our health; on the other hand, in extremis people can become ill or die from rejection or isolation. Alan Collins and Adam Cox suggested in March 2020 that whilst the young suffered disproportionately little from Covid-19 itself, the isolation of lockdown would cost many young lives over time. Past downturns and crises have led to increasing unemployment, increased mental health problems and spikes in suicide rates in many countries, with the 2007 economic crisis leading to more than 10,000 extra suicides in Europe and North America alone.[12] A sobering thought when you consider the brutal nature of the lockdown and the scale of the economic impact, which will dwarf anything seen in 2007.

Szalavitz and Perry note that 'the fact that stress is regulated by social systems has tremendous implications for everything from medicine to politics to business to economics, and these make empathy essential for the survival of humankind'.[13] The authors also note that children brought up with parental input and with more bonding time developed with higher average IQ when compared with children who did not have the same relationships.

Even Adam Smith, the economist who coined the phrase 'the invisible hand of the market', highlighted the importance of empathy to a thriving economy. Smith once said, 'When we see a stroke aimed, and just ready to fall upon the leg or arm of another person, we naturally shrink and draw back our leg or our own arm; and when it does fall, we feel it in some measure, and are hurt by it as well as the sufferer.'[14] He went on to explain that this feeling is the basis of compassionate action. Empathy also forms the base for trust, which is needed for the proper and effective functioning of everything from relationships to economies.

We have examined how social media, while appearing to connect people, actually leads to less face-to-face time and can affect mental wellbeing. Szalavitz and Perry assert that a negative feedback loop could develop. In fact, the authors note, research suggests that those who are depressed 'actually fail to perceive smiles that are directed at them', which only serves to 'enhance or prolong depression and social anxiety'.[15] Simply feeling loneliness can, in fact, lead to a greater incidence of these misinterpretations. This leads to a vicious cycle of negative reinforcement, creating an even more alienating society. Any balanced view of social media in this context, though, must also take into account the positive impacts many influencers have on many of their followers, whether it be through bringing them views on the news, education, information or motivation. To get the full picture, we need the social media platforms to share data to help us better understand how social media affects us.

Meanwhile, we must in any event improve our understanding of, and attitude to, empathy. Lanier advances that 'our fate rests on human traits that haven't yet been defined in scientific terms, such as common sense, kindness, rational thought and creativity. Perhaps the most important question of our time is whether we will be able to see past the mirage created by technology and information systems in order to see the world clearly'.[16]

Technology and societal trends have caused a decline in the number and quality of situations where empathy can thrive. This is coupled with a real and worsening problem of 'relational poverty'. If empathy is as important to a well-functioning society as these experts say and I believe, we need to consider what action we can take to address the deficit.

Roman Krznaric, political sociologist and founder of the world's first Empathy Museum and Empathy Library, says empathy doesn't stop developing in our childhoods. We can nurture its growth throughout our lives. Rather, empathy is an attitude that we can elect to make a part of our daily lives. He identifies six habits of highly empathetic people (HEPs).[17]

1. They cultivate curiosity for strangers. In my experience, while Generation Z are curious about strangers online, they are reticent to engage with people they don't know face-to-face.
2. They challenge prejudices and discover commonalities.
3. They are willing to try another person's life. Volunteer at a food bank, visit someone else's church in a different faith.
4. They listen hard and open up. HEPs listen very carefully to others and try to share emotions from their own feelings. This, of course, requires one-on-one and face-to-face conversation, not instant messaging.
5. They inspire mass action to engineer social change. We will see how clicktivism, if properly harnessed, can lead to physical gatherings which can make a difference.
6. They develop an ambitious imagination. Empathise with people outside your echo chamber; better yet, with those with whom you disagree.

Mastering empathy is also a key business survival skill because it underpins successful teamwork and leadership. The Consortium for Research on Emotional Intelligence in Organisations reports a correlation between empathy in sales people and increased sales.[18]

One of the striking observations about Generation Z is how many youngsters realise they are distracted by technology and have taken steps, sometimes just to escape technology for an hour here and there, to explore mindfulness and mindful listening. A study by Sodexho of Generation Z college students said nearly a third would be interested in taking classes in mindfulness.

What precisely does this mean? According to Jon Kabat-Zinn, mindful listening involves 'paying attention in a particular way, on purpose, in the present moment, and nonjudgmentally'.[19] Mindful listening cannot take place while the listener is simultaneously reading a text or email, or really even holding a smartphone but instead requires being actively present through the removal of distractions. In order to listen mindfully, mobile phones should be muted and screens should be turned off, giving the listener enough time to not rush the conversation. Mindful listening is purported to have physical and psychological benefits, reduce anxiety, and increase positive feelings.

Most of us do not have a coping strategy for this distraction crisis. We dabble occasionally in 'digital detox' by engaging in something totally absorbing where we cannot use our phones and yell at our kids to get off theirs, but it's very haphazard. One of my wife's more brilliant suggestions was that we should buy a hot tub. We persuade the kids to join us and go there for family time. The kids can't use their phones because they are terrified of getting them wet, and the proximity breeds good conversation.

I believe having empathy is central to being happy. Professor Richard Layard at the LSE is a world-leading academic on happiness. He notes that critical factors that underpin an individual's state of happiness include mental and physical health, human relationships, social support and trust.[20] Empathy is central to having all of these. The trouble is that happiness is not good for the surveillance economy on which big tech business models depend.

Social media actually abuses natural empathy to induce more social media use. The irony is that it is the human tendency towards empathy that drives the very addiction to social media which destroys empathy. For Zuboff, 'Facebook is the crucible of this new dark science'; it seeks to manipulate our natural tendency for empathy in order to 'modify behaviour towards others' ends ... This synthetic hive is a devilish pact for a young person. In terms of sheer everyday effectiveness – contact, logistics, transactions, communications – turn away, and you're lost. And if you simply crave the fusion juice that is proof of life at a certain age and stage – turn away, and you are extinguished.'[21]

Matthew Lieberman, Cognitive Neuroscience Lab Director at UCLA, points out that 'our brain is profoundly social. Our social wiring motivates us to stay connected. It returns our attention again and again to understanding the minds of people around us ... to ensure that we harmonize with those around us.'[22] This seems to suggest that empathy is hard-wired into the human brain, unless, of course, we are so distracted that we cannot focus on it.

We need to learn to log off. Karen Faith, Director of Empathy and Intelligence at Barkley, a company that specialises in building modern brands for modern consumers, says she 'anticipates that just as those who don't have to do hard physical labour pay trainers to work their bodies, those with the time and freedom to step away from tech for an hour, a day, or a week, will be considered the most exclusive, privileged group'[23] in the future. Generation Z must seize this opportunity. But to provide the time to rebuild empathy, it will first need to reclaim ownership of attention away from the distractions of technology. Williams posits that 'future generations will judge us not only for our stewardship of the outer environment, but of the inner environment as well'.[24] Given our limited attention spans, our mission should not only be to 're-engineer the world of matter, but also to re-engineer our world so that we can give attention to what matters'.[25] Technology currently works against us in this regard, as it encourages us to constantly juggle competing demands on our brains. But the fundamental point is not about the amount of time Generation Z spends on screens, it's about how that screen time is used and what doesn't get done as a result. As Haig says, 'The problem clearly isn't that we have a shortage of time. It's more that we have an overload of *everything else*.'[26]

6

LET'S TALK ABOUT THE JUGGLER'S BRAIN

My youngest son is at home with my wife and me; my older two are in London. We are all glued to Chelsea (who they all avidly support) playing Manchester United in the semi-final of the FA Cup. Chelsea scores, and my son screams with excitement and then starts his hilarious victory dance in front of the TV. The family WhatsApp channel bursts into life. Ping, ping. My wife has sent a picture of my youngest in front of the TV. My eldest has replied saying 'doing exactly the same'. Everyone is high on a cocktail of Chelsea scoring, WhatsApp pinging and the humorous pictures and messages that it conveys.

Pleasurable human experiences result in the release of dopamine in the brain. The dopamine attaching itself to receptors in the brain causes the feeling of pleasure we experience. Most pleasurable experiences cause the release of a small amount of dopamine. Broadly speaking, to start with, the more dopamine, the more pleasure.

Normally, this release of dopamine is a good thing. It encourages us to seek out what is healthy or beneficial in our environment. It's so import-ant, in fact, that neuroscientists have given it a central role in a type of fundamental human learning called reinforcement learning. I will explain how technology companies abuse reinforcement learning to modify human behaviour so that we maximise time on their platforms and apps. What scientists have found is that dopamine is related to the *prediction* of rewards. If a reward is received but not anticipated, an increase in dopamine is seen. And if a reward is anticipated and not seen, a decrease in dopamine is seen. Since our brains are wired to optimise rewards, this means that humans will be motivated to seek out new rewards in any given situation, do anything they know delivers a reward repeatedly and avoid anything which gives them negative effects. Technology companies design their platforms and apps to make them addictive using this science. Receiving a notification, a like on Facebook or Instagram, a match on Tinder or a win in Fortnite all trigger dopamine releases. Being blocked by a friend or killed in the game causes a decrease in dopamine.

The problem starts when you seek out dopamine regularly and repeatedly as most people could be tempted to, given the pleasurable effect. The brain starts to develop a tolerance for dopamine. So more dopamine is needed to generate the *same* degree of pleasure. In the natural world, the availability of rewards is largely out of humans' hands. On technology platforms, it is designed in and can be made almost infinitely abundant. Addictions develop because two things happen. The brain produces less dopamine per stimulus, and the brain feels less stimulated by each new release. So more, larger stimuli are needed, requiring the addict to seek them.

Sean Parker, Facebook's Founding President, said in 2017, 'We need to give you a little dopamine hit every once in a while ... exploiting a vulnerability in human psychology ... the inventors, creators ... understood it consciously. And we did it anyway. God only knows what it's doing to our children's brains.'[1]

Mirror neurons fire in the brain when an animal acts and observes the same action in another. You smile, I smile back. This may explain why some people unwittingly imitate their companions, sitting similarly in terms of leg positions or with their heads cocked at a similar angle. Some neuroscientists believe that mirror neurons form the basis of emotions such as empathy. If true, to develop and display empathy requires the physical observation of a counterparty during the intercourse – something, of course, that social media chat doesn't deliver.

While neuroscientists debate precise mechanisms, it seems reasonably well accepted that bonding situations – a mother feeding or hugging a child – result in the release of oxytocin, which itself triggers the release of dopamine and serotonin. This leads to pleasurable feelings of comfort and security and builds the bond between the baby and the parent or carer. We have seen that dopamine leads to pleasure, and serotonin boosts feelings of wellbeing and collegiality. Paul Zak, one of the original researchers into the effects of oxytocin, described this as Human Oxytocin Medicated Empathy ('HOME'). Bonding and empathy require at least physical proximity or engaged face-to-face engagement to occur. This is one of the reasons why it is so important that babies are not distracted with iPads fixed inches in front of their faces in their recliners before they are two, and equally important that parents must not be distracted from fixing their baby's gaze, eye to eye, by combining feeding or bonding time with use of their own devices.

Eye-to-eye contact seems to be critical not just as a baby, but throughout life. 'Whether it's affection, amusement, arrogance or annoyance, our eyes convey how we feel. And the ability to read another person's eyes, face to face, is one of the best predictors of a person's social intelligence,' says King. Referring to the conclusions of Simon Baron-Cohen's 'reading the mind in the eye test', she says. 'The better you are at inferring someone else's mental state by looking at their eyes, the more likely you are to be prosocial, perform well in groups and respond empathetically.'[2]

The self is a blend of how we think different important people in our lives view us and what they think of us, according to the 1930s American philosopher and social theorist George Mead. High self-esteem develops if someone thinks others hold them in positive regard, and vice-versa. Psychologists refer to different aspects of self-esteem: *social* – relating to how parents, siblings and peers see us; *academic* – relating to success in relation to classmates; and *physical* – relating to perceptions of physical appearance and abilities. Low dopamine levels are often associated with low self-esteem, hopelessness, inability to handle stress, a desire to isolate and unexplained lack of concern for family and friends.

Famous developmental psychologist Erik Erikson, best known for coining the phrase 'identity crisis' to describe failing to achieve a settled identity during adolescence, first explained how during adolescence children focus on their view of their identity, becoming absorbed by this identity-formation process in what, he argues, is the most important personality achievement of their lives.

Don Tapscott, who has written extensively about the role of technology in society, says in *Growing Up Digital* that 'adolescents during this period question important assumptions that defined them in childhood. They question, rethink, analyse, explore and eventually create a foundation that provides a sense of sameness as they shift through different roles in life.'[3] It is for these reasons that the impact of social media interactions during adolescence is so great. In particular, negative feedback from, or trouble with, friends and peers, can have a dramatic effect on an adolescent's sense of identity and self-esteem. It doesn't even matter whether the content is negative or malicious; just looked at in terms of time, if teens are spending hours a day on social media, it will be affecting their sense of identity in untold and potentially significant ways.

The prime challenge of emerging adulthood is 'to become the author of your own life,' says Zuboff. But she suggests that due to social media, third parties interfere more than ever. 'Adolescence has always been a time when acceptance, inclusion and recognition from the "others" can feel like matters of life and death,' she writes.[4]

When kids compare themselves with the 'golden individuals' on social media, their self-esteem falls, so found Susan Greenfield, a leading UK neuroscientist who has studied the effect of technology on the developing mind. Haig says, 'it is often unhealthy, because to make people want to transcend themselves, you first have to make them unhappy with themselves'.[5] Greenfield worries that this could create a self-reinforcing negative loop. Social media becomes more attractive because it doesn't require more 'painful' face-to-face interaction. She says that 'bizarrely, people with low self-esteem tend to make updates which emphasise their negative features at the expense of their positive, compared to those with high self-esteem'.[6] This leads to them attracting fewer likes, lower scores and less approbation. She says, 'ironically, the conviction that it is safe enough to disclose their feelings on Facebook', for example, 'may encourage people with low self-esteem to reveal things that then lead to the very rejection they fear'.[7]

In some cases, social media comparisons will also spur positive motivation. Eduardo says, 'If you are a positively minded, confident person, comparing can also spur you on to the very high competitiveness we see today. I see a lot of my peers working much harder, having a lot more ambition and accomplishing a lot more due to seeing others be successful on social media.'

As children develop their identities on and offline, so they socialise and cybersocialise into society. Socialisation means the process, beginning in infancy, where one acquires the attitudes, values, beliefs, habits, behaviour patterns and accumulated knowledge of one's society and modifies one's behaviour to conform with the demands of the society or group to which one belongs. The point here is that if children operate online for several hours from an early age, they are 'cybersocialising' in a world which is very different from the way they would socialise in a purely physical or real world and probably in ways totally opaque to their parents. We should expect, therefore, their behaviours to be hugely different as a result, particularly if, during their time online as children, they witness violence, pornography, murder, suicide, self-harming and the like. The eminent psychologist and expert on screen addiction Nicholas Kadaras, author of *Glow Kids*, has referred to this online move as the 'erosion of socialisation', arguing that digital media are 'digital heroin' which can turn kids into 'psychotic junkies' and that, much like learning to drive a car, we need to learn to drive the internet safely.[8]

Dr Mary Aiken, leading global cyberpsychologist and campaigner for the rights of children online, believes that when it comes to children's exposure online, we are all 'looking the other way'. As a result, she says we are witnessing a crime against innocence.

Neuroscientists believe that what we pay attention to affects our happiness and sense of wellbeing. In any given set of circumstances, what you choose to focus on exerts significant leverage on your attitude going forward. Remember being told to look on the bright side of life? How as a child you had to learn to be happy? To focus on the good things in your life? Well, it could in fact have some scientific basis. The point is, you may choose to focus on certain things, or find yourself pulled along by your busy life, distracted into largely irrelevant postings on social media with a negative effect on your wellbeing. Winifred Gallagher, behavioural science writer and author of *Rapt*, says that 'the idle mind is the devil's workshop',[9] and that when you lose focus, your mind tends to fix on what could be wrong with your life instead of what is right. Worse, if your default pastime is to reach for your phone and browse social media, social media platforms are often designed to convey and amplify negative emotions because they are better at keeping your attention.

If social media preoccupies your idle time, then there will be less time for focused effort on more worthwhile activity. The psychologist Mihaly Csikszentmihalyi found that 'the best moments [in life] usually occur when a person's body or mind is stretched to its limits in a voluntary effort to accomplish something difficult and worthwhile'.[10] He calls this activity 'flow' and believes flow generates happiness in contrast to unstructured time. Whilst social media wasn't his focus, 'surfing' or browsing through social media with no particular objective other than 'chilling' would be a good example of unstructured time.

It is clear that the young, developing brain is more impressionable and vulnerable than an adult's. During childhood and early adulthood, we develop our 'identity' as a human. What's different in the digital age is that children now develop their identity in a world dominated by their internet interactions, rather than just their family, school and locality. This means a much wider range of information and behaviours than would have affected previous generations will play a part in that development. This wider information will likely reach the child earlier than the physical equivalent would have for previous generations. And rather than the child driving their own development by experimentation in and outdoors, it is partly being driven by the technology with which they are interacting for so much of the day. The technology may not have a preconceived developmental agenda (other than possibly fostering addiction), but by virtue of what it presents to the child, it will have a significant influence. Understanding this influence is no doubt why Silicon Valley tech stars carefully control their children's screen time and, as has been well publicised, often send them to tech-free schools. As long ago as 2011, 200 teachers, psychiatrists, neuroscientists and others wrote to the *Daily Telegraph*, identifying the drawbacks of digital devices and expressing alarm over what they called 'the erosion of childhood'. Greenfield identifies that in the pre-internet world, children played at home and went 'outside' under controlled conditions – in safe places, or with a parent or carer to supervise. Now children venture onto the internet, the new 'outdoors', often completely unsupervised and uncontrolled. She argues that, in relation to the internet, we need to rapidly develop a 'shared culture of responsibility'. Otherwise, we are allow-ing our children into the digital equivalent of the 'great outdoors' with potentially very harmful consequences.[11]

The 'predator in the home' is how Aiken describes the danger of 'missing parents' when it comes to kids spending time alone online. Talking of boys playing group video games, sometimes with people they don't know, she says that if you imagine looking through your front window and seeing your son talking to three men they didn't know over the garden wall, you would wonder what was going on and probably intervene to find out. Instead, she says, you think 'your boy is sitting in his bedroom. He's quietly playing his game. He's at home. He's safe right?'[12] Maybe not.

Not developing the same attitude to risk or understanding of the conse-quences of dangers and that things go wrong is one of the implications of children spending a considerable amount of time on the internet, rather than playing offline. On the internet, things are often either programmed to 'work out' or at least the consequence of them 'not working out' is not terminal – instead, you are tempted to try again. If you get shot or blown up in a computer game, the game ends, and you start again with a new life. This can lead to children being insufficiently risk-averse or even reck-less. It is a dangerous lesson to learn that death (in the game) seemingly has no real-life consequence and only lasts until you start the next game.

Harvard scientists have demonstrated that sharing personal informa-tion about oneself, as promoted on social networking sites, activates the same reward systems that eating and sex stimulate. Greenfield says, 'conse-quently, the appeal of social networking is rooted in a biological drive of which we are unaware and which we find difficult to control voluntarily'.[13] We get a dopamine hit every time we post, which excites us, and posting is therefore physiologically exciting. Greenfield argues that this, together with the new way identity is formed online, is why some have buried the tradi-tional concern for privacy. 'If identity is now constructed externally and is a far more fragile product of the continuous interaction with "friends", it has uncoupled from the traditional notion of, and need for, privacy.'[14]

Why is sexting and cyber-exhibitionism commonplace? Many academic studies have shown that when we go online, relative to the way we behave in person, many of us become show-offs, exhibitionists, braver, less inhibited, more prepared to demonstrate anger, use worse language and generally show less judgement! This has been termed online disinhibition. The studies suggest that this is because we feel more anonymous, 'invisible' and lack eye contact or immediate feedback from a nearby human being. Escalation, where again, because of the lack of personal proximity to any reaction, low-key disputes can quickly become inflamed online, can lead to online abuse. Lack of empathy seems to play a part in all these traits – in the sense that visual clues and personal reactions in the real world might moderate some of the behaviours that go unchecked on the internet. People often access the internet from seemingly 'safe' places, like home. Insufficient assessment is made of the fact that the internet is not *in* the home, it is elsewhere. This leads to some people assuming they are safer online than they are.

Why are our devices so difficult to put down? Because, as is well documented, they are designed by some of the best neuroscientists in the world, based on huge consumer trials in specialist laboratories, to hook us by giving us regular dopamine hits.

Adam Alter – who I think first coined the term attention crisis – states, 'the problem isn't that people lack willpower' to stay off their devices, but rather 'that there are a thousand people on the other side of the screen whose job is to break down the self-regulation you have'.[15] And 'as an experience evolves, it becomes an irresistible, weaponized version of the experience it once was … In 2004, Facebook was fun; in 2016, it's addictive.'[16] Alter further suggests that in our desire to get more done faster, 'we've forgotten to introduce an emergency brake … or more relevant, the people who produce the engine don't want us to have a brake'.[17] Since 2016, other platforms like Instagram, Snapchat and TikTok have grown rapidly in competition with Facebook, which is now used by the younger generation more for messaging and event planning than for its original purpose.

'Technology companies are trying to get more out of our brains per unit of time,' says Matt Richtel, *New York Times* journalist. 'It's as close to a business model as you can imagine. The more engaged you are in what they create, the more successful they are.'[18] In his book *A Deadly Wandering*, he points out that this drives consumers away from what they are intending and trying to focus on, as technology designers aim 'to figure out how to engage us as immersively as possible'.[19] Perhaps our devices are so compelling that, however disciplined we might be, we just can't put them down. According to Richtel, 'Increasingly technology is appealing to and preying on the deep primitive instincts, parts of us that existed aeons before the phone … for the power of social connection, the need to stay in touch with friends, family, and business connections.' Technology becomes 'a brain hijack machine'.[20] Richtel observes how the phone brilliantly combines the effects of Moore's law and Metcalfe's law, with Moore bringing increased personal information even faster, and Metcalfe making the information as personal as possible to make the gadgets seductive and addictive. He concludes that 'Fundamentally, the extraordinary pace at which consumers adopt these programs and gadgets is not the product of marketing gimmicks or their cool factor, but because of their extraordinary utility. They serve deep social cravings and needs.'[21]

One tangible result of the socially normalised appetite for fame, celebrification and attention has been the revolutionary notion of having to be always on. Turkle says of adolescents, 'They experience their friendships as both sustaining and constraining. Connectivity brings complications … it can be hard to escape from new group demands. It is common for friends to expect their friends will stay available – a technology-enabled social contract demands continual peer presence. And the tethered self becomes accustomed to its support.'[22]

Teens today occupy a space 'already tilted by surveillance capital to tip them into the social mirror and keep them fixed on its reflections,' Zuboff suggests. And most concerningly, this space is inundated by 'genius and money ... devoted to this one goal of keeping users, especially young users, plastered to the social mirror, like bugs on a windshield'.[23]

Let's examine the history here. Google and Facebook executives have long acknowledged the potential to harness human desire for dopamine in the way phones and apps are designed and, moreover, that technology can be addictive. In 2012, Richard Fernandez, an executive coach at Google, noted that 'consumers need to have an internal compass where they're able to balance the capabilities that technology offers them for work, for search, with the qualities of the lives they live off line'.[24] The truth is, however, that phones and apps are designed to disable that compass, which makes it difficult to use or even *want* to use this internal tool. The younger and less experienced a user may be, the less likely they are to realise this. Social media and smartphone designers are well aware that we are programmed to survive by paying attention and design into our devices signals we can't ignore.

Freed asserts that 'across the video gaming industry, scientists bring kids and young adults into state-of-the-art labs to observe them as they game. One-way mirrors and cameras record the facial expressions of subjects while they play. If children look away from the screens, they're questioned to find out why. Behavioural techniques are used to fine-tune the game to make an end-product kids can't look away from and can't put down.'[25] So gaming in particular is designed to very precisely target key human drivers: 'behavioural addictions consist of six ingredients: compelling goals that are just beyond reach; irresistible and unpredictable positive feedback; a sense of incremental progress and improvement;

tasks that become slowly more difficult over time; unresolved tensions that demand resolution; and strong social connections,' says Alter.[26] And 'numbers pave the way to obsession ... most people become obsessive when they're focussing on numbers'.[27]

The UK government's recent white paper on online harms identifies that some online products are designed to encourage continuous use. Infinite scrolls on social media, typing bubbles, quantifying friends, notifications and likes and Snapstreaks are all identified as powerful tools for keeping people online and exacerbating addictive behaviours.

When faced with successive governments who have failed to regulate big tech platforms, scientists have argued about whether society's collective use of devices represents addiction, is compulsive or is just inappropriate and potentially dangerous to our wellbeing. Richtel quotes an addiction researcher: 'whether the word is "impulse" or "compulsion" or "addiction", clearly there is an overtaking of rational, logical processing of information and judgement like we see with ... drugs,' he says; 'even though technology is not classified as "addictive", some neuroscientists point to stark similarities between how technology use and drug use trigger chemical release in the brain'.[28] He cites a Yale neurological study suggesting that the release of dopamine by players of a computer-based racing game was similar to that produced by amphetamines and crystal meth and concluded that 'taken together, these findings suggest that (internet addiction) is associated with dopaminergic neural systems in a fashion similar to substance addictions'.[29] Alter makes a similar point, citing a psychologist; 'Peele sees no difference between substance abuse and behavioural addiction. It's just another 'extreme dysfunctional attachment to an experience that is acutely harmful to a person, but that is an essential part of the person's ecology and that the person cannot relinquish.'[30]

These distinctions, whilst important to the technology industry, could be seen as semantic. There can be little doubt that spending inordinate amounts of time on our mobile devices is an increasingly commonplace practice which underlies a generational shift from the offline world of face-to-face interaction – with the opportunity for deep attention and empathy – to the online world where many of these elements are not as readily available.

Alter explains why 'human behaviour is driven in part by a succession of reflexive cost-benefit calculations that determine whether an act will be performed once, twice, a hundred times or not at all. When the benefits overwhelm the costs, it's hard not to perform the act over and over again, particularly when it strikes the right neurological notes.'[31] In other words, the technology is designed to make it impossible for us to resist revisiting it, over and over again. Scientists believe that in many respects, substance addictions and behavioural addictions are very similar. 'They activate the same brain regions, and they're fuelled by some of the same basic human needs: social engagement and social support, mental stimulation, and a sense of effectiveness.'[32]

Richtel explains that devices appeal to our bottom-up attention and distract us from our top-down attention. 'Top down attention is what we use to direct our focus … [it] allows us to set our objectives and focus on them … and is crucial to survival … bottom up attention operates unconsciously, automatically driven by sensory stimulus and contextual clues.'[33] Richtel's book examines why a boy driving a car sent a text whilst driving which caused a serious car accident: 'his brain is flooded with anticipatory dopamine. He knows on a primitive, neurochemical level that he's about to get a squirt … That's why he pushed the fucking button. He's not conscious of it.'[34]

Adolescents are most vulnerable to the rewards offered by entertainment technology. Freed observes that 'using the latest brain imaging techniques, scientists have found that as kids enter adolescence, there's a dramatic remodelling of the dopaminergic system, the brain areas responsible for reward. Chemical reward sensitivity peaks in adolescence, so that for teens, rewards feel mega-rewarding.'[35]

American author Frank Scoblete, writing about slot machines, says that they 'sit there like young courtesans, promising pleasures undreamed of, your deepest desires fulfilled, all lust satisfied'.[36] This could surely be said of smartphones today. Wu says, 'Instagram has not stirred any new yearning in us, merely acted upon one already there, and facilitated its gratification to an unimaginable extent.'[37] Richtel says, 'When you add it all up – the social lure of information, receiving and disclosing; the intermittent delivery mechanism; the stimulation of inactivity and the neurochemicals associated with reward – you wind up with something powerful to the point of being overpowering. To some researchers, it feels like the process of neurological hijacking.'[38]

Talking of athletes addicted to the endorphin hit and ever-expanding exercise goals, heavier weights, longer runs, faster times, Alter says, 'the same technology that drives people to over exercise also binds them to the workplace 24 hours a day. Until recently, people left work behind when they left the office, but now, with the introduction of smartphones, tablets, remote log-ins and emails that find us wherever we happen to be, that stopping rule is obsolete.'[39] During Covid-19, technology has exacerbated this problem, as for many work is at home. The distance between home and the office is that between the part of the bed you sleep on and the part you use your laptop on. Commuting time has become subsumed into the working day rather than used for reading or relaxing, and many of us are completely 'Zoomed out'.

I observe two particular traits in Generation Z which demand explanation and worry me. One is the inability to do nothing, which I believe is born of technology training them to expect constant stimulation. My own children, despite living in what they would acknowledge is a stunningly beautiful countryside location, would no more sit, do nothing and stare at the views from a garden armchair than they would cut off their own arms. Within a minute of coming off the gaming console, my youngest might say, 'Dad, I am bored,' despite having a host of potential fun activities like football, swimming or tennis at his fingertips. Of course, the more stimulation offered by technology and apps, the easier it is to be bored with the offline world. The second is the inability to do one thing for a prolonged period with sole focus on that activity. Not only does technology seek to addict us, but it also modifies the skills our finite brains prioritise. Carr, in *The Shallows*, studies the work of academics recognising the phenomenon of neuroplasticity – where our brains change the way we function as a result of the way we use them. 'Neuroplasticity provides the missing link to our understanding of how informational media and other intellectual technologies have exerted their influence over the development of civilisation and helped to guide, at a biological level, the history of human consciousness.'[40]

My youngest says, 'Dad, as an outgoing person who at school doesn't spend much time at all on technology, I find it very disconcerting to realise how much time I spend on screens at home. At some point, it just became the default thing to do. When I try to analyse why I find myself distracted and bogged down in the technology, I think it's just how vast it is. There is always something going on. When you get bored of a game, a new update comes along, and it completely changes, maintaining your interest. When you get bored of one show on Netflix, there are 500 more. It can be very difficult to extract yourself from the various social media platforms I use, because there is always something to pull you back to spending more time on your phone. I think I understand why so many teens growing up have been sucked into its aura for the worse. Parents of young kids growing up need to set boundaries before their children's fun and happiness seemingly gets replaced by technology.'

Technologies train our brains into new behaviours. 'As particular circuits in our brain strengthen through the repetition of physical or mental habits,' Carr says, 'they begin to transform the activity into a habit. The paradox of neuroplasticity... is that, for all the mental flexibility it grants us, it can end up locking us into "rigid behaviours".'[41] Neuroplasticity comes with more and more device use. 'In some cases, the build-up of certain kinds of neurotransmitters, such as dopamine, a pleasure producing cousin to adrenaline, seems to actually trigger the turning on or off of particular genes, bringing even stronger cravings for the drug. The vital paths turn deadly.'[42]

The essential point is that by repeatedly doing something like playing a computer game for hours and hours, we get better and better at it, but the brain has a finite capacity. So we also lose the ability to do something else, potentially social skills around mixing and conversing with humans in person and the ability to do anything deep and focused for a long period – the deep attention required in a conversation or the deep reading required to properly read a book from cover to cover. 'The mental skills we sacrifice may be as valuable, or even more valuable than the ones we gain. When it comes to the quality of our thought, our neurons and synapses are entirely indifferent.'[43] 'Although any kind of tool can influence our thoughts and perspectives ... it is our intellectual technologies that have the greatest and most lasting power over what and how we think. They are the most intimate tools, the ones we use for self-expression, for shaping personal and public identity, and for cultivating relations with others.'[44]

As Szalavitz and Perry put it, 'social development requires multiple repeated face-to-face interactions. As we've said before, the brain becomes what it does. And the conditions of modern life conspire against allowing children time and space to repeatedly practice the social skills necessary to the true development of empathy.'[45]

For me, the propensity of devices and apps to train us to use them more and more raises two distinct issues: one concerns the loss of face time and empathetic experiences, and the other is the loss of ability to do anything deeply as a result of having to multitask. I call the latter 'Nothing Deep Multitasking Behaviour (NDMT)', and it seems to be a core survival skill for Generation Z and increasingly for all of us.

It isn't uncommon to observe a Generation Zer online with three devices. Let's say she's watching a film on Netflix on her laptop, with messages from, for example, Facebook popping up on her screen during the film and her mobile in her hand throwing up further messages from Snapchat, Instagram and WhatsApp. Or simply watching television with the laptop or mobile competing for attention and possibly combining messaging with earbuds playing music. Generation Z has been called the earbud generation. Seemiller and Grace note that 'Fifty-five per cent listen while eating and 70 per cent while on social media' and '87 per cent have music on in the background when doing homework', with 'nearly half spending at least 4 hours a day wearing earbuds'.[46]

Kees, twenty, says, 'I can go the whole day and never stop listening to music or podcasts through my earbuds. From the morning shower, to breakfast, the daily commute, studying, exercising, and relaxing, if I don't have music, I get bored or restless. It's become such a staple, I almost can't work or focus without music.'

Can you be focused while multitasking, or is it the ultimate oxymoron? As I watch children messaging while watching a film, listening to music with earbuds while browsing social media and messaging, and particularly gaming with headphones involving messaging alongside the game, I'm struck by the all-consuming nature of these activities.

Generation Z develops a 'juggler's brain', constantly moving between tasks, says Carr. 'In the choices we have made, consciously or not, about how we use our computers, we have rejected the intellectual tradition of solitary, single minded concentration, the ethic that the book bestowed on us. We have cast our lot with the juggler.'[47] In addition to everything else flowing through the network, we also have immediate access to all the other software programs running on our computers – they too compete for a piece of our mind. Whenever we turn on our computer, we are plunged into an 'ecosystem of interruption technologies', as the blogger and science fiction writer Cory Doctorow terms it.

And the problem is not just the interruption itself. It's the very significant amount of time it takes to get back to concentrating on the task you were trying to conclude before the interruption. This suggests that the benefits of avoiding distraction are enormous. Some, including me, believe the supposed benefits of multitasking are a myth. Your brain can cope with two relatively simple tasks at the same time, but most people cannot focus on two or more complex tasks successfully. Flip-flopping between tasks involves re-engaging with the old task, which wastes time, and the error rate for both probably increases. 'Instead of reaping the big rewards that come from sustained, focused effort, we instead reap empty rewards from completing a thousand little sugar-coated tasks.' What results, Haig says, is like a 'repetitive strain injury of the mind'.[48]

An engaged face-to-face conversation rules out multitasking. And multitasking is how Generation Z copes with life. For a while, WhatsApp video and Facetime might have been an answer to the conundrum of messaging not talking. But they have become unpopular as media for communication for long periods of time because they prevent multi-messaging. You have to hold the phone to your face, making it almost impossible to deal with multiple incoming message streams. Professor Katherine Hayles at Duke University observes that 'fractured attention is the sensibility of the 21st Century'. Turkle believes that *deep attention* is a thing of the past. During lectures, for example, she says students *google jockey* – bring up materials to audit or illustrate what the speaker is saying – or *backchannel* – bring up materials providing a running commentary on the lecture. And 'a life of multitasking limits your options so that you cannot simply pick up deep attention'.[49]

We have started to venerate multitasking. My son says, 'Dad, it's not *important* to be able to multitask – it's more than that, *it's a reflex*, it's what we do. But when I am creating music on my deck or writing an essay for uni, if I don't put the phone somewhere else, I am constantly interrupted, and it takes me time to get back into what I was doing. So it does waste a lot of time.' As Turkle puts it, 'Subtly over time, multitasking, once seen as something of a blight, was recast as a virtue. And over time, the conversation about its virtues became extravagant, with young people close to lionised for their ability to do many things at once. Experts went so far as to declare multitasking not just a skill, but as the crucial skill for successful work and learning in a digital culture ... now we must wonder at how easily we were smitten.'[50]

We will examine later the effect of multitasking on work. Carr says, 'when we go online, we enter an environment that promotes cursory reading, hurried and distracted thinking, and superficial learning. It's possible to think deeply while surfing the Net, just as it's possible to think shallowly while reading a book, but that's not the type of thinking the technology encourages or rewards.'[51] 'It is possible, I suppose, that the more we multitask, the better we get at it. But as Carr observes, 'you can train till you're blue in the face and you'd never be as good as if you just focused on one thing at a time.' We are learning to be 'skilled at a superficial level'.[52]

Given what we know about the way neuroplasticity works, if your mission in life was to create a mechanism to hook and reprogram a brain, the internet and social media are what you would have created. Collectively, they deliver perfectly designed and coloured notifications, pings and buzzes over and over again, begging for your attention, hooking you onto more and more dopamine hits and gradually and insidiously rewiring your mental circuits and functions so that you become the proverbial mouse running faster and faster round the wheel.

'The Net also provides a high speed system for delivering responses and rewards – positive reinforcements in psychological terms ... It also turns us into lab rats constantly pressing levers to get tiny pellets of social or intellectual nourishment.'[53]

Isn't multitasking more efficient than doing one thing by definition? 'When psychologists study multitasking, they do not find a story of new efficiencies. Rather, multitaskers don't perform as well on any of the tasks they are attempting ... In the years ahead, there will be a lot to sort out. We fell in love with what technology made easy. Our bodies colluded,' says Turkle.[54]

Pew Research found that 90 per cent of teachers said the internet is creating 'an easily distracted generation with short attention spans'. Alter cites a report which said that 77 per cent of 18–24-year-olds claim that they reach for their phones before doing anything else when nothing is happening. Alter worries that 'the ability of children to sustain attention is known to be a strong indicator for later success in areas such as language acquisition, problem-solving, and other key cognitive development milestones'.[55]

Newport explains that deep work is activity performed in a state of distraction-free concentration that pushes your cognitive capabilities to the limit. These efforts create new value, improve your skill and are hard to replicate. He believes most major physical feats, mental achievements and breakthroughs have occurred as a result of deep work, not the kind of distracted shallow work the internet fosters.[56] Carr sums it up: 'new strengths in visual spatial intelligence go hand in hand with the weakening of our capacities for the kind of "deep processing" that underpins 'mindful knowledge acquisition, inductive analysis, critical thinking, imagination and reflection. The Net is making us smarter in other words, only if we define intelligence by the Net's own standards. If we take a broader and more traditional view of intelligence, if we think about the depth of our thought rather than just its speed, we have to come to a different and considerably darker conclusion.'[57]

Generation Z is no longer able to deep attend to a conversation, deep read a book, deep listen to music or deep watch a film. As a result, whilst they may be honing their multitasking, skimming high-level skills to perfection, they may be losing critical thinking capacity – the ability to 'deep think' and 'deep work'.

The business model which underlies nearly all the sites and platforms we have reviewed is that of behavioural advertising. Jaron Lanier, in his book *Ten Arguments for Deleting Your Social Media Accounts Right Now*, says, 'algorithms gorge on data about you every second. What kind of links do you click on? What videos do you watch all the way through? How quickly are you moving from one thing to the next? Where are you when you do these things? Who are you connecting with in person and online? What facial expressions do you make? How does your skin tone change in different situations? What were you doing just before you decided to buy something or not? Whether to vote or not?'[58] And by monitoring this data on you, the social media platforms use these algorithms to serve up hyper-personalised products and services to you at the very moment when your propensity to purchase that thing is at its highest.

Of course, proponents would rightly say that in our busy lives having products and services that are exactly what we want, laid out for us without us having to waste time searching for them is surely just more efficient. But I do find it spooky when, for example, last night I had a conversation with the family about trimming my lockdown beard, only to wake up this morning to an ad on my social media feed for a beard trimmer. We know, of course, that the price we pay for having more 'relevant' advertising is the loss of privacy, which comes from our data being harvested by the tech we use, including being listened to.

Generation Z will lead a life of unprecedented surveillance and manipulation. Williams says 'many of the world's most widely used platforms, such as Google, Facebook and Twitter, are at their core advertising companies. As a result many of the world's top software engineers, designers, analysts, and statisticians now spend their days figuring out how to direct people's thinking and behaviour toward predefined goals that may not align with their own.'[59] In other words, it goes beyond surveillance to influencing our behaviour.

The core process that allows social media to make money is behavioural modification; methodical techniques which change people's behavioural patterns (buying behaviours in particular). Lanier says these include the temptation of engagement with rewards – personal ringtones, notification sounds, more followers, more likes or candy images in Candy Crush. 'Behaviour modification entails methodical techniques that change behavioural patterns in … people. It can be used to treat addictions, but it can also be used to create them.'[60] But he says the 'problem isn't behaviour modification itself. The problem is relentless, robotic, ultimately meaningless behaviour modification in the service of unseen manipulators and uncaring algorithms.'[61] In *The Death of the Gods*, Carl Miller, founder and Research Director at the Centre for the Analysis of Social Media, observes that 'scattered through tech giants are graduates of the Persuasive Technology Lab at Stanford. It was founded in 1998 by behavioural psychologist B. J. Fogg, to systematically apply psychological insights to technology with the aim of getting people to do things they otherwise wouldn't do … he called it "captology".'[62] Lanier says the problem is the combination of us all carrying around devices capable of behavioural modification, that we are crammed into online environments that can bring out the worst in us, in a world where the advertising game is to find product and service vendors willing to pay the monopsonies which own the platforms we use to modify our behaviour.

'What might once have been called advertising, must now be understood as continuous behaviour modification on a titanic scale.'[63] And as we noted earlier in the social media section of this chapter, he believes the process of behavioural modification amplifies negative emotions more than positive ones. 'We in Silicon Valley like to watch the ants as they dig harder into their dirt. They send us money as we watch.'[64] One has to conclude, given the ignorance most of us have about how big tech works systematically on our data and the weight of resources pitted against us as individuals, that this is not a fair fight!

It isn't just that tech monitors your moods and serves you up with offerings at just your moment of maximum interest and least resistance. Tech can *change* your moods to increase your purchasing propensity. Zuboff writes about the concept of 'emotional contagion' – the idea that platforms can monitor your mood via your interactions with technology (what you write on social media or say to Alexa or Cortana) and then prompt you to change your mood.[65] This can lead you to experiencing different emotions without you realising your mood is being changed for you. The irony 'is that a person's susceptibility to subliminal clues and his or her vulnerability to a contagion effect is largely dependent upon empathy'.[66] In other words, these platforms use your empathetic nature to addict you to them and modify your behaviour in such a way that your potential for face-to-face empathetic experiences is reduced.

In May 2017, a document was leaked from Facebook which blew the lid off behavioural monitoring. It 'detailed the many ways in which the corporation uses its stores of behavioural surplus to pinpoint the exact moment at which a young person needs a "confidence boost" and is therefore most vulnerable to a specific configuration of advertising nudges and cues'.[67]

The idea of technology simply delivering the right product advert at a moment of maximum likelihood to buy is, though, too simple for Zuboff.

She says that with the advent of IoT, sensors can now be 'actuators', meaning 'the real aim is ubiquitous intervention, action and "control" ... [through] tuning, herding and conditioning', not just prompting purchases.[68] Law professor Eric Posner and Microsoft research economist Glen Weyl postulate that AI and machine learning could develop in such a way that we start relying on the platforms to know what we want in terms of entertainment, goods and services.[69] AI could be so good at knowing our every whim that we become accustomed to just accepting recommendations with goods and services arriving automatically just as we desire them without our intervention. But they point out that 'certainly such a world, characterized by the combination of massive computer power and big data supplied by a voluntary (or possibly legally mandated) system of continuous surveillance, poses obvious dystopic risks. No individual or small group of individuals could be trusted to direct such a system, as the temptations to abuse it would be overwhelming'.[70] I am not so sure we are very far from such a situation existing right now. In *The Social Dilemma*, Zuboff talks about big-tech companies creating market places in human futures at scale.

'Kids for sale, online advertising and the manipulation of children' is the title of a recent paper by Global Action Plan (GAP), a UK charity focusing on wellbeing. It identifies how children are exposed to an extraordinary and unprecedented volume of advertising online – what they call a 'tsunami' of advertising.[71] Data analysis by the digital monitoring agency Sprout reveals that one in every three Instagram posts is an advert. GAP's own teenage survey revealed that teens see one ad every ten seconds while scrolling their feeds, equivalent to 425 ads per hour. Rules have long existed limiting TV ads to 7 minutes per hour on Public Service Broadcast channels and nine minutes per hour on other channels. There is no online equivalent limit. The report says that whilst estimates vary, one suggests that a child in the UK, US and Australia saw on average 20–40,000 TV ads a year before online viewing took over from TV. Assuming GAP's survey is broadly representative, it would mean children would now see ten to twenty times as many ads online as they saw on TV alone. Just like adults, children are of course targeted with adverts tailored to them based on large amounts of sensitive personal data. Their research shows that children are relatively unable to discern when they are being sold to and are especially susceptible to manipulation and that targeted advertising to under-thirteens, whilst illegal in the UK, is widespread. GAP argues that targeting a child with advertising exploits a gross imbalance of power. 'Ad tech companies hold, on average, 72 million data points on a child by the time they turn thirteen. On the one hand vast data, harnessed by supercomputers and insights from behavioural psychology; on the other, a single, still developing child's brain.' In the UK in September 2020, a group of leading academics, lawyers and privacy campaigners wrote an open letter demanding that Facebook, Google and other tech platforms should stop allowing the advertising industry to target teenagers and called for restrictions similar to those which apply to advertising alcohol and gambling. Google is facing a £2.5 billion lawsuit in the UK High Court that alleges it has unlawfully profiled children under the age of thirteen on YouTube.

Depression arising from device addiction is a major concern, say Seemiller and Grace. Many studies including their own confirm that more and more youngsters have had major depressive episodes. It seems to be an even bigger issue for girls where '22 per cent of girls treated for a mental health issue had a diagnosis of depression, more than twice the rate for boys'.[72] This may relate to girls' propensity to spend more time on social media whilst boys game more. It is also a particular problem in the LGBTQ+ group, where '41 per cent … indicated having received coun-selling or psychological services in the last 12 months to address struggles related to their identities'. They go on, 'in addition to the growing rates of anxiety and depression among members of Generation Z, there is also cause for grave concern around issues related to suicide. Rates have been on the rise for hospital medical professionals' diagnoses of suicidality/self-inflicted harm in young people as well as actual teen and young adult suicides.'[73]

The GAP report cited earlier notes the coincident timing of the widespread access of teens to social media, the rise in teens owning smartphones and rises in mental ill-health. It discounts the idea that these rises are explained by increasing awareness of mental health or the increased willingness of Generation Z to report distress, because increases are simultaneously seen in behavioural acts such as self-harm, suicide attempts and actual suicides, which increase at roughly the same time as self-reports of anxiety, depression and suicidal ideation. It concludes that, whilst 'correlation does not infer causation, it is worth noting that the rise in smartphone use and access to social media and hence increased exposure to targeted advertising, is coupled with increases in mental disorders in young people'. Common Sense Media recently published a report 'Tweens, teens, tech and mental health', which included reviews of most of the major recent studies into links between screen time, social media and teenage mental health. It found that associations between adolescent mental health and their use of social networking sites were inconsistent, links were small, and there were almost always other correlated or third factors which couldn't be ruled out. It observed that inferring causation is never straightforward when considering complex problems. It did note, however, that even small effects can matter when exposure is widespread (as in the case of social media) and the outcome is severe (as in the case of depression and suicide risk).

In the UK, the Samaritans' most recent suicide statistics report notes that it is the biggest killer of young people and that in 2018 there were 16.9 suicides per 100,000 of those aged 20–24, the highest subgroup amongst young people, with a 30 per cent year-on-year increase. Suicide-related internet use (in other words, evidence that a suicide victim had researched the subject online before committing suicide) was found in 26 per cent of deaths in the under-twenties. The Samaritans do make it clear, however, that there are typically multiple factors involved in someone's decision to end their life. Even more worrying is the growth in self-harm, rising in all youth groups in their study between 2000 and 2014: it is a strong risk factor for future suicides, and over 25 per cent of women and nearly 10 per cent of men between sixteen and twenty-four reported self-harming at some point during their lives in 2018. Sadly, LGBT youth are almost five times as likely to have attempted suicide compared with heterosexual youth according to the Trevor Project. Each episode of verbal harassment or abuse increases the likelihood of self-harming behaviour by 2.5 times on average, and in a national study 40 per cent of transgender adults reported having made a suicide attempt.

Teenagers who spend more than 5 hours a day on electronic devices are 71 per cent more likely to have suicide risk factors than those with 1 hour's use, and eighth graders who are heavy users of social media have a 27 per cent higher risk of depression, according to the findings of a Bankmycell study in the US in 2019.

There are good scientific reasons which might explain this. Human neural architecture is developed under conditions of close, mostly contin-uous face-to-face contact, including but not exclusively oral and auditory senses. And it is well known that if you remove a system's key inputs (e.g. by moving from face-to-face to online communication), this can lead to destabilisation of the system. Many studies have found that there are robust connections to suicidal ideation from two key factors: perceived burdensomeness (perceiving yourself to be a burden) and thwarted belongingness (being prevented from feeling like you belong). These are factors which we know bad experiences that occur frequently on social media would exacerbate.

As the Common Sense Media report noted, technology use is only one of the factors at play. Seemiller and Grace note in their studies that Generation Z's top three worries are the fear of failure, money and larger societal issues. They believe they 'carry the weight of the world on their shoulders like never before'. And that Generation Z 'is shouldering the burden of large scale macro issues facing the world while trying to balance their school and personal lives as youth and young adults'.[74] Worrying about the world's issues may be taking a toll on their mental health. This was, of course, written before the Covid-19 pandemic hit its peak, and one can only worry about the extent to which this will exacerbate current and future mental-health issues. In *The Social Dilemma*, Tristan Harris, former design ethicist at Google, describes the smartphone as a 'digital pacifier' and says that it is atrophying our ability to deal with anxiety.

Generation Z, it seems then, is worrying about not living up to their own expectations, disappointing others and not making a difference. So, while the period in which Generation Z has grown up is partly to blame, the potential to disappoint reflects the importance of peer-group review and feedback which technology facilitates and amplifies. Participants in Seemiller and Grace's studies expressed their worries about making mistakes, rejection, missed opportunities, regret and just being *average*. Whatever is wrong with being at the 50 per cent quartile, some people might ask – it means you are better than nearly half the population in reality, albeit you may not be as good as 99 per cent of what appears on social media. These worries aren't surprising in that rates of perfectionism in college students have linearly increased between 1989 and 2016 due to young people believing that 'others are more demanding of them, [they] are more demanding of others, and [they] are more demanding of themselves'.[75]

'What are the costs to a society of an entire population conditioned to spend so much of their waking lives not in concentration and focus but rather in fragmentary awareness and subject to constant interruption,'[76]

Wu asks. If we cannot deep attend, deep think or address complex cognitive tasks as effectively as we used to, there must be an economic cost. He is right when he says, 'it would no doubt be shocking to reckon the macroeconomic price of all our time spent with the attention merchants.'[77]

I had a go at calculating it. UK GDP is around £2.8 trillion per annum. The maximum legal working week is 48 hours. So, supposing every worker spent just one hour less per week on their devices and spent that hour working instead, the increase in working hours could create around an extra £58 billion in GDP just for the UK. Statisticians will point to many holes in this grossly oversimplified analysis. But it doesn't matter if it is wrong by orders of magnitude; the effect could obviously be huge. To put £58 billion in context, the entire NHS budget for the UK last year was around £140 billion. And to the extent online activity is ultimately found to be partly responsible for declining mental health, it is worth considering separately what the costs of that might be. In a report written by Lord Dennis Stevenson and Mind Chief Executive Stephen Farmer for the UK government in 2017, Deloitte estimated that there was a large annual cost to employers of between £33 billion and £42 billion from 'presenteeism' – where individuals are less productive due to poor mental health in work. The annual cost of poor mental health to the government was around £25 billion in providing benefits, lost tax revenue and NHS costs. The whopping annual cost of poor mental health to the economy overall was estimated at between £74 billion and £99 billion.[78] The point is that even if online activity is responsible for a small proportion of mental health costs, it would be a very substantial sum.

That's just the economic cost. Is it possible to determine the net effects on fitness of screen time? Some, wishing to look like the fittest on social media, are definitely motivated to do more exercise and eat more healthily, and we have noted how this can itself become obsessive due to the combination of wearables and social media. Others, due to the sheer amount of time spent on screen, may do less. Certainly Seemiller and Grace found rising rates of obesity in Generation Z, due to the combination of fast and snack foods, sugary drinks and less exercise due to screen time, video gaming and e-sports. The US Report Card on Physical Activity for Children and Youth, in the category of sedentary behaviours which measures screen time, found that just around 31 per cent of 12–19-year-olds studied met the screen time guidelines of 2 hours or less a day.[79]

We have covered the negative impacts on girls of social media. On the flip side, the body-perfect motivation thrown up to young men by social media and the propensity of boys to body build and take protein powders, steroids or other muscle-enhancing substances should also be concerning. Studies suggest that body-enhancing behaviour in US middle and high schools is pervasive: more than one-third of boys take protein powders, 6 per cent use steroids and more than 10 per cent admit using what they believe to be muscle-enhancing substances. Long-term use of steroids, in particular, is of course associated with depression, rage attacks, suicidal tendencies and heart issues.

To sum up this chapter, Baptiste says, 'On emotional intelligence, social media reduces our capacity to talk face-to-face or focus on anyone or anything properly. And while social media has democratised celebrification, everyone wants to be unique, different and best, and this leads to a never-satisfied state.'

PART 3

THE NEW NORMAL

7

WHAT MAKES
GENERATION Z TICK?

'OMG, that shirt is so sick.' I come across my middle son with his friend, Arthur, also a twenty-year-old Bristol University undergraduate. Arthur is obsessed with his fitness and loves fashion. He is extolling the clothing recommendations of his favourite influencer, Tom Austin, whose Instagram handle is tomaustin.fits. Here he posts outfit recommendations daily. Whilst I wouldn't have got much beyond British Home Stores in my local high street to buy clothes at that age, his favourite new brand is Obscura Store, Youth Lab, based in Seoul, South Korea. On investigation, I discover South Korea's young designers are taking the low-cost fashion world by storm, building on global popularity of the Korean Pop (K-Pop) scene with, according to fashion site Hypebeast, 'imaginative staples made sustainably'. There are tags on the influencer's Instagram images, which after one click, take you straight to the Korean website. In English, the site efficiently offers you delivery to the UK within a few days. Arthur gets *very* excited about a new pair of military-style trainers.

Generation Z is conditioned in terms of its values by its use of technology. From constant distraction comes the need for rapid, convenient, 'frictionless' consumption, but which allows for the expression of personality, individuality and flexibility. The gig economy (where people work on temporary or short-term contracts) is built around choice, convenience and efficiency with one very important additional notion built in – that of minimal commitment, for both customers and employees. Generation Z wants 'options not arrangements' as to how and when they consume and work.

Recommendations are most valued when they come from 'friends' (whether real, celebrities or just connections) and when they involve *experiences* rather than *objects*. There is a healthy regard for the cost of consumption, both in economic and environmental terms, and value for money – unsurprising given that this group has been made aware of the potential financial challenges that will haunt their entire cohort.

These traits did not simply appear out of thin air. Generation Z has grown up in the shadow of the traumas we have discussed: the war on terror, the global financial crisis, the climate crisis and most recently Covid-19. The negativity of these traumas has been amplified by social media, and this has led both to the feelings of unease and concern for world issues and financial security and to the entrepreneurial spirit and desire for independence that we have observed.

Seemiller and Grace conclude that this generation tends to be liberal or moderate on social issues and conservative on financial issues.[1] This is not particularly surprising when we consider the context in which they have grown up; indeed, their mantra seems to be, 'Don't impinge on my personal freedoms but do make sure I am safe and healthy.'[2]

According to Seemiller and Grace's study, 93 per cent of Generation Zers were somewhat concerned about unemployment, 72 per cent would pay more for sustainable offerings, 58 per cent cared or cared a great deal about environmental issues, and inclusion was a recurring and strong theme. Generation Z as a whole is thrifty, charity-minded and surprisingly financially literate despite their relatively young age. A study by a TransUnion indicates that nearly half of the 13–17-year-olds surveyed are familiar with what a credit score is and, more importantly, how this score is calculated.[3] And 91 per cent of those familiar with credit scores are currently saving. Sixty-two per cent purport to know a great deal about their family's finances, and 50 per cent of those in Generation Z believe themselves to be more knowledgeable about saving money than their parents were at their age.[4] Indeed, while Generation Z is worried about climate change, they are much more worried about money.[5]

In a way, Generation Z expects to have what they see some of the older generation having had in the good times, when they want it and where they want it. And their significance to the population in terms of scale and proportion means that their purchasing power will be huge. In their book *Marketing to Gen Z*, Jeff Fromm (President of FutureCast, the advertising agency) and Angie Read (VP of Growth Insight) suggest Generation Z's impact on US consumer spending alone could be $665 billion per annum.[6] But the service offering and the brand character of the supplier being consistent with their values will be very important to attracting Generation Z buyers.

Generation Z wants what it wants now and with minimal effort – in short, they desire frictionless access. Speed is absolutely critical. Apps available on a smartphone, like Amazon and eBay, enable consumers to buy just about anything from their sofas and have these items delivered to their doorsteps tomorrow. Product or service comparison websites, one click to purchase and free delivery are all part of this equation. As Alter notes, 'Life is more convenient than ever, but convenience has weaponized temptation.'[7]

Fromm and Read believe that in order to connect with Generation Zers – or in their words, Pivotals – technology ought to practically disappear, rendering user experiences seamless. Speeds should be so rapid as to be effectively imperceptible, and mobile access is absolutely key. Google search results now favour websites that are mobile-optimised. The authors note, 'If Pivotals notice the technology, you're doing something wrong.'[8]

In many ways, this obsession with efficiency makes sense. 'In a community where social status is deeply tied to net worth and company valuations, the more work you're able to get done, the more social capital you're likely to attain,' the authors argue. 'If you can take the time you were spending thinking about food, or getting dressed, or any of the myriad of other micro-decisions that clog up daily life, and dedicate it instead to writing code and getting rich, you'll be more productive, more profitable, and generally better off.'[9]

James, a nineteen-year-old Bristol University undergraduate, says, 'I have noticed that with ever increasing efficiency, speed and convenience of services like those Amazon and eBay offer, my ability to organise myself and productivity have diminished. I think of doing something in good time but believe I can leave it to the last minute, e.g. to order that calculator for my exam the day before the exam. When I then pull up Amazon on my phone one hour *after* the deadline for next-day delivery has expired, I cause myself unnecessary stress and wonder why I didn't order it when I first thought of it! We have become so reliant on technology providing service that we sometimes fail to hold ourselves to account for even the most basic tasks.'

Gen Z's search for value for money follows from the fact that, as of 2020, Generation Z is either studying or early in their careers, so its members do not tend to have much money, and it hasn't forgotten their parents' experience of the GFC. As a result, Generation Zers are often on the hunt for value. Price comparison websites enable them to assess the combination of price and location of source that fits with their budgets and urgency to purchase. As Seemiller and Grace put it, 'as much as millennials may like the notion of sharing for a profit, those in Generation Z have some criteria that must be met in order to see the sharing economy as one that meets their needs. They need these experiences to be convenient, efficient *and economical* all at the same time.'[10]

Many Generation Zers have several part-time jobs, or their own entre-preneurial activities to support their incomes. While the 'side-hustle' is a popular way to make extra money, for many it may be more of a necessity than a choice.

Generation Z is entrepreneurial, whether out of necessity or by inclina-tion. Many of its members have not only made purchases on the internet, but also sold items online thanks to platforms like eBay. Seemiller and Grace observe that 14 per cent of 13–15-year-olds, 22 per cent of 16–18-year-olds and 28 per cent of 19–21-year-olds have already made money online.[11] Generation Z won't be a generation like mine, which is sometimes accused of understanding the price of everything and the value of nothing.

Rent not buy is shorthand for the sharing economy, but it goes much further than this. Airbnb, Uber, WeWork and Netflix have all trans-formed the way traditional service models have worked in the property rental and hotel, taxi, office and video rental markets. But they all address a need – the customer wants what they want *just* for as long as they need it, as cheaply and conveniently as possible, with no further commitment. Generation Z may also impress its peers by temporarily 'owning' some-thing aspirational and using it to enhance their fame. Similarly, many employees wish to combine part-time work with working for themselves or working in multiple part-time roles.

The wish to 'rent not buy' extends beyond major capital items to home furnishings. At least, that's the thinking behind several web start-ups seeking to lease everything from sofas to throw pillows. These new subscription services, including the New York-based Feather and Los Angeles-based Fernish, differ from established furniture-rental compa-nies. As their eco-evocative names suggest, the new companies present renting as an environmental virtue – instead of buying cheap, disposable furniture that ends up in landfills, you can rent better-quality pieces that others use when you're done with them. They aim at people who have graduated from college but haven't settled down and who may appreciate fine things but don't necessarily feel the need to own them just yet.[12]

Even companies like IKEA, known for their cheap, quotidian furnishings that encourage a 'use-and-toss mentality', have begun to adjust their business model. The firm is currently testing subscription-based consumer leasing programmes in Poland and the Netherlands and is planning on expanding to thirty countries including the United States.

Generation Z's desire to be thrifty, combined with its tendency to fill shorter-term and sometimes part-time jobs combined with the onerous conditions in the consumer credit market, have led to an unending search for a new business model for consumption. For those who are not going to settle down with a partner, stay in a job for more than a few months or stay in one geographical location for long, there is no reason to buy a house, a car or even a bed or sofa. In the housing market, most of Generation Z cannot afford the large deposits now required to get a foot on the housing ladder. Shortages of lower-price houses and higher average prices have constrained Generation Z's ability to buy homes. In the UK in 1960, the average first-time home buyer was twenty-three and paid a deposit of £595. Today, most are over thirty, and their deposit is over £20,000. In previous decades, home buyers benefited from inflation, which meant that mortgages stayed constant, and the value of the property rose rapidly over prolonged periods. That phenomenon has gone as Western economies have moved into a new, lower-inflation environment. As a result, the potential for creating wealth through home ownership may not be such a driver for Generation Z. Consequently, for this generation, allowing someone else to take the risk of asset ownership and keeping their limited resources for other purposes makes complete sense.

'Options not arrangements' describes another aspect of the minimal commitment which underlies Generation Z's approach to life. I was contacted through LinkedIn and arranged to meet Luca, twenty-one, who had a startup business providing temporary insurance for the gig economy he wanted to discuss. We arranged a week in advance to meet at 10 a.m. on Monday morning. I grew up with a diary and then started using an online calendar. Most of the young entrepreneurs I meet seem to regard a meeting arrangement as a kind of option, and many don't keep diaries, just informal notes. As I was parking the car, I noticed Luca had texted a few minutes earlier to say, 'Sorry, got to do something this morning, can we do Thursday instead?' Kind of maddening, since it's by then too late to organise anything else, and of course the diary on Thursday is already full. So why does this happen? It may be due in part to a new work environment that does not tie Generation Zers to their desks, allowing them to juggle their commitments more flexibly. But I believe it is also due in part to a Generation Z-specific mentality that says commitment only starts when you are actually on your way to, or practically in, a meeting. Until then, you have an option. This includes events with their own generation. In my generation, last-minute dropouts from previously accepted formal invitations would happen very rarely. For our kids, however, not only are last-minute cancellations exceedingly common, but many decline to even formally respond to an invitation. Perhaps Generation Z's propensity to multitask means they have trouble organising their time, because they are always doing several things. Or perhaps it's that social media connections are so immediate that it allows users to almost always organise something to do at the last minute, negating the need to plan ahead.

Generation Z has grown up in the hyper-personalised world of targeted advertisements and social platforms and is often willing and used to trading privacy for a more personalised experience. In other words, you can listen to my conversation with Alexa as long as, if I ask her to come up with suggestions for the theatre, the ads that come up on my Instagram feed tomorrow morning include more current shows. 'Previous generations were afraid to share their personal information online. Gen Z

133

is fearless when it comes to sharing personal data, but in return, their expectations for a personalised experience are high,' according to Dorsey and Villa.[13] Indeed they say, 'Over one-third of Gen Z expect the Internet to predict what they need and alert them before they need it.'[14]

A study commissioned by WP Engine and undertaken by the Center for Generational Kinetics found that 44 per cent of Generation Z would stop visiting a website if it didn't anticipate what they needed, liked or wanted.[15] But their demand for customisation and personalisation as a way of expressing the personal brands they spend so much time online cultivating will extend well beyond the digital world. Fromm and Read call it 'Brand Me'. 'Pivotals are attracted to brands that can help them curate and manage Brand Me. No matter what you sell or promote, your priority should be helping, empowering and even collaborating with Pivotals. Take your logo out of the spotlight and let their image shine.'[16] Generation Z then sees its role as contributing to the shared knowledge economy, and in the process its members develop their own identities and pride as experts in their particular niche interests. Screen time is necessary to cultivate these identities, and so it's dangerous for our generation to automatically assume the 'geeks' stuck on devices are wasting time. In the words of the immortal song, 'the geeks will inherit the earth'.

More engaging content will be required from advertisers and in Generation Z's preferred form, video. 'Gen Z is the first generation that uses the Internet for entertainment first and information second,' WP Engine CMO Mary Ellen Dugan shares. 'Gen Z's entertainment-first approach to the Internet means brands need to think about their EQ – that is, entertainment quotient – perhaps for the first time ever.'[17] Between 2018 and 2019, Dorsey and Villa found that 18–24-year-olds grew their rate of video consumption by 57 per cent.[18] And the video will need to be personalised and engaging with interaction and gamification built in. Secure Broadcast, a company in Belfast, has pioneered a new way of making hyper-personalised video. Whilst the basic messaging or advertising is standard to all the videos it distributes for any campaign, the particular video shown to a potential customer is created on the consumer's mobile device in real time as he or she watches it, so that it can interrogate relevant data and bring into the video personalised content including name, age, location, language and any relevant previous interaction with that advertiser, e.g. an account balance or loyalty points. This gives the user a much more personally relevant, useful and engaging video.

Apparel companies in particular are jumping aboard this hyper-personalised bandwagon. For example, Lacoste now offers completely customised combinations of fabric colours, neck bands, logo position and waistbands on their classic polo shirts. Order in shop or online and have your very own shirt delivered to your home or available to pick up in shop 24 hours later. Nike offers a similar customisation service for trainers by way of 'NikeiD'. A company I know well which makes swim and underwear was working with Calvin Klein to create the capacity for US citizens to order and receive the following day at their home or office personalised clothing made in the precise colour, fit and banding combination they selected from those on offer on their website. This trend is important because Generation Z believes that what they wear is part of *their* brand, who they are and what they stand for. It will reflect the tribes they belong to and the causes they support.

McKinsey says that businesses must rethink how they deliver value to customers, rebalancing scale and mass production against personalisation.[19] Generation Z does not seek to define itself through a single stereotype but rather encourages individuals to experiment with different ways of being themselves and to shape their unique identities over time. According to McKinsey, Generation Z will be prepared to pay more for personalised offerings.[20]

Apple has arguably built its whole business by recognising and appealing to Generation Z's value system. As Zuboff observes, 'Apple's "miracle" is typically credited to its design and marketing genius.'[21] Indeed, the iEmpire was 'among the first to experience explosive commercial success by tapping into a new society of individuals and their demand for individualised consumption'.[22] This particularly twenty-first-century notion of having '"my life, my way, at a price I can afford" was the human promise that quickly lodged at the very heart of the commercial digital project,'[23] Zuboff argues. However, Apple has repeatedly broken the implicit social contract with its adoring young customer base by not paying enough attention to their views on sustainability.

'Brands Taking Stands' is the name of the movement which reflects Generation Z's focus on the environment, economic and social issues and, related to that, this generation's propensity, despite limited resources, to pay more for sustainable offerings. As such, every business needs to be thinking about how to make its offerings sustainable (and market this sustainability) if they are to attract Generation Z's attention.

In 2020, a survey by the consulting firm DoSomethingStrategic found that two-thirds of Generation Z consumers surveyed had experienced an increase in positive feelings about a brand because of an association with a social cause, and for 58 per cent such an association could spur a purchase.[24] Similar surveys from SAP and Sprout Social found similar results.

Sustainability was found by the international accounting and consulting firm PwC in recent research to be significantly more of a factor amongst the young; so much so that, when buying gifts at Christmas last year, 73 per cent of the under-25-year-old age bracket claimed to have chosen more sustainable gifts, including buying second-hand and giving homemade presents. PwC also found that the under-35-year-olds were more likely to be planning to change their diets for sustainability and environmental reasons.[25] I believe the new 'conscientious consumer' in Generation Z will quickly expect every aspect of their purchases to be sustainable. They will call out or boycott brands who fail to meet their exacting standards. As PwC observes, it is increasingly hard to see how a new premium brand that did not have significant and genuine sustainability credentials could be brought to market in the future.[26]

Patagonia, the outdoor apparel company, is a great example of a brand that has embraced Generation Z's values. It was one of the first companies to adopt a sustainability mission – 'build the best product, cause no unnecessary harm and use business to inspire and implement solutions to the environmental crisis'. They donate 1 per cent of sales to environment groups all over the world and have very high employee and customer retention. In cosmetics, Lush has made a similar brand pitch, 'creating a cosmetics revolution to save the planet'. It has integrated climate change advocacy into every aspect of its business and in 2019 closed its stores to allow its employees to attend the youth-led global climate strike.

Whilst every generation has to some extent sought to customise its look and found ways of trading in second-hand items, acquired from markets and boot sales, the rise of apps like Depop and the simplicity of eBay have enabled Generation Z to take buying and selling worn clothes to a new level, appealing to both their desire for sustainability and their entrepreneurial ambitions. Over the past three years, the resale segment has grown twenty-one times faster than the traditional retail apparel market and is expected to reach $51 billion in five years, according to a 2019 report by ThredUp.[27] It also says Generation Z is adopting second-hand 2.5 times faster than older age groups. I will never forget walking into the kitchen one morning when my son asked me to help him pack a ski jacket into a jiffy bag. I asked him where it was going, to which he replied, 'Oh, I have found a cooler one, so have sold this one for £150 to a guy in Norway.'

Peer-to-peer recommendation is more effective than paid advertising in digital marketing. Social media lends itself to recommendation, combining as it does pictures, words and life experiences. As Dorsey and Villa explain, 'Gen Z is the new "it" generation and will be for at least the next decade. This generation makes up the group of diverse, hyper-connected, short-attention-span influencers, who are fast becoming the tastemakers across industries, brands and digital platforms.'[28]

Morning Consult's survey of Generation Z and millennials in 2019 found that in terms of deciding when to purchase a good or service, 82 per cent of Generation Z trust their friends and family most, 52 per cent trust influencers, and 44 per cent rely on their favourite celebrities and athletes: 22 per cent had made a purchase inspired by an influencer or celebrity, higher than for millennials.[29] In a 2019 report, MediaKix found that influencer marketing spend on Instagram had reached $1.8 billion and forecast influencer spend to be $5–10 billion by the end of 2020.[30] Fromm and Read found in their survey of Generation Z that 89 per cent of what they call Pivotals said they would be more likely to enter a store based on where their friends shop.[31]

According to Keith Niedermayer, Adjunct Professor of Marketing at Wharton, Generation Z's time online, along with their extensive reliance on social media, means 'they're also highly influenced by others' opinions and word of mouth'.[32] They can view product and service reviews left on retailers' comparison websites or apps and access social media niche influencers' reviews on just about anything. Seemiller and Grace say that social media has created the platform for the 'non celebrities to flourish'. I think it would be more accurate to say that these non-celebrities are the *new celebrities* as far as Generation Z is concerned, and the recent rapid growth of TikTok has taken the trend to a new level.

Influencer marketing and celebrity endorsement are unsurprisingly bigger than ever, with one in three Generation Zers stating in the survey that they now find brands via online ads rather than on TV. Brand-made video, apps and games are playing an increasingly important role –29 per cent of Generation Z had watched a video made by a brand in the last month and were 35 per cent more likely than the average internet user to have played a branded game and 26 per cent more likely to have downloaded or used a branded app.

YouGov produced some recent research which shows that 49 per cent of those who have seen endorsements from people they follow agree that their profiles are not a genuine representation of the person promoting the product and 46 per cent think the endorsements aren't believable at all. YouGov's survey also found, however, that, despite their scepticism, only 24 per cent of people who had been exposed to influencer ads ignored them altogether. As YouGov put it, 'Brits might not always like internet personalities, they might not trust their motives, they might in some cases consider them outright dishonest, but they're still paying attention'.[33] During 2019, the first court case where an influencer was prosecuted by the FTC for not disclosing brand sponsorship income occurred after a study by them found 93 per cent of influencers were not following FTC guidelines about disclosure of brand sponsorship.

Influencers with the biggest profiles and most followers are not necessarily the most effective. I know from my own Italian restaurant business – Margot in Covent Garden, London – that Generation Z likes 'micro influencers', those with niche interests. This perhaps reflects their wish for individuality and customisation. We have had more success in attracting customers by advertising with niche influencers specialising in, for example, 'traditional Italian cooking' than the biggest restaurant critics in London, despite them having many fewer followers.

Sharing-economy businesses like Airbnb recognise Generation Z's desire for experiences over possessions and are reworking their business plans to harness it. Brian Chesky, the CEO of Airbnb, was recently quoted in the *Financial Times* as saying that he intended to double down on experiences – like hosting activities for travellers to his rented properties, including cooking classes. 'Experiences,' he said, 'I am more convinced than ever, is going to be a massive business.'[34]

During Covid-19, we struggled in my businesses to work out how to replace for colleagues the experience of community that comes with being in an office. I had one brainwave. The office summer party was in everyone's diary, but was about to be cancelled due to lockdown. Should we just send colleagues a cancellation? I had been shown by one of the young entrepreneurs I work with a brilliant twenty-year-old chef called Will Hughes on Instagram. He couldn't work, as his employer's restaurant was shut, so he had quickly built 42K followers doing witty 'cook-along' videos on Instagram under the handle 'WhatWillyCook … recipes not stressipes'. We turned the office party into a group Zoom call – sent every colleague a voucher to go and buy the ingredients for one of Will's dinners and got him to do a live comedy cook-along, following which we all ate what we had cooked whilst staying on Zoom.

Prioritising experiences over products was an attribute which millennials had already developed. A study by Harris Group found that 72 per cent of millennials would rather open their wallets for experiences than material items.[35] It seems that Generation Z has picked up and taken this to the next level; over the past few years, the US has witnessed a tectonic shift in spending with four times more spending devoted to experiences rather than physical goods.[36]

While all generations value 'experiences', the nature of those vary greatly between each age group. Generation Z values adventurous experiences (such as exploring and trying new things), while baby boomers see traditional travel experiences such as sightseeing or touring as the top priority. Millennials and Gen X (born 1965–76) value relaxation, such as beach or spa time. The Harris Group report notes, however, that age isn't the only defining determinant of travellers' preferences: income bracket also played a factor. Lower-income travellers prioritise spending time with family and loved ones, middle-income prioritise sightseeing, and higher-income travellers want to relax.[37]

Spending money on experiences is, relatively speaking, good value for money – another Generation Z value. 'Spending money on experiences tends to have a longer-lasting and more substantial payoff,' Jean Chatzky, financial editor of NBC's *Today Show*, wrote in her latest of eleven books, *Women with Money*.[38]

In Generation Z's world, where physical contact with friends is constrained by screen time, experiences can be used to engage friends. Michael Norton, a Harvard Business School professor and co-author of the book *Happy Money: The Science of Happier Spending*, found that spending within reason to strengthen relationships is generally a good use of money.[39]

Businesses need to reflect on the fact they will become dependent on the content of Generation Z's digital wallets. McKinsey claims three overriding themes will drive Generation Z's approach to goods and services: consumption as access not possession, consumption as an expression of personal identity and consumption as a matter of ethical concern.[40]

SOCIAL LIFE

8

THE HOOKUP CULTURE

OK, so try and imagine yourself as a single twenty-something in 2021, with a relentless focus on comparison and perfection. Generation Zers have found, though, that where they do have a relationship with a partner, access to social media in general and dating apps in particular hasn't always been helpful to maintaining that relationship. Generation Zers will often tell you that, whilst many have had some good experiences dating through technology, there are pitfalls too. Indeed, the supreme visibility that technology gives us can lead to toxic, unhealthy and even abusive encounters. After all, the search for true love, which may be one of the hardest any of us undertakes, can be illusive and quickly exposed if not based in reality. But is Generation Z looking for love or *encounters* not *relationships*?

The digital revolution has changed the way people meet each other and start relationships. Thirty years ago, finding a partner might take you to the youth club, the pub, the disco, or to a sporting or work event. Generally speaking, you approached the individual you found most attractive, who, of course, frequently declined your advances. You turned your attention to your next choice. The pool of potential partners, however, was small and relatively limited to your immediate location. When compared to modern, technology-facilitated methods of seeking and approaching potential partners, the old method was a much less efficient and potentially less effective way of meeting a potential partner.

Thanks to dating apps, today's daters can search or 'swipe through' hundreds, if not thousands, of individuals, reviewing their personal information, validating that information by cross-checking against social media or other internet resources and having an initial online chat – all before physically meeting. Logically, this should make the likelihood of a meeting on the basis of mutually compatible objectives much higher and is, arguably, a much more efficient process with a much higher chance of success.

More people will meet their partner online than offline by 2035, according to a 2019 survey by eharmony and Imperial College Business School, London. A third of UK relationships started between 2015 and 2019 started online, up from 19 per cent between 2005 and 2014.[1] Research from Michael Rosenfeld and Sonia Hausen of Stanford University and Reuben Thomas of the University of New Mexico found that people now take fewer words to tell their meeting stories. Whereas in 2009, an average respondent needed sixty-seven words to explain how they met their significant other, in 2017, they needed only thirty-seven. It doesn't take long to say 'I swiped right'. Just over a decade ago, only 22 per cent of heterosexual couples in the US said they met online; in 2017, that number grew to 39 per cent. The number of folks who were introduced by friends, once the most common method of meeting, dropped dramatically, possibly because online dating has now become culturally acceptable.[2]

Dating apps certainly provide a useful service for many. And of course, dating apps play right into the values which drive Gen Z: efficiency, frictionless transactions, multiplicity of choice, little commitment and plenty of value (most of these apps are free). However, some of my generation see the advent of dating apps as 'terrible' or even 'disgusting'. But these normative judgements may not be justified – instead, the new way is just different from the way we met partners. A dating app is probably a much safer way of meeting someone with a much higher probability of finding a partner with compatible objectives – whether it's company, a hookup or a relationship.

Turkle points out that for some people, particularly those who are shy or find it difficult to take the conversation to the next level, dating apps take away the tricky parts of the process and 'do it for you'.[3] In a sense, there is no need to be romantic. The app puts every encounter in a romantic context.[4] But Turkle also observes that using a dating app encourages users to see their romantic life in terms of you being a proposition – what business people call 'product placement'. You are the product and you are direct marketing yourself – or, to be more specific, the best version of yourself.

Alberto, twenty-one, says, 'A worrying trend is that relationships are becoming more and more a narcissistic expression of how one wants to be seen by the social media community, played out in his or her sentimental life. In this sense, many of my generation are becoming used to tailoring their feelings and behaviours to satisfy external expectations.'

A study by eharmony found that more than 50 per cent of online daters lie in their profile, and most do so about their age, height, weight, job or income.[5]

Now that so many people live alone or work remotely, many people find themselves isolated from meeting new people. Covid-19 has exacerbated this isolation. Here dating apps come into their own, allowing people to search for partners by reference to particular attributes they seek. Bloomberg reported that a 2017 survey from the parent company of Tinder found that financial responsibility was ranked as a very or extremely important quality in a potential mate by 69 per cent of 2,000 online daters surveyed[6] – more important even than sense of humour, attractiveness, ambition, courage and modesty! Dating app operators can use what they know about you from the information in your profile to make or source assessments of you, e.g. give you a likely credit score.

Baihe, China's biggest matchmaking service, recently teamed up with the financial wing of Alibaba, China's leading e-retailer, to showcase clients with better credit scores!

Is the hookup culture, which dating apps have facilitated, an issue? What has become known as 'hanging out' or 'Netflix and chill' may not be quite as innocent as it sounds. In her book *The End of Sex – How Hookup Culture is Leaving a Generation Unhappy, Sexually Unfulfilled and Confused About Intimacy*, Donna Freitas defines a hookup as brief – potentially mere minutes – lacking in emotional involvement and likely to involve sex. A hookup can theoretically boost self-esteem. And while hookups have always been endemic to human interaction, they have newly become the dominant form of intimacy, particularly within the American college campus environment. 'It is a defining characteristic of social life on many campuses,' Freitas claims. 'To reject it is to relegate oneself to the sidelines of college experience.'[7]

Dr Lisa Wade's study of hookup culture on US campuses underscores this hypothesis; she finds that 45 per cent of respondents were self-confessed 'dabblers,' and a further 14 per cent 'enthusiasts' of hookup culture.[8]

Sexting has become widespread. According to a report from La Trobe University's Center for Sex, Health and Society, nearly 75 per cent of 15–18-year-olds have sexted, and around half have sent nude or nearly nude photos or videos of themselves; 84 per cent have received sexually explicit messages by phone or email.[9] Anne Mitchell, author of the report, noted that in the 'social, online world kids live in … sending these images and messages is part of the sexual relationship'. Indeed, Mitchell claims, sexting has become a new method of courtship.[10] Generation Z, of course, includes cohorts over and under eighteen, and it's important to note that in the UK sharing even self-generated imagery of minors is a criminal offence. Sexting has become so commonplace, however, that prosecution is not a realistic way for society to stop young people from engaging in this activity. There is a significant distinction to be made between two over-sixteen-year-olds or two adults swapping pictures of themselves and an adult asking for a picture of a minor.

Technology-assisted child sexual abuse (TA-CSA) has increased as a result of sexting, including with images, becoming commonplace. The UK's leading children's protection charity, the NSPCC, commissioned a report on child sexual abuse which looked at the effects of technology by interviewing 15–19-year-olds recruited through the NSPCC, Childline and the National Crime Agency. It found that technology gives perpetrators of CSA easier access to young people, particularly at night-time, when they are at home and they can control their 'night-time space'. The online environment can hide abusive dynamics that would be more obvious in face-to-face relationships. Being unable to escape from an abusive person because they are in frequent contact through technology can make young people feel powerless. Importantly, 'a key feature of TA-CSA is [the abuser] threatening to share sexual images of the young people with their friends and family' and the 'technological dimension can prevent some young people from recognising their experiences as abuse'. Worryingly, it also found that children who experienced CSA offline were less likely to be blamed or stigmatised than those who experienced TA-CSA.[11]

If you split with the partner you once trusted enough to send explicit images, these images could come back to haunt you should your ex-partner post this content online without your permission in a phenomenon known as 'revenge porn'. The 2015 'Cybercrime tipping point' report notes that teens 'are not overly concerned about revenge porn', but this laissez-faire attitude may be problematic later in their lives.[12]

As I was reading Freitas's book, I found myself thinking that hookup culture must be a US college phenomenon limited to that side of the pond. So, to test my hypothesis, I asked a few members of a sports club I belong to from the Generation Z cohort in London to fill in a simple questionnaire about their use of dating apps. Whilst it is in no way representative, being a small sample from a relatively heterogeneous group, the results were interesting. I received ten responses from 19–23-year-olds to a questionnaire with twenty questions about their dating app usage. All of those surveyed had at least a high-school education; I have included some of the most typical responses below.

How many times a day did you look at the dating app?
- 'At my peak, I was looking at it eight to twelve times a day, even more if I was actively messaging multiple people' (D, twenty-one).
- 'Many, many times, uncountable at the peak, like checking WhatsApp' (J, twenty-five).
- 'It became my go-to distraction during lectures or while bored in my bedroom. About 30 per cent of my total online time at times' (G, twenty-one).

Did you find it became addictive?
- 'Absolutely yes. Dopamine hit every time someone "likes" you. Dopamine hit every time a new match. Rush every time a new message from someone who you could potentially hook up with that night comes through' (J, twenty-five).
- 'Absolutely, the validation received from obtaining "matches" and the resulting direct messages would feed my self-esteem. Also the ease at which I began obtaining hookups, through it in itself almost felt like a hobby at one point. I would be actively going on five to seven Tinder dates a week at my peak' (D, twenty-one).
- 'For a short while I found it addictive. With each year that passes, young people crave a progressively more intimate social media experience, and dating apps offered just that. Not to mention how accessible dating became, as well as hookups' (G, twenty-one).

- 'On and off, cyclical phases of "OK, I'll try my luck on Tinder" … Few weeks later … "Tinder is shit, I am deleting it" … few weeks later … "Hm, I think I will try Tinder again"' (J, twenty-five).
- 'I think addictive is a strong word … it satisfied cravings I had on many levels. Tinder, through sheer volume, allowed me to find people who would be very difficult to find in a bar. But it's very easy to fall into the trap of chasing the next shiny thing. In a weird way, it helps me assess my own place in the pecking order. The application itself looks like a cross between a slot machine and strip club. Arguably it's the best feature of the whole experience. Not actually meeting the person themselves later, but swiping furiously and getting a dopamine hit when you match' (M, twenty).

Were you looking for dates, hookups or finding a long-term partner?
- 'I would use it for sport, and developing my social skills mostly. I wanted to become good at – among other things – hooking up, both as an act and the lead-up to it' (D, twenty-one).
- 'Hookups, with an open mind it may lead to more, but hookups first. Open-minded to being monogamous once committed but then realised meeting on Tinder is not a foundation of anything long-term' (J, twenty-five).

How much pre-qualification chat was there prior to meeting?
- The answers to this query were universal. Not a lot. As little as possible.
- 'The chatting leading up to the meeting was what I hated most. If they were good-looking and had good chat, then I was always keen to meet as soon as possible' (D, twenty-one).

What proportion of chats ended up in meeting?
- Universal answer: very low, 3–10 per cent.

What proportion of meetups involved sex?

- Universal answer: very high, none below 50 per cent. Most reported significantly higher proportions.

Did meeting people and having sex make you feel good in the main?

- 'I liked the attention. I feel I always needed the admiration of girls to feel good and confident in my daily life. Didn't have much time for school work when it was going on. I wouldn't even really care for the sex. I just liked the attention. I have found that a much healthier dating experience can be obtained from just being a social animal. Tinder for me was when I wanted attention but was too lazy to go out' (D, twenty-one).

- 'Yes absolutely. Another notch. Another war story for the lads. Another conquest' (J, twenty-five).

- 'In all honesty, it never felt as good as I would have liked it to. Being able to talk about it with the boys was almost the best bit of it. That said, it kept me busy and was an essential part of growing up and learning' (G, twenty-one).

- 'Yes, I like sex very much, and it's a confidence boost. It's also good practice. I enjoy meeting new people and getting to know them. It helps me learn more about what my type is too' (J, twenty-three).

Did this typically involve sending body images?

- 'If perhaps I slept with this person on the occasion that I met them, it would be quite regular that I would end up receiving nude pictures from them in the coming days. I guess the girl sending them would feel pretty and appreciated if I told her she looked good in the pictures. It's almost like the whole sending a nude pic, especially for girls, is a test of comfort. Also, I present myself as being a very non-judgemental person, which makes me an easy target for nude pictures. There is no downside to sending me a nude picture. I won't judge them. I won't save the picture and spread it. I won't think of them as a slut. I literally feel nothing when I receive them, though, which is weird' (D, twenty-one).

- 'Maybe after extended texting and getting to know there might be an exchange of pics' (J, twenty-five).

Were the profile pictures of the people you met accurate?
- 'Always a little disappointing on social media being a shrine of false pretences, so rarely did I meet someone who was actually as good-looking, intelligent and successful as they portrayed' (J, twenty-five).
- An equal number of respondents said the person in real life looked better than their photos, better in real life, or the same.
- 'Mostly they were reasonably accurate, but I have heard some horror stories from friends about catfishers. And some of my friends' photos have been used for fake profiles' (J, twenty-three).

Were your profile pictures accurate?
- 'No less accurate than the pictures I received LOL. Accurate, but sprinkled in glitter. You're just selling yourself. Definitely some Photoshop editing and filters used!' (J, twenty-five).
- 'I had my best pictures on my profile, but they were all real and unedited' (J, twenty-three).

What proportion of meetings ended up in relationships?
- The nearly universal answer to this questions was 'none'. Quite often, in-person meetings involving sex led to a series of hookups.

How would you rate your experience on dating apps?
- 'Thoroughly enjoyable, the perfect companion to my younger years at university' (G, twenty-one).

- 'I think it's healthy to date and meet lots of new people. It's a very explorative experience and helps you identify your wants and desires … don't get disheartened due to the lack of likes. Remember your personality doesn't shine through in these apps. And don't overuse the app, use with caution, it can affect your mental health' (J, twenty-three).

What advice would you give to other people just starting out on online dating apps?

- 'Please don't. Go and meet someone the right way. Speak to them. Have a face-to-face conversation. Get used to going up to people you are attracted to and saying "Hi" to them and starting a real, human, conversation properly. This has more value now than ever' (J, twenty-five).

Whilst my survey is male dominated and in no way representative, and use elsewhere in the world may be very different, clearly the hookup culture is alive and well in London.

One of the early successful dating apps was Badoo. It was designed by Andrey Andreev, a young Russian who had already built a successful gaming business. He combined several features including SEO theory and the use of dopamine to ensure Badoo's success. The app operated using a freemium model: it was free to start with, but if you wanted your picture to continue to be displayed on the front page, you had to make a micropayment to retain ideal placement. Chat was free until the algorithm spotted you were about to meet or move to communicate off the app, at which point chat would be frozen until you made a further micropayment.

For men, hooking up can become a competition and turns into a game. 'It's not about finding a suitable partner. It's about beating last time's score on how many dates will talk to you or agree to meet.'[13] This is only compounded by Freitas's study, which suggests that 'the motivation for hookup culture usually stems from self-esteem problems'.[14]

The rise in popularity of app-based dating has resulted in a paradox of choice. Tech encourages Generation Z to want unconstrained choice; in dating apps the choice can be huge. Schwartz observes, though, that limited choice can lead to more satisfied lives. He identifies the difference between satisfied satisficers and never satisfied maximisers.[15] This perhaps explains why Freitas observes that the most common group was the '41 per cent of students who expressed sadness and even despair about hooking up. These students suspected that it robbed them of healthy, fulfilling sex lives, positive dating experiences, and loving relationships.'[16] And she observes that *most* men were actually sad, ashamed or ambivalent about hooking up but cannot admit it to other men for fear of not being 'real men'.

'Dating apps are a good recipe for disaster from the perspective of affection,' says Alberto, twenty-one. 'Abundance of choice online means that once things start to go wrong in a relationship, which happens all the time, it is very easy to find an apparently more suitable replacement to the current partner. This commodification of feelings is the true plague of my generation and one that undermines empathy at its very base.'

Dating apps are yet another manifestation of the relentless predominance of technology in our lives, the pace at which we live, the new pressures it imposes and the impersonality which it has fostered. Hookup culture serves as a demonstration of these trends played out in a potentially dangerous way in some of our children's lives. Freitas argues, 'Hookup culture teaches young people that to become sexually intimate means to become emotionally empty, that in gearing themselves up for sex, they must at the same time drain themselves of feeling. They are acculturated to believe that they are supposed to regard sex as a casual, no-big-deal type of experience, yet many of them discover that sex is in fact a big deal.'[17] The implications of this mentality extend beyond sexual activity.

As Freitas notes, 'If we live in a culture that teaches young people to care less about their own feelings, and everyone else's, that bodies are to be used and disposed of afterward, we can be sure that those lessons are going to spill over into everything else they do, and everything else they are.'[18]

While technology certainly aids in efficiency, this desire for speed and frictionless access has now infiltrated every element of our lives. And, as Turkle notes, 'When technology engineers intimacy, relationships can be reduced to mere connections. And then, easy connection becomes redefined as intimacy. Put otherwise, cyberintimacies slide into cybersolitudes.'[19]

The opportunity for and fear of multiple rejections is the flipside of the abundance of choice in potential suitors provided by dating apps. George, a participant in my survey, says, 'One of the safety nets of online dating is that you can approach girls virtually without meeting in person. Would you ever approach thirty girls in one day expressing an interest in them? No. But you can via these apps. I found that this sense of security allowed me to jump right into the world of online dating without much hesitation. However, there is a negative side to mass-marketing yourself on the dating market. Rejection. The rejection is less tangible, however, as the frequency of it rises and becomes a feeling you experience on a daily basis. That combined with the pressure to "deliver" and "close" makes rejection feel very real and poses an unspoken dark side to dating apps. I'm guessing, but I'm sure this is experienced by most users, whether it is conscious or subconscious.'

Are we experiencing a new age of sexual liberation? Freitas says, 'I have come to believe that students are becoming more callous about sex – and perhaps other things as well. This callousness does not read to me as liberation, but rather as the face of hookup culture's dominance. The "rise and progress" of hookup culture rests in the fact that young adults are simply getting better at being uncaring.'[20]

It is perhaps a particular irony that dating apps are called dating apps. After all, the one thing they *don't* lead to is what my generation would have understood as a date: a meeting with a drink or food or entertainment that involved talking, uninterrupted face-to-face time, deep attention and an exchange of information and views. These interactions were not expected to lead to sex on the first date. Seemiller and Grace's study found that more than 60 per cent of Generation Z have never actually been in a relationship or romantically involved with someone, and when compared to baby boomers and Gen Xers, the number of those in Generation Z who date is much lower.[21] Freitas observes, 'The idea that "nobody ever dates here" was one of the most common refrains of my study, and it is something I continue to hear constantly from students on campus lecture visits.' Most students could not cite relationships that had developed from dates. Rather, a new process has developed that starts with a first hookup which involves sex, a 'classic' hookup, which potentially leads to serial hookups between the same people and finally a relationship. As Freitas says, 'What could be better than sex without strings? Yet in fact, many of them – both men and women – are not enjoying it at all.'[22]

Studies on the hookup culture identify other worrying factors and trends which are likely related to Generation Z's lower level of empathy that follows from more screen time and less face-to-face interaction. 'How do you learn to talk and flirt and date and end up in bed if you've only mixed with other people online?' Dr Cash of the reStart online addiction clinic asks. 'Our guys get sidetracked, and they develop intimacy disorders. They don't have the skills to bring sexuality and intimacy together. Many of them turn to pornography instead of forming real relationships and they never seem to understand true intimacy.'[23]

Some participants in hookup culture struggle to juggle their 'need' to participate in sex with their desire to comply with personal religious constraints or other value systems. This leads to the concept of 'non-sexual sex' (e.g. oral sex), maintaining 'technical virginity' (sex not involving penetrative sex) and the propensity to watch pornography.

Freitas says 'what virginity means when oral sex has become the new making out is not only a question for students and young adults, but the wider public as well'.[24]

It seems to me that whilst the hookup culture is neither entirely new nor all bad, there are several issues. First, the loss of the connection between romance, a relationship and sex. Whereas Generation Zers may feel as though they have been 'liberated' from traditional views around relationships, this has also led to a decline in romance and authentic relationships. As Freitas argues, 'Hookup culture has taught college students that they should skip the romance and go straight to sex.'[25]

Second, despite the transactional nature of a hookup – which is commonly conceived to be of the 'no strings attached' variety – many Generation Z participants in these hookups don't manage to stay emotionally disengaged in the way envisaged. This leads to disappointment with the hookup and low self-esteem. In fact, Freitas notes that when men are given anonymity to speak, many reveal that hookup culture fosters performance anxiety.

The hookup culture is blamed for an increase in unwanted sex. Freitas's research revealed that '44 per cent of the women participating in the study reported at least one unwanted sexual encounter while in College, and 90 per cent of the unwanted sex took place during a hookup. Of all the reported incidents of unwanted sex, 76.2 per cent involved alcohol, which played a significant role in blurring the lines of consent.'[26] Indeed, many women note that during a hookup, it does not occur to their partner to ask or wait for consent. Alcohol only further complicates the matter, as 62 per cent of unwanted sex in Freitas's study was a result of impaired judgement due to drugs and alcohol.

Worryingly, Seemiller and Grace note that 11 per cent of Generation Z college seniors disagreed or strongly disagreed with the notion that 'sexual activity that occurs without the presence of explicit, affirmative consent (i.e. yes means yes) is considered sexual assault'.[27]

The UK's National Crime Agency in 2016 reported a sixfold increase in online-dating-related rape offences over the previous five years. Aiken says dating online can result in an irrationally fast development of trust, which she refers to as 'instimacy'.[28] Rapid escalation of romantic chat leads to what she refers to as 'misdirected expectations' between the parties. Seventy-one per cent of the rapes the NCA reported took place in either the victim's or offender's residence, and the profile of the offenders did not match normal sexual offender profiles.

Kids are getting exposed to porn earlier and earlier. Seventy per cent of all 18–34-year-olds are regular porn viewers and perhaps most shockingly, the *average* age to begin viewing porn is a mere eleven.[29] Some suggest that the peer pressure amongst boys to lose their virginity has been over-taken by the pressure to have viewed porn. A survey found that in 2013 Pornhub was the thirty-fifth most visited website for children aged six to fourteen in the UK. One in three British boys is now considered a 'heavy' porn user, watching more times than they can count. Another survey in the UK found that the average boy watches nearly 2 hours of porn every week. A third of the 'light' users said they had missed an important deadline or appointment because they could not break away from their pornographic adventures, leading Zimbardo and Coulombe in their survey of young men to coin the phrase 'arousal addiction' for this phenomenon. In a survey called 'The pornification of Generation Z' published by Understanding Teenagers in Australia, 88 per cent of 16 and 17-year-olds believed that looking at sex sites on the web was commonplace for their age group.[30] *Psychological Science* found that the more teens were exposed to sexual content in movies earlier (not necessarily even porn), the earlier they started having sex and the likelier they were to have casual, unprotected sex.[31] White notes further that 'beyond sexual activity, similar research has found that early viewing of pornography among children leads to higher-risk sexual activity, sex addictions and sexual violence'.[32]And he concludes, 'Even though Generation Z may not be worried about porn, those who care about the generation should be.'[33]

Ninety-four per cent of all therapists are reporting dramatic increases in the number of people addicted to online pornography, White also says. And just like social media and online gaming, 'porn is something that can dominate the thought lives of those in its grasp, leading to them needing ever increasing degrees of exposure and experience to provide the same level of stimulation over time'.[34] Denny Burk, a Baptist pastor, worries that 'a growing number of young men are convinced their sexual responses have been sabotaged because their brains were virtually marinated in porn when they were adolescents. Their generation has consumed explicit content in quantities and varieties never before possible, on devices designed to deliver content swiftly and privately, all at an age when their brains were more plastic – more prone to permanent change – than in later life.'[35]

The risks of over-exposure to porn as identified by the Understanding Teenagers report are:

- the disconnection of sex from emotional intimacy;
- the need for more extreme material to achieve the same level of arousal or interest;
- increased risk of developing a negative body image;
- increased risk of depression or eating disorders;
- self-authoring or allowing others to take sexual images of yourself;
- submitting to sexually extreme behaviour;
- an acceptance of promiscuity as a normal state of interaction;
- increasing objectification of people, especially women.[36]

Over-exposure and addiction to porn is believed to lead to many Generation Zers feeling some degree of guilt and, in fact, a *reduction* in sexual desire. If you can turn sex on and off when you want it, watch precisely what turns you on best, not have to buy the partner dinner or put up with a conversational game or process before, during or after the act, have zero risk of not performing to either your own or someone else's expectations and reach orgasm by yourself, why, some might ask, would you bother with a human being?

Soon virtual reality video will be so good that it will seem like you are the person having the sex when you watch a porn movie. This will further threaten the need for real physical human interaction.

Deep-fake porn videos are another concern. Here someone is able to take a porn movie and superimpose someone else's facial image on the scene, so that the porn actor looks like that person. And they are reported to be very realistic, just like the deep-fake videos used to attempt to distort political discourse, which we shall examine later.

Exposure to porn for some Generation Zers doesn't mean just viewing it. Through sites like Instagram, some take the celebrification model to the next level, providing links on their Instagram profile to other platforms not subject to Instagram's content guidelines which ban some forms of nudity and sex. Here they post pictures and videos of themselves naked or having sex. Launched in 2016, Only Fans, which is like a digital version of Soho's clubs during the 1960s, has no content restrictions and members are charged a monthly fee for access. As of May 2020, Wikipedia reports that Only Fans has 30 million registered users and claims to have paid $725 million to over 450,000 content creators. Twitter is also provided as a link to user-created pornographic material. Twitter insist that those posting such material include a warning that the content contains sensitive media and do not allow it in live video, profile or header pages, only once a warning message has been acknowledged by the viewer. Both are ways celebrification can be taken to another level.

In their book *Man Disconnected*, Philip Zimbardo and Nikita Coulombe argue that the combination of excessive video game playing and porn use creates a deadly duo, 'as it results in heightened withdrawal from social activities and an inability to relate to others, particularly girls and women'. In their survey, 62 per cent of boys aged thirteen to seventeen chose digital entertainment (i.e. video games, pornography) as factors contributing to their motivational problems; 57 per cent of adolescents aged thirteen to seventeen said there was a strong relationship between excessive video game playing and/or porn watching and various aspects of a romantic relationship, with emotional immaturity and lack of interest in pursuing or maintaining a romantic relationship/social isolation as the two highest scores.[37]

In a variety of recent studies, up to 80 per cent of college students purport to have engaged in sexual activity outside of their committed relationships. This is likely due to a decrease in social stigma around infidelity, an increase in parties with high levels of alcohol (and potentially recreational drug) consumption and a culture on many college campuses where sex is built into the party plan. For critics, the high rate of casual sex is an epidemic, negatively affecting women in particular and reducing the likelihood of creating and maintaining stable, meaningful relationships.

Some believe the rise of casual sex is a sign of social progress. In an *Atlantic* article from 2012, 'Boys on the side', Hanna Rosin urged women to avoid serious partners so that they could focus on their own lives. Despite apparently believing that the hookup culture is an engine of female progress, Rosin concluded that casual sex cannot be a meaningful end goal. 'Ultimately, the desire for a deeper human connection always wins out, for both men and women,' she writes.[38]

The weight of evidence suggests that the combination of very early exposure to sexually explicit material in mainstream movies, porn and the hookup culture create new norms which will have very major consequences for the way Generation Z socialises, forms and experiences 'relationships'.

9

SEXUALITY? WHATEVER ...

'It's not even so much that I am totally sure I am pansexual yet,' says John, Dutch university student, twenty. 'It's just that I don't want to be categorised as anything. I want to be free to choose what I do and with whom and change my mind too if I want to!'

Three decades ago, we laboured under the delusion that 5 per cent of society was homosexual and 95 per cent was heterosexual. And that was that. We now realise that it is much more complicated. Many people are on a spectrum which, whilst it includes these two classifications, has many others on it, and people don't necessarily only fit into one, nor do they necessarily stay in one. Fluidity, meaning the potential to be more complex than simply gay or straight and/or move between points on the spectrum, has become better understood. Whilst electronic dating has facilitated more choice, privacy and convenience in seeking preferred choices and exploration, habits may not have changed as much as the increased social acceptability of different behaviours, meaning people can just be more honest about their choices. And this fits with Generation Z's search for individuality, enabled by technology, projecting an image that is uniquely theirs.

This is one of the few trends I explore in this book which is probably least affected by technology. But perhaps the private exploration the internet allows does in some way contribute to its development. Turkle notes that 'connectivity offers new possibilities for experimenting with identity, and, particularly in adolescence, the sense of free space'.[1] The internet provides the ideal backdrop for developing minds to explore new ideas and concepts. Whereas the physical world does not always allow for this kind of facilitation, the internet does so in spades.

Pansexuality has quietly become acceptable to many of the younger generation. According to Human Rights Campaign's (HRC) 2017 LGBTQ Teen Survey, the number of individuals identifying as pansexual has increased 100 per cent since 2012. A similar survey five years prior reported only 7 per cent of individuals identifying as pansexual.[2]

White notes that Generation Z may be the first for which diversity is a natural concept.[3] Because Generation Z is globally connected, their social networks are similarly expansive. In fact, '26 per cent of Generation Z would need to fly to visit most of their social network friends'. This diversity also leads to being accepting or inclusive. White believes Generation Z has become 'sexually and relationally amorphous'.[4] As White notes, 'What is being revealed is an increasing sexual fluidity that refuses either the homosexual or the heterosexual label. The idea of labels is repressive … Sexuality should be allowed to follow their desires, moment by moment.'[5]

More than 25 per cent of Britons identified as *not* 100 per cent heterosexual when asked to place themselves on a sliding scale of hetero-to-homosexuality. Moreover, 54 per cent of people aged eighteen to twenty-four did not identify as entirely heterosexual, which may make them the most sexually liberated, or least socially repressed, group in the history of the nation.[6]

The uptick in the number of individuals who identify as pansexual is reflective of the positive shift in recent times towards acceptance of the LGBTQ+ community, and more fluid identities in particular. The very concepts of gender and sexuality are being redefined to better reflect modern identities and lived experiences.[7] Activist Faith Cheltenham told ThinkProgress, 'As a person who identifies as pansexual and bisexual,

I'm openly flaunting my attractions to more than one group of people, while also expressing and loving myself through a pansexual lens that feels different for me, "free-ass motherfuckering" if you will, when it comes to my expression and experience of my own gender-queerness and of myself as an intersex woman and femme.'[8]

'Being pansexual, to me, is loving someone for their soul and connecting on a level that isn't directly physical,' twenty-five-year-old conceptual artist and art curator Emily Getsay told ThinkProgress. She noted that she 'adopted the term "pan" when I realized I didn't fit into the bisexual binary. Pansexual meant that my sexuality could be more fluid and encompass gender non-binary people and genderqueer people.'

'Those adopting pansexual identities were younger than those adopting lesbian, gay, and bisexual identities,' a 2017 study in the *Journal of Sex Research* reported of the 2,200 non-heterosexual adults surveyed.

This is to say that identifying as pansexual is particularly prevalent among younger people who have grown up in a world where fluidity – in many senses of the word – has become more accepted and normalised. In fact, in 2018, 'pansexual' was momentarily Merriam-Webster's most searched word of the day, following singer Janelle Monáe's announcement that she defined herself as pansexual. Other celebrities who have identified as pan include Panic! at the Disco frontman Brendon Urie and Miley Cyrus. Demi Lovato, meanwhile, identifies as 'sexually fluid' or 'having a shifting gender preference'.[9] In 2020, Howard Donald of the band Take That said on Instagram that he wondered whether he should be pansexual. Describing himself as a happily married man for now, he observed that you can still be attracted to men and women. He said he had been inspired by Christine and The Queens frontwoman Héloïse Letissier, who is openly pansexual. The comedian and author David Walliams hinted at being pansexual in the book *Inside Little Britain*, but said he did not like to be labelled by that word. In an interview in the *Radio Times* in 2013, he said, 'I think it's all about falling in love with the person … I hate it when people "confess" or "reveal" their sexuality and also things can change for people over the years … you don't just fall in love with someone's body do you? You fall in love with someone's soul and heart and brain.'[10]

In the device- and technology-dominated world described in the preceding chapters, where attitudes to sex are potentially becoming more callous, relationships are decreasingly valued, and empathy is on the decline, the rise in and acceptance of pansexuality may be one ray of sunshine on the Generation Z horizon. Loving someone because you are attracted to them, unbound by historic, cultural or religious norms, is an endearing characteristic of some members of Generation Z. It may be one trend that saves Generation Z from a less loving world thrown up through device addiction.

John, who is currently trying to determine his sexuality and has had different feelings at different times, says, 'I feel society, particularly the older generation, view sexuality in a binary way, either straight or gay. I find it impossible to put these complex and changing feelings into one of these boxes. I am concerned that coming out as bi, or merely questioning, will be interpreted as gay. And worse, it will be a label that stays with you forever. One does not simply "switch sides". To assign this level of commitment would mean that coming out in any way would be a daunting decision.'

Only 48 per cent of Generation Z identify as exclusively heterosexual and, relatedly, are less likely to ascribe traditional gender binaries and are more open to gender fluidity.[11] A majority of those in Generation Z know someone who utilises gender-neutral pronouns (i.e. *them* or *ze*).[12]

While Generation Z is generally more open-minded than previous generations, the bigots remain. The Human Rights Campaign found in a recent study that 11 per cent of 13–17-year-old LGBTQ+ youth have been 'sexually attacked or raped' because of their actual or assumed LGBTQ+ identity, and a shocking 70 per cent of them reported having been bullied at school because of their sexuality.[13]

10

FORGET RELIGION, MARRIAGE AND TWO OPPOSITE-SEX PARENTS

In a time when people thought the world was flat and science remained a developing field, there was more need for religion. It served a useful purpose. It gave a context for life, it presented hope and comfort and suggested rules that were useful to the orderly running of society. But as someone who has spent most of his early life in and around churches, believing in Christianity at some level, I have always wondered if the Christian story isn't simply a case of brilliant marketing. Religion has long served as a useful way of explaining the unexplainable. Churches were also key institutions of community, including for news dissemination and spreading public information to parishes where literacy was low. The digital revolution has arguably displaced any need for this function. The trend amongst millennials to disengage with church and religion was quite dramatic. And in Generation Z it has accelerated.

The proportion of young US adults who purport not to subscribe to any religion now stands at 23 per cent, according to White. Moreover, 'about 19 per cent of Americans would call themselves "former" Christians'.[1] About one in four adults under the age of thirty are non-religious.[2] A Pew Research study suggests that even of those who purport to believe in God, 62 per cent never pray.[3] For White, 'The pattern is indisputable. The younger the generation, the more post-Christian it is.'[4] The same trend applies in the UK, where 45 per cent of the population, and nearly two-thirds of those under the age of twenty-five, are non-religious.

The 2009 British Social Attitudes Survey indicated that 53 per cent of those surveyed would classify as not religious at all.[5] The European Social Survey showed that 53 per cent of those surveyed identified with no religion.[6] In 2018, London's St Mary's University Centre for Religion and Society produced a study suggesting that 70 per cent of the population aged sixteen to twenty-nine identified as not religious.[7]

The trend towards no religion has become self-reinforcing. Two factors make this so. Since the biggest factor in driving religious affiliation tends to be parental affiliation, as Generation Z's parents and older siblings have disengaged, so Generation Z has been encouraged to engage less. And as the proportion of non-religious folks has grown, so too has the acceptability of such a position. To the extent that younger generations engage with religion, for many the trend is towards 'religion lite' – attending services sporadically and during holidays or cultural events: convenient, an experience, but not driven by belief.

Uniform societies tend to drive religious affiliation. Multicultural communities with exposure to diversity do not drive religious affiliation to the same extent. As White notes, Generation Z is 'facing radical changes in technology and understandings of family, sexuality and gender'. The younger generations occupy multigenerational households, and moreover, 'the fastest growing demographic within their age group is multiracial'.[8] As a result, Generation Z is the most diverse generation to date – in terms of ethnicity, race and religion.

'If the US has a national religion, the closest thing to it is faith in technology.' So jokes Freed, based on his observations of young patients at his clinic. 'Bill Gates, Steve Jobs, Mark Zuckerberg, and other industry leaders are today's gods.'[9] Indeed, with 2.2 billion active users, Facebook gives the world's largest religions a run for their money when it comes to scale. The 'church' is certainly not the same institution that we saw a few decades ago. It may have been replaced by other institutions, like the fitness class, or by other processes of communion and idolisation like celebrification. The idols of modern consumerism – popularity, sex, experiences – can now all be pursued from your bedroom at the click of button, whilst you indulge your adorations led by your tailored news feed.

'My generation has not been taken to church,' says Alberto. 'This absence of spiritual confrontation means there is no process to take a personal perspective toward something superior. This deprives one of the intimate knowledge of one's inner self and can lead to one following virtual idols and beliefs. The internet brings individuals to think of themselves as invincible and eternal and it gives space for reckless behaviour and time away from reality.'

Casper ter Kuile, a researcher at Harvard Divinity School and executive director at On Being's Impact Lab, has spent time studying millennials and Generation Zers. He says that as they are progressive and spiritually open, these generations are still looking for elements of religious experience. Kuile's research focuses on religious identity in a secular age. In his 2015 study 'How we gather' (co-authored with Angie Thurston), Kuile explores ways modern millennials seek out meaning, community and ritual in the absence of organised religion.

He quickly homes in on fitness studios. CrossFit and SoulCycle are not just offering their students a way to get fit. While individuals come to these studios for health purposes, they stay for the communities they discover. Indeed, he notes, 'It's really the relationships that keep them coming back.'[10]

One of the big growth products in fitness recently has been Peloton, a mounted stationary bike fitted with a large digital screen that enables the user to join group fitness classes from the comfort of his or her living room.

While Peloton also offers in-person classes in a studio (like SoulCycle), this product gives users even more flexibility; for those who are busy but want competition in their exercise without going to the gym, the Peloton at-home bike may be the perfect compromise, offering a community you can access and then turn off whenever you want it from the sitting room.

The new celebrities of social media may have replaced God as Generation Z's idols. Wu discusses the intensity of celebrity worship in the twenty-first century, noting that the 'ecstatic possibility of transcending the ordinary and glimpsing the infinite' defines modern obsession with film, music and media stars. Perhaps, he notes, as the sociologist Chris Rojek theorises, this is secular society's response to the decline of religion and loss of belief in magic.[11]

Can celebrification really be a religion? While Wu distinguishes between celebrity culture and religion, he notes that 'whatever the neurological basis of religious experiences, something of the same mechanism seems to be activated by the existence, and particularly the proximity, of the illustrious'. The media is able to create the 'illusion of intimacy' or 'intimacy at a distance'. Platforms like Instagram, which turn everyday people into celebrities, creates a sort of 'attention economy [throwing] up its own mirage for the discontented masses: fame for everyone'.[12]

As a result of the ubiquity of devices and technology, the summative effect of all these requests for our attention creates a sort of religion in and of itself. Indeed, as Williams posits, this results in the 'installation of a worldview, the habituation into certain practices and values, the appeals to tribalistic impulses, the hypnotic abdication of reason and will, and the faith in these omnipresent and seemingly omniscient forces that we trust'.[13]

Marriage was the glue which kept a family unit together at a time when women couldn't work or earn as much as men and it was socially unacceptable to have children out of wedlock. It was an economic necessity for women to look after the family and for men to finance the family, and socially necessary for the parents to be married. At the same time as engagement with religion itself has declined, for different reasons women's ability to work has increased, the gender pay gap has declined, civil partnerships have become commonplace, single-parent families have also become common, and the social stigma of children being born out of marriage has dramatically declined. Consequently, marriage and the traditional nuclear family unit has become more of a choice than a necessity. Perhaps this is a much more logical way of being – after all, the idea that you could meet someone at age twenty whom you were likely to continue to want to spend the rest of your life with seems ambitious. Given the increase in life expectancy, the potential partnership for life could be eighty years, making it even more unlikely to be happily sustainable. It is no surprise, then, that the gap between sexual maturity, or the space between initial exposure to sex, and marriage or civil partnership is more pronounced today than at any point in history.[14]

If fewer youngsters believe in a religious God, why would they get married? Marriage, perhaps the ultimate long-term deep commitment, of course runs contrary to the 'no commitment' principle identified as a key part of Generation Z's new value system and the transactional nature of the encounters illustrative of the hookup culture. In a recent YouGov survey, a third of 25–39-year-olds and more than a quarter of 18–24-year-olds thought marriage was an outdated institution. Only 39 per cent of those surveyed overall thought you needed to get married to have kids, and 25–34-year-olds were 51 per cent less likely than older age groups to believe this to be the case. Social mores have changed, it seems, so that it is much less socially unacceptable to have kids without getting married than it was.

Generation Z has, of course, experienced a changing family environment. Pew Research Center found that, as of 2018, 65 per cent of children in the US didn't live with two married parents, up from 15 per cent in

1968.[15] There has been a big rise in single-parent homes over the same period, and in 2017, 32 per cent of children lived with one unmarried parent, up from 13 per cent in 1968.[16] Over 20 per cent of children in the US now live in multigenerational households.[17] Same-sex couples are much more common, with over 20 per cent raising children under the age of eighteen.[18] Overall, Pew found that very few US households resembled the traditional nuclear family.

The decline of strict Christian beliefs has had a negative effect on the nuclear family too. White notes that family is no longer defined strictly as having a heterosexual couple with children. 'Male with male, female with female, children with surrogates, multiple parents, polygamy, and polyamorous unions abound,' White argues.[19] And in 2015, Britain became the first country in the world to recognise three parents to a single child.

Seemiller and Grace observe that Generation Z is very accepting of evolving gender roles. As long ago as 2013, '40 per cent of homes with children under 18 years old had mothers who served as the exclusive or main income source for the family, up from only 11 per cent in 1960'.[20] And it's not that Generation Z don't value family – the opposite is true: 65 per cent call family one of the five most important elements of an ideal life.[21] Rather, it is simply the case that what constitutes a family has evolved.

Szalavitz and Perry argue that we need to focus on the decline of the 'extended' family rather than the core. The authors argue that society has ignored the critical role that extended families play; while significant attention has been paid to single parents and divorcees, 'virtually no one looks at the effects of the massive breakdown of extended family that has come with industrial and post-industrial society. When extended families and related social networks are examined, they show great benefits to children – especially for single parents but for two-parent families as well.'[22]

Henry, twenty-one, says, 'I grew up Catholic and went to a very Catholic state school, but it seems nowadays that anyone with some reason and scientific knowledge doesn't subscribe to a religion – it doesn't play a huge importance in my life. Family is very important for me, perhaps because it's very easy to truly be myself around them (maybe a result of social media / portraying yourself differently in public and online and getting some respite when at home). For me personally, I think a lot of psychological issues can arise from traumatic childhoods and the lack of a parent. For this reason, I believe I will raise kids in a traditional nuclear family.'

Since families (whether nuclear, single-parent, extended or in whatever form they happen to take) are where most kids grow up and get their first exposure to technology, we must examine the relationship between the two even as the family metamorphoses. We had an interesting discussion on holiday about the fact that, as a family of two parents and three children, we had spent four months of lockdown together and generally still spend our family holidays together. And we get on reasonably well. But in the context of the boys inviting friends to spend time with us, they observed that they felt blessed and that their experience was not necessarily typical. Some of their friends' homes were very different. There are many broken homes where marriages have ended and others where stress levels due to economic or health issues run high most of the time. The dominant theme was parents working hard to make ends meet and the kids feeling this pressure vicariously.

'Decades ago, we built families out of necessity. Now we must work consciously to create strong families,' says Freed.[23] He also says that parents often fool themselves about the value of technology in the family setting. For example, Pew Research found that most US parents believe that technology allows their family lives to be as close as, if not closer than, their own family upbringings. Kids Industries found that 77 per cent of US and British parents felt that tablet computers benefited their children. But Freed points out that they are confusing connection with facetime when it comes to technology.[24] In fact, empirical evidence suggests that these devices *reduce* the amount of time parents spend *with* their children. As Raffi Cavoukian, singer and founder of the Center for Child Honouring, observes in *Lightweb, Darkweb*, 'Family space has been hijacked by the very devices that are supposed to enhance our lives. They've taken over the family dynamic.'[25] Freed cites Stanford University research showing that for every hour an adult spends on the internet at home, family time is reduced by twenty-four minutes.[26]

One area where digital communication with parents has been shown to be valuable is in reducing stress. Kids often contact parents when something goes wrong, and all the research suggests a parental response can often be very effective in dissipating stress.

Szalavitz and Perry note that by the age of three months, 40 per cent of children in the US are regular video and TV viewers; by the time they reach two, 90 per cent watch 2–3 hours a day; this trend continues as children age. Before they complete elementary school, research suggests, a child witnesses 8,000 on-screen murders and more than 100,000 other acts of video violence. This is made all the more problematic by studies that suggest 'a consistent link between viewing on-screen violence and aggressive behaviour. This connection is strongest for the youngest children.'[27]

Freed concludes that technology, when misused, 'denies kids the connection with parents and other caretakers that's at the very heart of effective parenting and healthy child development'.[28] When technology impinges upon the bond children have with their parents and hampers their ability to focus and perform at school, this obsession with technology leads children to be anything but happy.

Parent–child interactions are crucial during early development. Freed advances that such interactions 'trigger the release of chemicals that promote pleasure and bonding into young brains'.[29] These chemicals, including dopamine and oxytocin, are released during family times, and facilitate a child's attachment to his or her parent. 'On a personal level,'

Freed notes, 'Such loving moments are vital to building the relationship your child needs with you to grow up happy and successful.'

These relationships are not just nice-to-haves. Rather, the ways in which children interact with their parents 'profoundly impact nearly every facet of their behaviour'. Freed suggests that having a healthy relationship with their parents allows children to 'regulate their emotions better, score higher intellectually and academically, and have higher self-esteem when compared to children without a healthy parental bond'.[30] This effect carries forward into adolescent years as well; teens who are close to their parents are 'less likely to be depressed; they also receive better grades in school and fewer behavioural problems'. Sibling relationships can be just as important as parental relationships, and perhaps more at risk from technology. Freed notes that 'research confirms the power of positive sibling relationships to boost children's self-esteem and contribute to other important qualities. Increasingly, I see the profound draw of technology denying kids a relationship with a brother or sister.'[31]

In addition to the usual distractions children face in the family environment in the form of smartphones, social media, video gaming, and entertainment software more generally, the technology industry specifically targets children with products, starting with stand-mounted ipads on cots and prams, designed to attract their attention during family time.

Technology can have yet another insidious effect on a child's development – a reduced level of language exposure. Both parental attention and language exposure affect brain development. Szalavitz and Perry posit, 'Verbal ability appears to be strongly related to impulse control; we encourage toddlers to "use your words" when they get frustrated for a reason. Language builds cortex – and the cortex modulates the lower, more reactive brain regions.'[32] Time spent on screens, however, reduces the time for verbal interaction with parents, siblings and others. It also means the party with whom you are 'conversing' is, in the case of TV, film, and most social media, passive and, in effect, ignoring you. 'You can't learn empathy from something that can't empathise – and without reciprocity and interaction during teaching, language learning is severely impaired.'[33]

It would appear, then, that three of the most basic elements of my generation's traditional model of life – religion, marriage and the nuclear family – are not going to be as typical for Generation Z. This, combined with the impact of the relationship between technology and some of these changes, will further exacerbate the loss of opportunity for 'empathy time' with potentially life-damaging consequences.

11

FOOD ON THE GO

My wife and I headed to the Donmar Theatre in Covent Garden just before lockdown, planning to meet in our favourite tapas restaurant next door. We found, however, that it had disappeared and been subsumed into a huge new food hall containing fifteen different artisanal food-on-the-go bars. We tried it, raising the average age of those eating by two-thirds as Generation Z stood around us, eating, drinking and chatting while monitoring their phones and messaging. I concluded that whether food halls create effective new communal eating opportunities for social and work meals remains to be seen – they could just present further opportunities for Generation Z to be 'alone together' on their devices when it comes to eating.

The growth of the food hall in the US and increasingly Europe and elsewhere is a development which illustrates both the dynamics of Generation Z's sharing economy and the high value placed on experiences, or in this case experiential consumption. According to Cushman and Wakefield's recent report on food halls, they are not just a fad, but a new normal in the experience economy. Food halls are the hottest growth trend in retail property and are usually a celebration of regional or cultural authenticity and farm-to-fork approaches rather than the mass-market concepts we have become accustomed to with the likes of McDonald's and KFC.

They focus on independent and artisanal vendors, often including a heavy local sourcing bias, including local craft beers, appealing to Generation Z's search for authenticity and hyperlocalisation. They are spreading to offices, campuses and roadside service stations. They are designed to have inviting rest spaces which appeal to the Instagram culture, some featuring open studios for live cooking demonstrations that can be turned into videos – digital assets that can be used and played all over the world. They can be used for a variety of options that create a vibrant social environment. Seventy-eight per cent of digitally native brands and 61 per cent of digital immigrants (broadly millennials – those for whom smartphones arrived part way through their lives) said food halls would influence their decision to visit a mall. The media and entertainment industry has realised this is a place to capture Generation Z's attention: Time Out has built what is probably the premiere food hall in the world in Lisbon, Portugal, and has planned others around the world. Vice Media has opened the 'Munchies' Food Hall in New Jersey, using their media to drive footfall. Google and Twitter have food halls as key amenities in their Toronto and San Francisco offices, respectively. These are designed to appeal to Generation Z, which is trying to create some life/work balance, and their design is heavy on the 'experience' factor.[1]

Eating together with family members, friends and business associates has been a core part of life throughout my lifetime. It has been a key source of communication, happiness and shared life experience, and has led to the fostering of the most important communities in my life. There are two primary types of shared meals: those with family and friends, and those with business associates. Sadly, communal eating in both settings seems to be on the decline, which seems to give rise to potentially negative implications for our collective wellbeing.

It's concerning, then, to discover that in a recent post-Covid study by Oxford University, a third of weekday evening meals eaten by those surveyed were eaten in isolation, and the average adult eats ten meals out of twenty-one alone every week. Sixty-nine per cent of those questioned had never shared a meal with any of their neighbours and 20 per cent said it was more than six months since they had shared a meal with their parents. Twenty per cent said it was a rare occurrence to eat an evening meal with other people during the week. One in eight said it had been more than six months since they'd shared a lunch with friends or family – either at their home or in a café, pub or restaurant – and 20 per cent said they hadn't eaten an evening meal out with a good friend or family member for more than six months.

'One place where families used to talk, exchanging experiences, ideas, values and more was around the dinner table. That is now an ancient tradition, honoured more in the breach than in practice,' say Zimbardo and Coulombe,[2] who have studied the modern meltdown of manhood and how this is manifest in the lives of young men today.

'The dining room table no longer exists,' says Stephen Fry, the British comedian, actor and author. 'Families go into their house, everyone has their own bedroom, their own game console, their own laptop, and they don't see each other … I think that – more than any other aspect of the digital world – may well be deleterious to our species. The fact that we no longer, every day, sit around with the family, friends, whatever and in common share stories, share the day, plan the future.'[3]

Students who do not regularly eat with their parents are significantly more likely to be truant at school according to the OECD – about 30 per cent compared to 15 per cent for all families throughout the world on average. Children who do not eat dinner with their parents at least twice a week were also 40 per cent more likely to be obese. Children who do eat dinner with their parents five days a week or more were found to have less trouble with drugs and alcohol, eat more healthily, show better academic performance and report being closer to their parents.[4]

Oxford University found that communal eating increases social bonding and feelings of wellbeing and enhances one's sense of contentedness and embedding within the community. And furthermore, people who eat socially are more likely to feel better about themselves and have a wider social network capable of providing social and emotional support.[5]

From a scientific point of view, communal eating activates beneficial neurochemicals – experiencing a sense of connection (like that resulting from a shared meal) results in the release of endogenous opioids and oxytocin, which stimulates pleasant feelings. The Archives of Paediatrics and Adolescent Medicine in the US found that the more often that families ate together, the less often adolescents (ages eleven to eighteen) smoked cigarettes or marijuana, drank alcohol, had poor grades, were depressed or had thoughts of suicide.[6] Family meals are a time to check in, for parents to assess what is going on in the child's life, and an opportunity to relax, share, reconnect, discuss and hopefully laugh (or cry!).

As educational consultants Kim John Payne and Lisa Ross note in their book *Simplicity Parenting*, 'The family meal is more than a meal. Coming together, committing to shared time and experience, exchanging conversation, food and attention … all of these add up to more than full bellies.'[7]

Of course, in some countries, culture dictates that the mealtime is still sacred. France and Italy come to mind as havens of food idolisation or as cultures where eating with family and friends are core to their identity. Africa and Asia also still maintain higher propensity for communal eating.

Communal eating takes on an even more important role in a world where technology may drive online connection but can leave people physically isolated. Professor Robin Dunbar of Oxford University notes, 'We know from previous studies that social networks are important in combating mental and physical illness. A significant proportion of respondents felt that having a meal together was an important way of making or reinforcing those social networks.'[8]

Cohesive networks become particularly important in times of crisis, and as such, 'Making time for and joining in communal meals is perhaps the single most important thing we can do – both for our own health and wellbeing and for that of the wider community,' Dunbar argues.[9] Many traditional UK universities still encourage communal daily dining; this serves as a hallmark of both Oxford and Cambridge colleges, as well as places like Durham. Eddy, nineteen, an Oxford undergraduate, says, 'For me, it has been the informal and social and academic discussions that have probably helped me develop my ideas more than anything, and 90 per cent of this takes place at College dinners.'[10]

In business, too, the benefits are clear. Kevin Kniffin, Professor of Applied Behavioural Science at Cornell University, recently concluded, 'From an evolutionary anthropological perspective, eating together has a long, primal tradition as a kind of social glue. That seems to continue in today's workplaces.' His study suggests that the act of eating meals together is associated with increased cooperation (about twice as high as among those who didn't) and collaboration, bringing to the business better work-group performance. Companies that encourage this sort of behaviour will see more productivity out of their employees in the long run. Consequently, employers should not only think carefully about providing shared meal opportunities within office environments but also consider the design of the dining experience so that it creates the likelihood of communal eating.

Another important benefit of eating together, particularly in client relationship building, is that it creates a relaxed setting for professionals to know their customer better, share experiences and develop empathy and trust. It facilitates 'selling' in a relatively neutral environment.

In her book *Eating Together*, Alice Julier argues that dining together is a kind of levelling experience and can radically shift people's perspectives and reduce people's perceptions of inequality. Communal diners tend to view those of different races, genders and socioeconomic backgrounds as more equal than they would in other social scenarios. Eating together creates a safe space where people can share daily experiences as well as their most intimate thoughts and feelings – in a way, this may be the physical version of Instagram.

Ultimately, the shared meal offers a key opportunity to develop empathy. But even where communal eating still occurs, the phone is generally omnipresent, and many believe this has a negative effect on relationships. King cites a study involving 300 friends and family members who were randomly assigned to either have a phone on the table or put it away, which found that the mere presence of a phone on the table during a meal made it less enjoyable. The effect was found to be greater when the subject of conversation was more meaningful rather than purely casual, and perceptions of empathy and trust also declined.

We have seen how the nature of families has changed, with more single parents or both working parents leading to fewer opportunities for communal eating. The traditional family mealtime has become less of an opportunity for deep conversation. And the old concept of the business lunch may now be on the wane, as we shall see – with the trend towards food being taken in a simpler and more casual way, at the desk or on the move.

Generation Z requires more flexible meal patterns, limited-service restaurants and home delivery due to studying, working long hours and busy lives, partly driven by technology and resource constraints. But wherever they decide to eat, they take their smartphones with them. It's an interesting question as to whether lifestyle changes drive their tech habits or tech habits are driving their lifestyles. But either way, when participating in group meals, members of Generation Z are often multitasking, juggling their attention and their participation in the meal with incoming messages and notifications.

The food-service business is reacting quickly to Generation Z's emerging needs. This favours 'to go' meals at times convenient to them, not necessarily traditional mealtimes. As such, limited-service restaurants like Pret a Manger and Subway are becoming more popular, and grocery retailers are improving their offer of 'grab to go' food. Home delivery of both shopping and prepared food is another big trend that is rapidly transforming eating habits.

Food delivery's rapid growth is fuelled by the availability of new apps, which aggregate restaurant products from multiple suppliers and delivery mechanisms created by the sharing economy, including Uber Eats, Deliveroo, Glovo, Doordash and Grubhub. These apps and platforms play to Generation Z's preferences for choice, convenience and efficiency. Deloitte estimates the food delivery market to be worth $25 billion by 2030 in Europe alone.[11] PwC believes that food delivery will represent about 20 per cent of the restaurant market within ten years.[12] But given the statistics we saw earlier about the propensity for people to eat alone, I fear that the rise in home delivery could further lower the likelihood of communal eating. And the attraction of home delivery is highest among the youngest – PwC says 88 per cent of the UK population between eighteen and thirty-four has used food delivery services compared to only 30 per cent of those over fifty.

Both the growth of the gig economy, where more people work outside the traditional office environment, at home or on the move and now Covid-19 have fuelled the growth of home delivery. Baptiste said, 'I've seen a fair few of my friends who work in New York, London and DC focus less and less on their own personal health and more on their work. This is directly linked to their use of computers and social media, as they spend so much of their time on it either for work or, when they get home, to relax. As a result, their health is declining/plateauing as they choose to just get a burger from Uber Eats or Deliveroo, rather than cooking.

Productivity and social "connection" trumps things like eating and exercising. This addiction to their devices has led to the very bare minimum effort being made when it comes to cooking or eating, preferring to get takeout than cook a decent meal.'

Leon, in the UK, is a great case study of a fast-food restaurant that has picked up on Generation Z's thinking. This fast-casual chain offers 'naturally fast food' that espouses the notion that you can eat out cheaply, efficiently and sustainably and enjoy food that 'both tastes good and does you good'. They recruit their best customers to work for them, appealing to Generation Z values – asking for colleagues who are positive and passionate about wellbeing (before any mention of food), with benefits like free meals on shift, discounts for staff and up to four friends, long holidays, discounted gym memberships, free yoga, Zumba, boot camps, massages and quarterly parties.

Numerous apps have been designed to appeal to the latest trends in Generation Z thinking. Generation Z places a premium on sustainability and often focuses on the negative impact on the environment of packaging, particularly plastic, as well as the negative side-effects of eating too much meat. A recent study found that 67 per cent of Generation Z claim to watch what they eat, examining labels and nutritional content.[13] And 57 per cent are willing to pay more for sustainable food, compared with 43 per cent of the general population.[14] 'Generation Z has come of age during the food messaging wars, a time when companies heavily promote features and phrases such as non-GMO, organic, locally sourced, fewer than five ingredients, food allergy labels, and countless fad diets.'[15]

Clever entrepreneurs, then, have developed business models to appeal to the conscientious buyer. Karma is a Swedish app which fights food waste by selling restaurants' excess stock to customers at discounted prices, thereby reducing restaurant wastage and reducing consumers' cost. The Barn in Holland focuses on organic local ingredients delivered in fully compostable packaging. The Urban Farmacy in Brazil grows most of its own products, attracting the hyperlocalists. Swiggy Pop in India, operated by the popular Swiggy delivery company there, appeals to younger consumers and caters exclusively for solo diners. Mori Sushi in Egypt has produced a gaming app based on the popular Candy Crush game where consumers compete to win discounts on meals. Lunch:On in Dubai appeals to the busy business customer, suggesting in a text message each day a meal based on the customer's preferences for office delivery at lunchtime so it can be eaten at the desk. Unfortunately, none of these apps focuses on the value of communal eating, and in most cases they seem to be likely to promote its further decline.

Marco, Italian Generation Z, says, 'I liked your chapter on food on the go. Both my brother and I are passionate about cooking our own meals and we try to eat with friends and family where possible. As you pointed out, this is generally the case with Italians. I felt the consequences of neglecting this when at uni by having many vending-machine dinners in the library. With poor nutrition, I'd get sugar crashes, terrible mood swings, and my concentration was poor. Not to mention the weight gain and lack of time eating and talking together with friends!'

CIVIC LIFE

12

CLICKTIVISM, SLACKTIVISM AND HACKTIVISM

Let's talk about the political -isms.

Clicktivism is a term applied to those who pursue their political activity through social media, e.g. liking a post about Black Lives Matter. Traditionalists in my generation who remember going on marches use the word Slacktivism disparagingly to criticise this kind of 'armchair' passive political activity. *Slacktivism* includes retweeting, sharing posts, signing online petitions, following activists on social media and liking organisations and causes. In the grand scheme of things, all of these are relatively easy actions in which to engage. Slacktivism is derived from the term 'slacker', suggesting that those engaging in digital behaviours are willing to expend very little effort in pursuit of their beliefs. Turkle notes that 'technology gives us the illusion of progress without the demands of action – just give a thumbs up or join a follow or WhatsApp group and it's done!'[1]

I think we are unfairly maligning Generation Z if we accuse them of engaging in nothing but clicktivism or being slacktivists. Indeed, the digital arena for this generation has become a vital space for imagining, implementing and engaging in activism to create the change they hope to see in the world, whether in regard to climate change, gender politics or race. As Miller says, 'people can protest, mobilise, coordinate, and act without needing to have institutions in place … this drastically alters the relation-ship between the powerful and the powerless, those with their hands on the reins of power, and those that disagree with what that power is used for'.[2]

Changing the world for the better is something that Generation Z believes is necessary and, more importantly, that they can influence. The word *hacktivism* has been used to capture the way this generation is disrupting traditional thinking and innovating. Hacktivism entails intro-ducing creativity and innovation to just about anything, doing things differently for better results. Generation Z is going to make an impact by infusing their unique approach to traditional forms of civic engagement and instituting novel ways of creating social change.

Some of the highest-profile campaigns of recent history – whether it be Greta Thunberg's ongoing climate-change campaign, the 2019 global school boycott protesting the climate crisis, the 2018 'March for Our Lives' gun-control school walkouts or the 2015 ALS Ice Bucket chal-lenge for motor neuron research – have been started by youngsters and very effectively amplified by social media. The 2019 school strikes urged parents to take responsibility for their greenhouse emissions, and more than a million young people in 125 countries participated. In several countries, including Germany and the UK, Generation Z also demanded a reduction in the voting age from eighteen to sixteen so that they could influence policy. Greta Thunberg now has over 10 million Instagram, 4 million Twitter and nearly 3 million Facebook followers and has used social media very effectively to maximise her impact, but social media played a major role in all of these campaigns.

Generation Z is disenchanted with traditional politics. They don't see political leaders as role models, generally aren't influenced by them and yet are potentially very politically and socially engaged. Generation Z sees social media influencers as more important role models than traditional politicians. Social media influencers are sometimes journalists, but often just characters who have set themselves up as bloggers or vloggers on YouTube or Instagram and started sharing their opinions. If their content is interesting, they can often attract large followings quickly. As we have noted, Generation Z doesn't find its news from traditional sources, turning instead to social media and other channels that offer bite-sized content meant to be consumed on a mobile screen. This does not lend itself to depth of analysis, but rather small nuggets of news that can be seen while multitasking. Naturally, Generation Z reacts to the news in the same place they consume it.

Generation Z is the first post-WW2 generation to grow up with populism. The term 'populism' may be dangerous because the very name implies that the 'ordinary people' (whoever they may be) are always right as a result of their views being popular and in the majority. Somehow, however, these popular views are usurped by the elite minority who rule through corrupt institutions. Populism maintains anti-elite and poten-tially anti-traditionalist overtones and as a result seems appealing to Generation Z. Sometimes, but not always, this may be true. The Brexit debate in the UK was presented by the Leave campaign as populist – when Nigel Farage painted the EU as corrupt, wrong and elitist and suggested that leaving the Union was a victory for the ordinary people. On this occasion, however, Generation Z, to the extent it voted, overwhelmingly voted against Brexit, preferring what it saw as the multicultural, more secure economic future within the EU.

The question for me, though, is whether social media actually facilitates real political discourse at all, rather than whether it supports populism. I would argue that the level of discourse in most social media is relatively fatuous, and the effect of social media is often to amplify the politically acceptable majority view and vilify the minority who express outlying views. James Williams is a member of the Digital Ethics Lab at the Oxford Internet Institute, and his research addresses the philosophy and ethics of attention and persuasion as they relate to technology design. He says, 'The technologies of the digital attention economy do not promote or select for the kind of reasoning, deliberation or understanding that's necessary to take political action beyond the white hot flash of outrage.'[3] Lanier says that the internet fuels loud-mouthed assholes more than young idealists because 'it is more suited to malevolent manipulation than to any other kind of purpose … it studies idealists, lining them up so they can be shit-posted … become more irritable, more isolated and less able to tolerate moderate or pragmatic politics'.[4]

Giovanni, twenty, says, 'With the transition of news to social media, I often notice the reduced depth of engagement with the detail of news content. The other day a friend sent me an article about the Minneapolis lawmakers' vow to disband the police department, following the George Floyd protests. When I commented on a point that was made in the article, I realised my friend had not even read it. Rather, she thought the title sounded interesting. I call this the culture of being the 'first to know', a race of sorts to be the first to share news with others, before they share it with you. The consequence is that we are constantly alert for headlines but often don't delve deeply into the story.'

If social media platforms are capable of influencing users to buy goods and services by offering up advertisements that are likely to pique interest, are they also telling their users what they want to hear from a political standpoint? Author and entrepreneur Eli Pariser, who is focused on how to make technology serve democracy, originally created the notion of a 'filter bubble'. He observed that while users often believe themselves to be seeing a balance of content, they are in fact seeing what is created and reinforced by algorithms.

Social media has structural weaknesses when it comes to promoting debate. Maybe it does the opposite, cloning groups of like-minded people into amplifying echo chambers or monocultures and expelling the outliers into their own niche groups. In a recent article in *New York Magazine*, Kevin Systrom, the founder of Instagram, said, 'Right now, it seems that we live in our own little bubbles on social media and we follow the accounts we believe in. You're not exposed to other opinions. That, to me, is a problem that's well within the reaches of the folks running these companies to fix.' I would say that most of us throughout our lives have tended to buy newspapers that reflect our general political views and watched news stations that were either unbiased or broadly reflected our views. Social media takes the potential for echo chambers to a new level, though, with its infinite niches allowing everyone to find a comfortable place to wallow in their own view.

Several other risks arise from the role technology plays in the political process. The first and most straightforward is distraction. Williams points out that the Android mobile operating system alone sends over 11 billion notifications every day to its more than 1 billion users.[5] Reading any article for any length of time without distraction has, as we have seen, become hard. Then there is the busy and distracting page on the news website or magazine in which the article appears. Williams notes that often this sense of distraction is not purposefully engineered. Rather, 'A news website might give me the option of viewing the latest update on my government's effort to reform tax policy, but it may place it on the page next to another article with a headline that's teasing some juicy piece of celebrity gossip, and whose photo is undoubtedly better at speaking to my automatic self and getting me to click.'[6]

Sometimes, however, these distracting demands on attention are purposefully placed. Williams advances that the Chinese government has created 448 million posts on social media per year as part of its 'strategic distraction'[7] programme, designed to distract the populace from stories the government wanted to suppress. President Donald Trump's Twitter campaigns, which use controversial tweets to distract attention either from opponents or difficult stories at key moments, and his highly targeted Facebook campaigns, have attracted much comment from the American press. In the 2016 presidential election, newspapers reported that he was microtargeting ads to those who liked HBO, Catholics, those who liked law enforcement and those who liked Audi cars. Some ads were placed in his own name, others in that of his running mate for Vice-President, Mike Pence. All were paid for by the Trump Make America Great Again Campaign.

'One of the tragic ironies of the internet is that such a decentralised infrastructure of information management could enable the most centralised system of attention management in human history,' says Williams.[8] In modern times, power is concentrated among just a few people in a small number of companies, who have the unique capacity to suggest not only what many of us should *do*, but what we *see and think* too.

Given the dominance of a small number of social media platforms owned by a small number of corporations or led by a small number of people, the question becomes whether and to what extent these platforms have been or could be misused to interfere in politics. A recent study from the University of Oxford's Computational Propaganda Project has found evidence of organised social media manipulation campaigns in seventy countries in 2019, up from forty-eight in 2018.[9]

In the wake of the 2016 elections in the US, Facebook, Twitter, Google Search and YouTube all announced policy changes to combat dark ads, malicious fake news and hate speech.

In June 2020, Twitter announced that it had closed more than 170,000 accounts linked to a 'manipulative' Chinese influence campaign. The accounts were removed after Twitter said they had attempted to influence perceptions of events including pro-democracy protests in Hong Kong, the US protests over George Floyd and the pandemic Covid-19.

In late 2019, Facebook said it had taken down four new foreign interference operations originating from Iran and Russia, including one targeting the 2020 presidential campaign in the US. The Russian campaign used consistent operational security steps to conceal its identity and location, said Facebook's head of cybersecurity. Fifty Instagram accounts and one Facebook account were used with 246,000 followers and 75,000 posts. The *Guardian* in the UK found a Russian handbook that described how this kind of activity might work, noting that 'the deployment of information weapons acts like an invisible radiation upon its targets; the population doesn't even feel it is being acted upon. So the state doesn't switch on its self defence mechanism.'[10] After this activity came to light, a paper by three Facebook cybersecurity staff concluded, 'We have had to expand our security focus from traditional abusive behaviour … to include more subtle and insidious forms of misuse, including attempts to manipulate civic discourse and deceive people.' The paper also observed that such bad actors were not subject to the usual commercial criteria limits on spending, as they are funded by governments.

One of the Iranian campaigns targeted the US and North Africa with content related to Israel, Palestine and Yemen. Zuckerberg said Facebook had been found on the back foot in 2016 and was now taking steps in advance of the 2020 elections to be better prepared. The company said it was launching a programme to secure the accounts of elected officials, tightening rules on who controls a page and better labelling content from state-controlled media outlets. Facebook now bans adverts which discourage voting. But McNamee asserts, 'Lack of empathy has caused Facebook to remain complacent, while authoritarians exploit the platform to control their populations, as has occurred in Cambodia and the Philippines.'[11]

Under the stewardship of ex-UK Deputy Prime Minister Nick Clegg, Facebook has made a series of changes to its policies relating to political materials. It now fact-checks some content, is attempting to reduce the number of fake accounts (which it says are the source of most fake news) and has invested in AI to reduce harmful content. McNamee notes, 'Moderation is not possible with Facebook's scale with Facebook's approach. Facebook has not accepted this reality. They continue to believe that there is a software solution to the problem and that it can only be successful without changing their business model or growth targets. Facebook is certainly entitled to that point of view, but policy makers and users should be skeptical.'[12] Facebook does not fact-check the output of politicians and has a newsworthiness exemption policy, which means that if someone posts material which breaks Facebook's own community standards, they may still allow it to remain online if they consider the public interest of seeing it outweighs the risk of harm. However, when a politician posts previously 'debunked' content including links, videos and photos, Facebook aims to demote that content, displaying it with information prepared by fact-checkers and banning its inclusion from ads. Clegg says that Facebook's job is to create a level playing field, not to be a political participant itself.

The issue of deep-fake videos, which are videos made to look like someone in real life, but actually made by someone else, are a new and worrying development for Facebook and other social media sites. In advance of the May 2019 European Parliament elections, Facebook announced its intention to set up two new regional operations centres that would monitor election-related materials in Singapore and Dublin. It also said anyone placing political or 'issue' ads would have to be 'authorised' before the campaign was launched. This followed a ruse in late 2018, when *Vice* magazine applied to place ads on behalf of all 100 US senators and gained Facebook approval for all the ads.[13]

Still, many commentators do not believe that Facebook's measures go far enough. In 2012, *Nature* published the result of an experiment involving 61 million users of the social network and concluded that about 340,000 extra voters turned out to vote in the 2010 US congressional elections because of one election-day Facebook message.[14] The significance of this was that if these voters had mostly been younger voters who were on social media, and they had a preponderance to vote for the Democrats, this kind of activity could have affected the election result.

Lanier and many others cite the targeting of the Black Lives Matter campaign in 2016 as an example of what can go wrong. This group of voters, researched originally for other purposes, were targeted by Russian information warfare agents to vote against Hillary Clinton in the presidential election.

In 2017, *The Atlantic* published a piece entitled 'What Facebook did to American democracy'. In relation to President Trump's 2016 campaign, the article noted Facebook's enormous distribution power and the rapacious partisanship it engendered, reinforced by distinct media information spheres. This was only exacerbated by the increasing scourge of 'viral' hoaxes and other kinds of misinformation that could propagate through those networks.

Alexander Stewart of the University of Houston completed a study in 2019 which concluded that a small number of strategically placed bots could influence a larger majority of undecided voters to change its mind.[15]

We should not assume that it is only since the arrival of Donald J. Trump onto the US political scene that these activities have occurred. Google is reported by media scholars Daniel Kreiss and Philip Howard to have been very close to the Obama campaign before his election in 2008, using their information on voters to support his campaign. Journalist Sasha Issenberg in his book *The Victory Lab* quotes an Obama political consultant as saying 'we knew who ... people were going to vote for before they decided'. Google's founder joined Obama's Transition Economic Advisory Board after the election and appeared next to him at his first post-election press conference. The relationship between Schmidt and Obama developed such that Schmidt's role in the 2012 campaign was even greater, and journalists covering it believed the campaign knew the identity of every undecided voter whose vote was needed for Obama to win and had worked out how to target ads to try to persuade them to do so. Following the 2016 US presidential election, Mike Greenfield, an early data scientist at both PayPal and LinkedIn, created the online polling platform Change Research. The company, whose polls produce results quickly and cheaply, was used by some Democrat candidates in the run-up to 2020's presidential election. It is one of a group of what have been labelled 'Democracy Tech' startups, funded by left-leaning voters, to level the playing field with the technology used by the Republicans.

If Facebook's news feed is now *the* primary source for news websites, we simply do not know enough about how it is controlled to make sure it doesn't interfere in electoral outcomes or mass views on major issues like immigration. BuzzFeed's reporter Craig Silverman undertook analysis that showed 'in the final three months of the [2016] US presidential campaign, the top performing *fake* election news stories on Facebook generated more engagement than the top stories from major news outlets such as *The New York Times, The Washington Post, The Huffington Post, NBC News* and others'.[16] What should we make of society viewing more fake news than real news? Research by Doteveryone suggests that 62 per cent of people do not realise that their social networks can affect the news they see.[17]

In a paper published by the US-based Internet Architecture Board in March 2020 entitled 'The internet is for end users,' researchers write, 'Most who participate in the internet Engineering Task Force are comfortable making what we believe to be purely technical decisions ... nevertheless the running code that results from our process (when things work well) inevitably has an impact beyond technical considerations. The impact of this trend is not to be diminished; the internet has become the mediator of essential functions within communities and has indeed become a political machine in and of itself. The web and tools on the web have helped overthrow governments, rejigger social order, change the outcome of elections, and control populaces.' In *The Social Dilemma*, Harris asks if social media now amplifies gossip, hearsay and fake news to the point where we don't know what the truth is any more, and McNamee suggests that Facebook may be the greatest tool of persuasion ever created.

The question, then, becomes whether we truly want to 'privatize the gatekeeping of our own public space for speech,'[18] as Lanier writes. And even if the answer is yes, will we always answer in the affirmative? Lanier goes on to ask, 'Do billions of users have the ability to coordinate moving off a service like that in protest? If not, what leverage is there? Are we choosing a new kind of government by another name, but one that represents us less?'

To be sure, Facebook has become a primary news source in many democratic countries. But it is crucial to keep in mind that this was not Facebook's initial mission or value proposition; ultimately, it remains a corporation focused on maximising profits, headed by a single individual.

Cambridge Analytica (CA) was a British political consulting firm that was accused of combining the misappropriation of digital assets, data mining, data brokerage and data analysis with strategic communication during electoral processes. The company closed its operations in the course of the Facebook Cambridge Analytica data scandal in 2018, but before closing, the CEO claimed to have worked on 200 elections around the world. CA certainly worked for Ted Cruz's campaign in 2016, Donald Trump's in the same year and the Leave EU campaign in the UK. Its role in these campaigns has been controversial and is the subject of ongoing criminal investigations. Facebook later banned CA from advertising on its platform, saying it had been deceived by CA's representations. Some of CA's work was based on a profiling system using online surveys, political campaign apps, as well as Facebook and smartphone data to micro-target messages to voters. The controversy resulted in Facebook's market capitalisation falling $37 billion. Facebook later admitted it had concerns about 'improper data gathering practices' at CA long before the controversy erupted. In 2019, the FTC imposed a $5 billion fine on Facebook when it became clear that CA had paid to acquire data on 87 million unknowing social media users.

Some academics have since asserted that CA's claims of success in micro-targeting voters and its effects of changing voting behaviours are grossly exaggerated. But it doesn't really matter who is right. If there are firms who claim to undertake this activity for money, it must be a matter of public interest and, in my view, likely to be of concern.

McNamee says of the US, 'Our country has built a Maginot Line – half the world's expenditures on defense – and it never occurred to anyone that a bad actor could ignore that and instead use an American internet platform to manipulate the minds of American voters.'[19]

Indeed, the same campaign can now espouse a number of different messages. As Jimmy Wales, founder of Wikipedia, notes, 'In the old days, politicians in order to win had to have a single consistent message, then reach across the middle … whereas now it's beginning to feel like they can run campaigns that completely contradict each other. They sell completely different messages to different audiences, and a lot of it's just voter suppression.'[20]

No one truly knows how many profiles on social media are operated by individuals who accurately self-identify. I shall examine later whether anonymity on the web should be curtailed, but in the meanwhile it is clear that fakes are everywhere.

Lanier observes that on social media, 'Fakes are present in unknown but vast numbers and establish the ambiance.'[21] The danger lies in the ability of these fakes – many of them bots – to act quickly and maliciously. For Lanier, these bots represent 'a *cultural* denial of service', which generally involves bombarding a site with bogus traffic to prevent real users from accessing its services. In much the same way, Lanier states, 'Armies of fake people … take up a lot of oxygen in the room and steer the world on behalf of their masters.'[22] In May 2019, Recode reported that Facebook had taken down 2.2 billion fake accounts in the first three months of 2019 alone, nearly equivalent to the total number of active users it claims to have had at that time altogether.[23]

The internet and media more broadly become an amplifier and self-reinforcer of trending social media stories. McNamee says, 'the slavish tracking of Twitter by journalists, in combination with their willingness to report on things that trend there, has made news organisations complicit in the degradation of civil discourse'.[24]

Does it matter that my news feed is subtly (or vastly) different from yours? Experts would suggest that the answer is a resounding 'yes'. According to Lanier, 'The most common form of online myopia is that most people can only make time to see what's placed in front of them by algorithmic feeds … the results are tiny changes in the behaviour of people over time'. But these minute changes compound; as Lanier notes, 'Not only is your worldview distorted, but you have less awareness of other people's worldviews … their experiences are as opaque to you as the algorithms that are driving your experiences.'[25] As such, the system decides, based on internally coded prescription, what to show each of us, which could lead to significant bias. As McNamee points out, 'The opacity of our times is even worse than it might be, because of the degree of opacity that is itself opaque.'[26] While the internet was meant to lead to increased transparency, it would appear that the exact opposite has taken place. Today, the problem has ballooned to such an overwhelming degree that social media sites alone are incapable of taming the monster they have created. As McNamee notes, 'With a shocking percentage of the country's population stuck in preference bubbles that blind them to fact, we need to think about ways to reconnect people in the real world, to encourage handshakes and eye contact with people who live differently and hold different views.'[27]

Kees, twenty, says, 'Due to social media curating a personalised news feed, I find it really hard to discuss politics with someone who doesn't have the same views as me. Our news intakes are completely different, and have been different for a long time, so we cannot even agree on the most basic of facts on which a discussion could begin. If one person brings up the headline of a study they read, the other guy would just recite the headline of another study that said the complete opposite, and neither person would be aware of the study the other person saw.'

The lack of tolerance for minority views on social media seems to be another growing issue. Seemiller and Grace identify what they call the 'cyberbalkanisation' of news and interest groups on social media platforms, which is the 'segregation of the internet into smaller groups with similar interests to a degree that they show a narrow-minded approach to outsiders or those with contradictory views'.[28] We noted earlier the concept of filter bubbles, more commonly called echo chambers. An echo chamber, however, may be a misnomer. Williams suggests that the more appropriate term may be amplifier feedback, effectively 'holding a live microphone up to a speaker to create an instant shrieking loop that will destroy your eardrums if you let it'.[29] The majority is amplified and the minority prevented from expressing its views other than in niche platforms dedicated to those with the same views. *The Social Dilemma* observes that recent Pew Research identifies the US population as being more polarised than at any point in history, but points out that polarisation is effective at keeping people online.

Events which the court of social media opinion find unacceptable can lead to the vilification of individuals. For example, in 2015 a dentist from Minnesota shot and killed Cecil the lion and then posted a picture of himself with the dead animal on social media. It quickly went viral, and on Facebook a 1,000-member strong group took control of assassinating the dentist's character. While many will say it served him right, it seems cruel to suggest that being cyberbullied and physically intimidated into disappearing was appropriate.

On the other hand, the debates about gun control which swept the US after a series of horrific school shootings, as well as the #MeToo campaign, following allegations of sexual abuse by Harvey Weinstein, may be positive examples of 'court of social media' campaigns. But as Williams points out, 'If justice is our goal – as it should be – then it is not at all clear that these dynamics of moral outrage and mob rule advance it. If anything, they seem to lead in the opposite direction.'[30] The problem with mobocratic justice is that it is driven by 'viral outrage' that is capricious, arbitrary and ultimately uncertain.[31]

Mob rule is hard-coded into the design of the attention economy, according to Williams. 'It creates an environment in which extremist actors, causes or groups who feed on outrage can flourish,' he notes. Increasingly, vigilante justice seeks to destroy individuals 'symbolically, reputationally, we might even say *attentionally*, for their transgression'.[32]

How much should we be worrying that a small number of people could control what we see on social media? Leading ethicists sound strong alarms in response to big-tech platform protestations of innocence. Williams says, 'Responding in the right way means treating the design of digital technologies as the ground of first struggle for our freedom and self-determination, as the politics behind politics that shapes our attentional world and directs downstream effects according to its own ends.'[33] The challenge, of course, comes from the fact that this new system of influence does not abide by traditional rules nor resemble traditional systems. It is precisely because this modern manifestation claims *not* to wield political power that it has the ability to be particularly insidious. And it hides behind the smokescreen of free speech. Zuboff says, 'Free speech fundamentalism has deflected careful scrutiny of the unprecedented operations that constitute the new market form and accounts for its spectacular success. The Constitution is exploited to shelter a range of novel practices that are antidemocratic in their aims and consequences and fundamentally destructive of the enduring First Amendment values intended to protect the individual from abusive power.'[34]

Social media has been repeatedly abused by extremist groups to express their views and circulate propaganda. This has led to calls for platform operators to create policies which prohibit such activity and 'take down' offending material. Most major social media platforms have community guidelines and aim to remove materials which are deemed to be in contravention of those guidelines. They employ a combination of AI and human intervention to weed out non-compliant content. There are many difficult issues for social media platforms in content moderation, notably the scale of their platforms and volume of new material which is user generated, the inadequacy of AI review programs resulting in them either missing a non-compliant post or removing ones which are compliant (raising freedom of speech issues), the limitations of language technologies, differing cultural norms and the inability of platforms to share information about posters of offending material with each other to coordinate take-down activity without breaching privacy or anti-trust laws. Zuboff says, 'nowhere is surveillance capitalism's outsized influence over the divisions of learning in society more concretely displayed than in this outcast function of "content moderation"' performed by the twenty-first-century version of janitors.[35]

After many years when the process of content moderation was little known, it has recently come into the limelight as a result of both journalist investigation and exposure, and more recently in books like Sarah Robert's *Behind the Screen*. A light has been shone on a vast global industry devoted to filtering vile images and graphic material from our screens, often despite the reticence of the big techs to talk about it openly in any detail. Sarah Roberts examines the issues raised by the application of detailed content moderation instructions given to staff employed to undertake the filtering, which, unlike community guidelines, are generally not public.[36] This leads to an opaque process prone to the limitations of the ability and judgement of both AI tools and the individuals engaged in detection and filtering decisions. Inevitably, the views of the individuals involved have some impact on what survives and what doesn't, meaning it is not an objective process. One man's justifiable protest can, after all, be another man's hate speech.

Change the Terms, a US advocacy group, has urged platforms to standardise and enforce content moderation policies, particularly around hate speech. Facebook has recently announced the intention to appoint an oversight board to make recommendations to its board about content-moderation policies. Other social media companies are looking at setting up such 'social media councils'. This is complicated, as different countries will define hate speech quite differently. As Joan Donovan, a contributor of the Centre for International Governance Innovation (CIGI), says, 'It's not simply that corporations can turn their back on the communities caught in the crosshairs of their technology. Beyond reacting to white supremacist violence, corporations need to incorporate the concerns of targeted communities and design technology that produces the Web we want.'[37] Until there is coherent international cooperation on content moderation, evangelists on the subject will focus on the laws of the most stringent countries. Germany, for example, completely bans hate speech and requires non-compliant material to be removed within 24 hours of a complaint; if this is not satisfied, offending companies may face fines of up to 50 million euros.

Following the death of George Floyd in the US in 2020, the Black Lives Matter campaign which was suborned in 2016 has had a major resurgence. Samantha Power, Obama's Ambassador to the UN, tweeted on 5 June, 2020, 'My daily appeal to Mark Zuckerberg to change Facebook's destructive and incoherent approach to misinformation and incitement by politicians. Please hear FB early employees: "Fact-checking is not censorship. Labelling a call to violence is not authoritarianism."'

There are many excellent applications of artificial intelligence used in policing, healthcare, finance, education and commerce designed to reduce costs to the operator of the service and improve the product experienced by the consumer. Individuals in society become hyper-indexed and hyper-quantified by the companies and governments they deal with. Judgements can then be made about them by scoring algorithms to make processing their application or purchase more efficient. Simple examples include the scoring of a healthcare insurance policy application by an insurer to determine the appropriate premium, or credit scoring by a credit card company to determine the appropriate interest rate, all on the basis of answers to a questionnaire completed by the consumer and processed by a computer. In policing, data analysis can be used to predict the likelihood of future criminal action from individuals or cohorts for the purposes of deciding to whom to devote limited police resources.

Bias can creep into these processes, however, and this has led to the call for a new human right to be recognised – that of the right to 'reasonable inferences'. The principle is to address the problem of computers making assessments with human bias built into their algorithms, which leads to unfair decisions – for example, being overcharged for an insurance product or being discriminated against by border authorities. We will see how the EU has focused on this issue in its proposals for regulating AI applications and how other organisations are building it into their thinking on potential global internet governance.

In her book *Weapons of Math Destruction*, data scientist Cathy O'Neil records that the models powering the data economy 'encoded human prejudice, misunderstanding, and bias into the software systems that increasingly managed our lives' with the result that they 'tended to punish the poor and oppressed in society'.[38] O'Neil explains that without human intervention and feedback, a statistical engine can produce 'faulty and damaging analysis' and 'poisonous assumptions are camouflaged by math and go largely untested and unquestioned'.[39] She concludes that 'promising efficiency and fairness, they distort higher education, drive up debt, spur mass incarceration, pummel the poor at nearly every juncture, and undermine democracy'.[40] Her solution is to create Big Data models that follow our ethical lead and observes that sometimes, this will involve putting fairness ahead of profit. The first step, however, is to conduct research, measuring the precise impact of models and employing algorithmic audits.

The 2018 report of the EU Ethics Advisory Group identifies a number of dangers within today's technological landscape – for example, the substitution of computational or algorithmic optimisation for human decision taking, the algorithmic spreading of fake news and the rise of micro-targeting and algorithmic psychographic profiling, which reduce people's ability to discriminate between what is reliable information and what is not. These dangers all serve as threats to human autonomy. As such, the Group poses the question of whether the individual human – as a legal subject – has a future.

The 2020 Black Lives Matter protests have led to the big tech companies pausing in their roll-out of facial recognition technology. These technologies match database photographs with facial images to identify people with higher speed and sometimes accuracy than people can. They have been provided to law enforcement agencies by companies like IBM and Microsoft for some time and in the UK have been used in conjunction with CCTV by the Metropolitan Police since January 2020. In June 2020, IBM said it was closing its facial recognition operation. Amazon said it would stop selling its 'Rekognition' system to the US police, saying that it would give time for Congress to pass appropriate rules. Microsoft did the same, encouraging Congress to pass rules that were grounded in human rights. America's National Institute of Standards and Technology examined nearly 200 algorithms used in facial recognition systems in 2020 and found that, whilst good systems were often very accurate, the worst produced many false identifications, which could exacerbate racial or gender biases leading to discriminatory questioning, surveillance and even loss of liberty.

In Generation Z's adult life, digital ethics will hopefully develop to stage where they eliminate technology's worst attributes. Generation Z has the opportunity to shape digital ethics' impact. Carr notes that 'the intellectual ethic of technology is rarely recognised by its inventors'.[41] Because these developers are so focused on solving a specific problem, they are unable to remove the blinkers to see the greater consequences of their work. Moreover, technology users are often unaware of the ethics underlying many tools, being more interested in the immediate and tangible benefits they derive from these tools.

Data ethics, one of the precursors to and cornerstones of digital ethics, refers to systemising, defending and recommending concepts of right and wrong conduct in relation to data and, in particular, personal data. The UK has established data ethics centres at both the Alan Turing Institute and the Centre for Data Ethics and Innovation (CDEI). Oxford University's Internet Institute houses a world-leading Digital Ethics Laboratory, and Delft University of Technology publishes a world-leading academic journal, *Ethics and Information Technology*. The Turing Institute has leading data ethics academics in it and aims to provide advice and guidance on ethical best practice in data science. The CDEI aims to create new governance structures for data-driven technologies including AI. On launch, its chair said, 'We want to work with organisations so that they can maximise the benefits of data-driven technology and use it to ensure the decisions they make are fair. As a first step, we will be exploring the potential for bias in key sectors where the decisions made by algorithms can have a big impact on people's lives.' The UK wants to be a leader in 'responsible innovation in data-driven technology'.[42]

The European Union has led the world in setting up laws to protect personal data in the form of General Data Protection Regulation (GDPR). The main aims of the GDPR are to harmonise data protection law across EU member states and to give the 'data subject' more control over how the 'data controller' uses their personal data. It seeks to protect EU citizens wherever they are in the world, including in the US. GDPR is world-leading legislation, and while some criticise the costs it imposes on smaller companies, some of its principles have been adopted or used in templates for legislation in other jurisdictions. This goes far beyond the use of data in politics. Governments, including the UK government, have issued data ethics codes meant to guide the use of public data. But of course the UK already has strict laws about what surveillance the state can exercise over your data and what they can use it for, with direct ministerial accountability, judicial oversight and intense regular parliamentary scrutiny. I never cease to be amazed that people complain about state surveillance or data collection when Google and Facebook already know far more about you, your location, friends and habits than the intelligence agencies would ever collect, unless you were one of a relatively very small number of suspected criminals.

The multi-page terms and conditions you now tick before installing an app will often include GDPR permissions. But the average consumer does not read these terms and conditions and with a single click gives up the power to control their data.

In 2018, the EU Ethics Advisory Group issued a report entitled 'Towards a digital ethics', grounding their thinking regarding the fundamental right to privacy and the protection of personal data as a crucial element to the protection of human dignity. The advisory group noted that the combination of big data, social networks and other online platforms – the internet of things, networked sensors, cloud computing, artificial intelligence and machine learning – collectively require a 'big data protection ecosystem', an interactive and accountable assemblage of future-oriented regulation, accountable controllers, privacy-conscious engineering and empowered individuals. The report noted that data protection is about protecting the person behind the data, not just the data. Once people experience life through the digital economy as well as in person, it changes the very nature of 'personhood'.

Generation Z has grown up with big-tech companies having their data. Recent studies have shown, however, that privacy was more important to them than being famous or liked online: 55 per cent of Generation Zers claim to want to decide what information they share with brands, and 54 per cent want to control how brands contact them. Sixty per cent of those in Seemiller and Grace's study said they were concerned about identity theft specifically.[43] Perhaps as Generation Z matures, it will pick up on the opportunity created by GDPR and turn the developing global thinking on data ethics into a transforming force for the better. Zuboff believes this can be the case, calling today's young people 'the Spirits of a Christmas Yet To Come' who 'live on the frontier of a new form of power that declares the end of human future, with its antique allegiances to individuals, democracy and the human agency necessary for moral judgement. Should we awaken from distraction, resignation and psychic numbing with Scrooge's determination, it is a future we may still avert.'[44]

According to Williams, an economy based on controlling attention can 'frustrate and even erode the human will at individual and collective levels, undermining the very assumption of democracy'.[45] As such, we ought to rewire the relationship we have with technology.

Most concerningly, Williams points out that the proportion of individuals who believe it is essential to live in a democracy has declined rapidly. The premium placed on democratic values is diminishing across cultures, languages and economies. This may be due in part to the fact that many countries share a dominant form of media, which 'just happens to be the largest, most standardised, and most centralised form of attentional control in human history'.[46]

Zuckerberg has said that privacy is no longer a social norm. Can democracy exist without privacy? More troubling still, is there free thought without privacy?

The conclusions seem clear. Technology has the capacity to interfere significantly with politics, both unintentionally by way of algorithmic newsfeeds that bias readers towards one viewpoint or another and intentionally by way of specifically designed platforms that are meant to influence voter behaviour in the same way that advertisers affect buyer preferences. Alex Karp, billionaire founder of Palantir, wrote in his August 2020 open shareholders' letter accompanying the stockmarket listing of his data analytics company: 'Our society has effectively outsourced the building of software that makes our world possible to a small group of engineers in an isolated corner of the country. Do we also want to outsource the adjudication of some of the most consequential moral and philosophical questions of our time? Silicon Valley's elite may know more than most about software, but they do not know more about how society should be organised or what justice requires.'[47] *The Social Dilemma* refers to the tools big tech has created for platforms to influence politics as 'remote control warfare'. Miller sounds the warning that this process is nascent: 'If politics has been one of the least disrupted things of the digital age so far ... it will be one of the most disrupted things in the years to come. Political power is shuddering through a transformation, layer by layer, from how it is won, how it is opposed, what it really is, and what it controls.'[48] 'The internet was designed with democratic principles in mind, especially freedom of speech and assembly. Non-democratic states have staged a counter-attack in the second decade of this century using the very infrastructure on which freedom has flourished. Rather than suppress openness, the aim is now to exploit it.'[49]

Victor Pickard has written about the global journalism crisis and has promoted the idea of taxing digital monopolies in order to redistribute media power and reinvest in public service journalism.[50] The Media Reform Coalition and the National Union of Journalists in the UK proposed allocating capital raised from taxes on digital monopolies to support public service journalism, an idea which the then-leader of HM Opposition, Jeremy Corbyn, echoed in his own plans before the 2019 election. The Cairncross Review of British news media called for a new institute to oversee direct funding for public interest news outlets. In April 2020, the Australian government announced that it would force companies like Facebook and Google to share advertising revenue with local, smaller media companies. While Pickard welcomes these national initiatives, he argues that a large global media fund is required to support investigative news activity around the world and protect them from violence and intimidation. Pickard says 'platform monopolies should not be solely responsible for funding global public media, but the least they could do is support investigative journalism, policy reporting, and international news coverage that they are complicit in undermining'.[51] He rejects the notion that the $300 million Google and Facebook have each promised to fund new related projects over three years will solve the problem. While he acknowledges that Google has said it will tailor its algorithms to better promote original reporting, and Facebook has promised to offer major news outlets a licence to its 'News Tab', he believes they fall well short of addressing the magnitude of the global journalism crisis.

Technology has, as usual, created some clear benefits to society, and Generation Z in particular, in terms of news distribution and their ability to participate in political discourse. What is also clear, however, is that the dominant platforms, if they decided to, could affect the content of newsfeeds and ultimately election outcomes. Other bad actors are already seeking to do so and, in some cases, have succeeded. If people stop believing democratically elected governments and are often persuaded by conspiracy theories, is democracy in crisis and hasn't technology created the tools to destabilise society? This is not a situation I would argue that we can afford to allow to develop unmonitored and unregulated.

PROFESSIONAL LIFE

13

PURPOSES NOT BUSINESSES

Following a contact and conversation on LinkedIn, I agreed to meet Jack Dyrhauge, a twenty-one-year-old social entrepreneur from Bristol, for breakfast. After some relaxing banter, he told me about the problems he had faced growing up with Asperger's syndrome, including the bullying he withstood at school. He said he had doubted he would ever have a job or a girlfriend. I could hardly believe that someone now so obviously bright, positive and sparky could have endured such experiences. He went on to tell me how he now works in sales for an enterprise software business, not a typical role for an autistic person. His boss allowed him to work flexibly so that Jack could set up a charity that encourages and supports autistic young people in his area who are entering their first jobs – this is particularly important in the UK, where unemployment amongst people diagnosed with autism is a shocking 80 per cent. He now works with my alma mater, Bath University, helping autistic undergraduates into the workplace, and I managed to link him to the CEO of the UK's largest autism charity, where we are collaborating. Meeting Jack was a moving, truly inspiring experience for me and very typical of the Generation Z meetings I have had over the last two years.

I have tried to meet a young entrepreneur every business day. I have been blown away by their entrepreneurial spirit, positivity and creativity and on many occasions have found that their elevator pitch for their 'business' is in fact a pitch for a social enterprise. Generation Z's aim is often to address a social issue, not necessarily to make money. As Emery White noted in his survey, Generation Z's high propensity to consider entrepreneurship is not simply about creating security. Instead, Generation Z is defined by its desire to make a difference and its belief that this is a possibility.

I also met William Pearson, another twenty-one-year-old, educated in Oslo before doing a degree in mechanical engineering at Exeter and a Masters in Management at LBS. He interned at four small businesses, including a Swedish industrial design company, before himself creating the Ocean Bottle, a permanent water bottle that each of us should buy and own. Each bottle is smart-chip-activated, and sales surpluses are directed to funding the collection of ocean-bound plastic in countries with poor waste recycling practices. Ocean Bottle helps set up recycling infrastructure in coastal communities with high levels of plastic pollution, stopping the plastic reaching the ocean. These sales surpluses are also used to fund plastic collectors' tuition and healthcare and, furthermore, to micro-finance their own businesses. Ocean Bottle has already paid collectors to recover 30 million bottles and has won numerous global awards for environmental impact. William had been a deckhand on a yacht where he had been shocked by ocean plastic levels and is now an ambassador for Plastic Planet. I was able to help him by introducing him to the UN Ambassador for the Oceans.

Charles Benet, twenty-one, educated in the US and interning with Europe's largest sports booking app in Madrid and a venture building incubator in Mallorca, arrived one morning to tell me about his 'anti-prejudice' dating app called Depixs. Profiles feature detailed descriptions of your interests, hobbies, passions and beliefs. Potential matches are identified and presented with the picture largely blurred. As you start to chat, more and more details of your bio become visible, and the picture becomes less blurred. Only through sustained conversation – indicating a mutual personality match – do the associated photos of the users become clear. The app is designed to eliminate immediate rejection based on prejudicial grounds like age, weight, race and beauty.

Giovanni Raiteri, educated in Lausanne and at Oxford, is a twenty-year-old who created Carbon Codes. He had taken himself through the Open University Fundamentals of Digital Marketing course and gained a Growth Master Certificate from Growth Hackers. Carbon Codes helps consumers who want to eat sustainably reduce their carbon footprint. Carbon Codes works with restaurants to attach carbon scores to each of their dishes and provide discounts to diners should they choose low-carbon dishes. These meals can be delivered or eaten at the restaurant. The restaurant in London I have invested in, Margot, is looking at the idea, as it appeals to our vegan and conscientious customer base.

Matteo Colledan, twenty, was educated in London, ending up with a Masters in Science from Imperial College, having won the Hult Prize in Tokyo. The Hult Prize Foundation is a global learning platform which enables the new generation to deliver social change through education and entrepreneurship. He co-founded Consciously Aware. This business seeks to address the issue that a lot of recyclable waste has to be destroyed because it is contaminated with organic matter, e.g. a yoghurt pot thrown away with yoghurt still in it. Tracing technology connected to recycling plants and consumer apps keeps users informed as to which residents are achieving clean waste with the aim of dramatically increasing the recycling rate.

When I joined the job market, my generation often sought to work for blue-chip companies with well-recognised brands and a track record of long-term profitability. We optimised for security, training and progression within the company and valued the prestige of the name. Generation Z, on the other hand, does not believe that companies should exist only to make profit and, in line with what is called 'Conscious Capitalism', want to see that they also have purpose. To understand purpose, it is worth reviewing how purpose has grown out of corporate social responsibility (CSR).

During my working lifetime, the concept of CSR became mainstream; I have been lucky to play a part in leading some CSR initiatives in a few of the organisations I have worked for. CSR often started with companies picking community projects where their operations were based and supporting their local communities. Centrica, for example, a major UK utility, started an excellent programme in rehabilitating former convicts from a prison near its HQ. Other large companies started national programmes around themes that were important to them or their mission statements; this gave rise to many brilliant schemes like Teach First, still successful today, aiming to attract clever graduates into teaching. HRH Prince Charles must be given credit for being a leading light in the CSR world. As patron of Business in the Community (BITC) in the UK, he and the organisation inspired companies to take on more corporate social responsibility. BITC created the CSR Index to measure what companies were doing and whether they had really embedded CSR in their thinking, rather than simply paying lip service to make it look like they were pursuing it. By 2000, BITC was moving on from CSR to a more holistic approach to responsible business.

CSR has developed through many iterations and is a major feature of the way many larger businesses now operate. With the increasing appreciation of the climate change crisis, however, and the degree to which it resonates with consumers, sustainability has become the new watchword, and companies have started designing their products and operations to be sustainable. Cranfield School of Management's Doughty Centre for Corporate Responsibility defines corporate sustainability as a business commitment to sustainable development, and an approach that creates long-term shareholder *and societal value* by both embracing the opportunities and managing the risks associated with economic, environmental and social impacts.

Businesses which commit to sustainability will typically either explicitly or implicitly follow the ten principles of the UN Global Compact, which defines the parameters of being a responsible business. Patagonia, Unilever, IKEA and Danone are all held up as examples of companies who have led in this area.

In his book *All In*, Professor David Grayson, Founder Director of the Doughty Centre, defines sustainability as how companies can ensure 9–10 billion people will live reasonably well within the constraints of one planet by mid-century. Grayson cites Peter Drucker, who said, 'Every global problem and social issue is a business opportunity in disguise,' and the Business and Sustainable Development Commission, which has calculated a $12 trillion opportunity for business in implementing the UN Sustainable Development Goals. Grayson believes that society moved in 2016 from the second of his three identified eras – where businesses saw that a more comprehensive means of addressing sustainability was required – to the third 'Purpose-Driven Era'.[1]

This Purpose-Driven Era, says Grayson, is one where the best corporate leaders focus what they do – from supply chain management to manufacturing to marketing – through the lens of the purposeful and positive impact they aspire to have in the world through the success of their business. He says it needs to start with an authentic, practical and inspiring explanation of why the business exists. The Chartered Institute of Management describes purpose for a business as the meaningful and enduring reason to exist that aligns with long-term financial performance, provides a clear context for daily decision taking and unifies and motivates relevant stakeholders.

'Three quarters of those in Generation Z believe work should have a greater purpose than making money,' according to Seemiller and Grace.[2] And whilst many roles in business may be relatively simple, employers will need to find ways of connecting a range of roles to something bigger and more meaningful if they are to attract and retain Generation Z talent. In the study 'Generation Z goes to college', 26 per cent of respondents said that making a difference was the most important factor in a future career. Ninety per cent believe it is important for their careers to contribute towards social change, and 93 per cent said that their decision to work at a company is affected by the company's impact on society.[3] A national study by Fuse, a brand marketing firm targeted at members of Generation Z and millennials, found that 85 per cent of members of Generation Z believe that companies should be obligated to solve social problems.[4]

Purpose is not just about brand values, but rather about the business model. In the early days of CSR, some companies thought they could have what Julia Cleverdon, CEO of BITC at the time, called 'a lunch, a launch and a logo' and stop there. In other words, they could pay lip service to CSR and get away with it. Forward-looking companies have already recognised that this kind of approach will not convince Generation Z. Authenticity is key to a company's CSR initiatives and, by extension, its broader purpose. A company's purpose must further be underpinned by its culture and values. A study by BBMG and Globescan concluded that Generation Z is three times more likely than any other generation to say that the purpose of business is to 'serve communities and society'. It also found that Generation Z is more likely to trust that large companies are operating in society's best interests *only* when the companies show it by their actions and their employees' actions.[5] It is perhaps no surprise that most of the brands thought to be authentic today are companies who are, in effect, being themselves, not putting on some kind of charade in the name of purpose. Take, for example, outdoor and adventure brand Patagonia, ice cream maker Ben & Jerry's or shoe purveyor Tom's.

Demonstrating a positive contribution to society, not just financial performance, is what in 2012 the Chairman of Blackrock, one of the largest international investors in quoted companies in the world, wrote in his first open annual letter to all Blackrock's investee companies was necessary for companies to prosper over time. Society includes shareholders, employers, customers and the communities in which they operate. Without a purpose, he said, no company can achieve its full potential and will ultimately lose the licence to operate from its key stakeholders. His letters have become more and more urgent in their claims, and in 2020 he called for a fundamental reshaping of finance and emphasised his view that 'climate risk is investment risk' and that ultimately 'purpose is the engine of long term profitability'.

In 2020, the US Business Round Table, a group of nearly 200 CEOs in the US which had been repeatedly criticised by some for a gap between its public statements and the actions of its members, issued a new statement of business purpose rejecting the idea of shareholder supremacy in favour of a more balanced approach. The Davos manifesto for the World Economic Forum in 2020 explicitly embraced stakeholder capitalism and suggests that purpose is to engage all its stakeholders in shared and sustained value creation. The best way to understand and harmonise the divergent interests of all stakeholders is through a shared commitment to policies and decisions that strengthen the long-term prosperity of the company. Grayson believes there is a long way to go before companies' actions fully reflect purpose, and in the meanwhile, we can count on Generation Z to call out any 'purpose washing', i.e. charading as pursuing purpose, whilst not actually walking the walk.

At Oxford University, I was closely involved in supporting the creation of Said Business School's Centre for Corporate Reputation. We examined 'which stakeholders a company has a reputation with' and 'how that reputation is defined'. We looked at why having a good reputation was important to the company's success and determined that whilst companies can get away with not living their stated mission for a while, they will always get found out, and the result could be catastrophic. BP, the British oil and gas company, discovered in 2010, when one of its wells – Deepwater Horizon – caused a massage spillage in the Gulf of Mexico, that it was not good enough to claim to operate safely: you actually need to operate safely. The cost to the company was about $65 billion in fines and settlements alone.

Forward-looking companies recognise that there is a high degree of trust inherent in the relationship between consumers and the businesses which supply them with goods and services and that includes the use of customer data. Data has become increasingly important to business as a result of the digital revolution, and leading companies have thought hard about how they ought to leverage customer data, and how transparent they ought to be with their customers with respect to their data treatment. This has led to data-use policies being designed and approved at board level in leading companies like Visa.

Visa has pioneered a consumer-orientated data policy under the leadership of Pier Luigi Culazzo, Chief Digital Officer. Visa's policy relies on two premises: first, never before has so much decision-making responsibility been delegated on an industrial scale and in ways that may not be fully comprehensible to stakeholders. Second, technology and systems have no built-in morality. We can't presume data science will be ethical – it becomes Visa's job as a trusted brand to design ethics into everything it does. Whilst there is increasing guidance from governments and relevant agencies, there is no comprehensive guide to what companies should do. Consumers are universally concerned about how their data is used and worry about a wide range of data, privacy and identity issues, with varying degrees of knowledge and understanding. Visa has therefore built its own data ethics policy and what they call a 360-degree organisational approach. This starts with a board-level Data Use Council, which has adopted three guiding data-use values. First, the customer should be empowered to manage his or her own data. Second, the customer should benefit from data-driven innovations. Third, it is Visa's job to be an accountable steward of customer data, protecting it and respecting customer privacy.[6]

Visa explicitly recognises that there exist some trade-offs in data ethics.

1. If Visa is excessively detailed in their explanation of data usage, customers are likely less likely to be able to understand these details.
2. If Visa is to prioritise customer privacy, it cannot be as fair or unbiased in its data collection.
3. If Visa is to prioritise customer privacy, the value of collected data may suffer.
4. Between the fairness or bias of data collected and its accuracy.
5. Between your privacy and the accuracy of the data collected.
6. Between the security and explicability of the data collected.

To address these trade-offs, Visa operates a 'privacy by design' policy involving specific privacy impact assessments on every product and service created. All staff must comply with the policy, which involves training and governance from the Chief Privacy Officer and Data Protection Officer.

14

PHIGITAL WORKPLACES

Visit the office of one of my digital startups today and you'll be amazed by what you find. The youngsters arrive, head for a cubicle, surround themselves with a laptop, phone and iPad, put on their earphones and get to work. Turkle coined the expression 'office pilots' to describe them. They may be surrounded by people, but not ones they are really interacting with. Indeed, they are so engrossed in communicating via multiple devices that the two people they don't speak to all day are the 'pilots' of the adjacent cubicles. And tomorrow, those cubicles will be occupied by different people, so the sense of continuity and community is very different from my experience of offices. Turkle calls this 'hoteling', and likens it to 'sitting in a room together but not sitting together'.[1] Even conference calls have changed in nature – Generation Z prefers not to take these calls in group meeting rooms and instead will dial-in on their own so that they can multitask on other devices without others seeing or 'distracting' them.

Stillman and Stillman, who have studied Generation Z's attitude to work and workplaces, coined the phrase 'phigital' to denote this marrying of the physical and digital worlds and note that an employer's ability to handle phigital blurring well will be crucial to attracting talent. Their survey found that 91 per cent of Generation Z say that a company's technological sophistication would impact their decision to work there.[2]

Throughout my career, working in a communal office environment has been the norm. Being able to meet colleagues physically has been a key way to learn and a vital source of understanding, as well as an effective tool in building empathy with colleagues and clients. But the rise of home working or telecommuting and hot desking (where employees just use an empty desk in the office rather than have one permanently allocated) has reduced the opportunities for in-person meetings. Conference calls and video conferences had already become the norm in some workplaces even before the arrival of Covid-19 in the UK in early 2020, which has made it difficult to meet in person and looks like it may have a permanent impact on many employees' desire to go to an office.

Covid-19 has dramatically – and irreversibly – advanced the home-working trend as more people and organisations have been exposed to prolonged periods of it. 'The notion of putting 7,000 people in a building may be a thing of the past,' said the boss of Barclays, while Morgan Stanley's chief said the bank will have 'much less real estate'. Businessman Sir Martin Sorrell said he'd rather invest the £35 million he spends on expensive offices every year in people instead. Even before the pandemic, the Office for National Statistics forecast that half the UK workforce would be working remotely by the end of 2020. In October 2020, Microsoft announced that its employees could choose to work from home permanently.

The ability to work remotely, or telecommute, is important to Generation Z. In response to its learnings from Covid-19, Twitter recently announced after Covid-19, employees can work from home 'forever'. Three-quarters of Generation Z would prefer to have flexible hours.[3] Because Generation Z uses technology to be 'always on', having flexible work hours may in fact allow for greater efficiency, as they are responsive regardless of time. Employees who work remotely at least once a month report being happier than their desk-bound colleagues, and happy employees are more engaged employees.

Generation Z will blur the line between work and home, much as it does the distinction between the online and offline worlds. Technology allows Generation Z's work to always be with them, but their work is just one of many tasks occupying their collective mind. Regardless of whether they are in the office or at home, Generation Z employees will be balancing work and socialising through technology. Employers must give them great experiences if they are to attract and retain them and keep their attention.

Generation Z is more interested in the environment they work in, how flexibly they can start and finish, whether the office is in a cool location, how much holiday they can take, the concierge services available and other benefits on offer from the employer. This is in stark contrast to my generation, which, having secured a job, focused on climbing the ladder and increasing salary and benefits.

Generation Z is cost- and resource-conscious and will not like corporate largesse. Seemiller and Grace note that Generation Z, as a whole, is open-minded, caring and diverse, with a strong sense of integrity and tenacity. The cohort values 'financial security, family and relationships, meaningful work, and happiness, and is motivated through relationships, engaging with their passions, and achievement'.[4] Candace Steele Flippin's research has found the generation to be eager, hardworking, creative and motivated.[5] And the College Senior Survey suggests that Generation Zers are perspective-taking, tolerant of different beliefs, cooperative and highly driven.[6]

Inclusivity may be one of the strongest characteristics of Generation Z. Because the members of this particular cohort are themselves diverse, they are uniquely comfortable with working with others who are unlike them. As such, Generation Zers do not think of diversity as something to be managed, but instead as a reflection of themselves.[7] Stillman and Stillman found that 75 per cent of Generation Z's decision to work for an organisation would be affected by the level of diversity of the company.[8]

On the flip side, a recent survey by LinkedIn found that only 42 per cent of employers agreed that their new hires had the emotional intelligence required for their position.[9] This may be a direct result of some of the effects of social media we discussed in earlier chapters.

Generation Z is three times more likely to job hop than previous generations, LinkedIn found. Given the context in which Generation Z has grown up, this is surprising, as one would imagine job security would be highly valued. LinkedIn found that 20 per cent of these individuals average four or more jobs even in the limited time they have spent in the workforce.[10] Moreover, a staggering 80 per cent of those under twenty-four said they would consider a complete change in function or industry. This may be a result of Generation Z's hunt for a job that aligns with their values.

Eduardo, twenty, says, 'Job hops occur mainly because it is nowadays impossible to progress high fast enough to satisfy our desire for constant stimulation and rapid advancement. Corporations are so huge. We will never get enough sense of responsibility. We are just ants fighting for crumbs really. What's a VP at Goldman Sachs these days? No one.'

Employers will need to think carefully about how best to communicate with Generation Z to appeal to their tech habits. As Stillman and Stillman say, 'Generation Z is the ultimate consumer of what marketers have called snack media. We like to be entertained in bite sizes. Any YouTube video that is more than two minutes is too long.'[11] Long emails will not be read, and senior executives may find that communication is best through short video clips.

Employers will also need to think about how to best harness technology in their recruitment, using online video to explain the opportunities, accepting video resumés in place of traditional written ones, and most importantly, making the process fun, using apps like Jobsnap. '40 per cent of Gen Z say they would use YouTube to determine if they wanted to work for a company, a close second of 37 per cent would use Instagram, and 36 per cent would use Snapchat,' according to Dorsey and Villa.[12] They note that Goldman Sachs has used Snapchat's College Campus Scheme Stories platform with short recruitment videos and that McDonalds use what they call 'snapplications' to attract Gen Z to interview with a career page from which you can swipe to book an appointment from your mobile. Covid-19 has accelerated the use of online interviewing. I have heard from numerous intern applicants over lockdown about their experiences of being interviewed in this way. But even prior to Covid-19, Wiser, a London-based Generation Z recruitment company, has transformed the way some large companies recruit. They leverage young staff in the process of contacting, educating and interviewing candidates and make the process fun and gamified rather than tedious and frustrating. Forward-looking employers seem ready to embrace this new approach. Seemiller and Grace say 89 per cent of employers say they would watch a video resumé if it was sent to them.[13] Salesforce use referral programmes to harness Generation Z in peer recommendation, a rapidly growing technique for recruitment of this age group. Recruitment happy hours and referral bonuses have led to this being Salesforce's largest source of new hires. This, of course, appeals to Generation Z's pension for peer recommendation.

Generation Z places a lower value on long-term commitment in jobs. Their mantra seems to be something along the lines of 'take, learn, move'. Stillman and Stillman note that Generation Z thinks of career progression as a video game: as soon as you have mastered one level, you want the next challenge. This means employers need to think about internship programmes, apprenticeships and project-based work. Accenture found that more than 70 per cent of Generation Z had completed an internship before entering the workforce. Paid and sometimes unpaid internships are now a completely standard part of any graduate CV. I never cease to be amazed at how many experiences the entrepreneurs I meet have had by twenty or twenty-one and in how many cities.

Giovanni says, '"Experiences not jobs" is the phrase which captures an important change underway in our generation. I realised this when evaluating internship opportunities last summer. I felt that an "experience" in a startup where I would have real responsibilities and the possibility to have a tangible impact was much more appealing than a "job" in a larger company where I was unlikely to leave a mark. Indeed, opting for the former was a very rewarding choice – a constant learning experience fine-tuned to my interests and skills in which I felt like I was able to bring some value to the team.'

Reid Hoffman, the founder of LinkedIn, has described employment with his company like a 'tour of duty': rotational, to learn; transformational to one's long-term career and for the company; and foundational, in terms of its long-term value.

A third of participants in Seemiller and Grace's study reported that enjoyment is the most important factor in their future career, and 93 per cent say their decision to work for a company is affected by the company's impact on society. Employers will need to think how to reinforce their company's purpose and their Generation Z employees' contribution towards it in the experiences they offer.[14]

Good training, to make the job a good experience, not just a job, will be key. Seemiller and Grace note that if companies reduce professional development opportunities, Generation Z employees will simply look elsewhere for opportunities to learn more. Indeed, the authors write, 'If employers drive their Generation Z employees out of the office to retool, those employees may find they retool themselves right into another job in another organisation.'[15]

Living up to Generation Z's expectations of customisation will be a major challenge. Since every product and service supplier on the web is offering individualised attention, employers will need to do so as well. By the time they reach the workplace, Generation Z will have spent a lot of time building their personal brands on social media. They will expect their employers to recognise their unique skills and assets and, as a result, to customise jobs to suit them. Stillman and Stillman's survey suggests that 56 per cent of Generation Z would rather write their own job description than be given a generic one. Not only should jobs be made specific, but entire career paths will need to be customised to the individual.

Generation Z is so accustomed to being 'monitored', in the sense that the big-tech platforms collect all their data, that they will expect the same in the workplace. The days of a simple annual employee survey, however, will not do for Generation Z. Stillman and Stillman found that 65 per cent would be comfortable with being monitored at work but would require customised feedback rather than standard appraisal processes. Employers may struggle to find ways of accommodating Generation Z's need for hyper-customisation in the workplace. Employers will need to develop new techniques to really listen to Generation Z and make them feel properly taken into account. Dorsey and Villa's 2018 State of Gen Z study found that two-thirds of Gen Z said they needed feedback from their supervisor at least every few weeks in order to *stay* at their job.[16] This regular feedback can, though, they say, be extremely brief and delivered entirely by technology.

Once-novel perks found at startups and tech companies are now becoming standard offerings for companies of all sizes and stages to appeal to younger talent. No surprise, then, that Netflix offers unlimited holidays and paid paternity and maternity leave for up to a year. For employers, putting employee loyalty, job satisfaction and work–life balance first pays off. Benefits like debt-repayment programmes, paid sabbaticals and remote work flexibility help companies to attract and retain top talent, lowering costly turnover rates. These perks speak volumes to the overworked, burned-out population looking for a respite from the 'always on' culture of the digital age.

When compared to baby boomers and older generations in the workforce, millennials were already more likely to choose benefits such as points- or budget-based perks (gifts from the employer based on points awarded to employees for achieving budget or by colleagues), a technology spending account, health and wellness options or flexible holidays. Glassdoor found that 89 per cent of millennials would choose better benefits over a pay rise. I believe this trend will accelerate as more Generation Z moves into work.

Glassdoor's career and workplace expert Rusty Rueff urges employers to consider and communicate clearly alternatives to traditional forms of compensation and how to keep employees happy. He suggests that non-traditional compensation like gifts from employers given against points awarded by colleagues for performance, technology spending accounts, health and wellness options and flexible holidays should all be prominent and that recruiters should take note that touting the benefits and perks offered can help win talent of different demographics, industries and occupations. Michelle Meyer, head of US Economics at Bank of America Merrill Lynch, and her associate Anna Zhou believe wages are becoming a shrinking share of total compensation and, furthermore, that wage growth will peak at lower levels than in past economic cycles. Twice as many millennials (12 per cent) as baby boomers said paid time off was the most important benefit, according to another study. And as millennials become the biggest cohort in the workforce, benefits are a growing portion of employer costs, a trend that should only increase, Meyer and Zhou write.[17]

Even before Covid-19, healthcare was seen as a crucial benefit, with Monster Worldwide suggesting 70 per cent of Generation Z see it as a 'must have' and Stillman and Stillman suggesting that Generation Z found it even more important than time off.[18]

In order to retain top employees for over five years, benefits and inclusivity have proven to have more of an impact than superficial perks. Unlike the cash-strapped previous generations, whose main driver for a career change was money, the idea of working from home a few days a week or reimbursement for family planning like egg freezing can relieve some of the mental burdens the younger generation faces.

Unlimited paid time off (PTO) policies are growing in popularity. While many employers are wary of unstructured or unlimited vacation policies, this extreme-sounding benefit has worked wonderfully for companies like Netflix, HubSpot, Dropbox, Github and GE. Deb Henley, founder of Henley Leadership Group, found that, by implementing a PTO policy, she enabled her employees to create flexible work and vacation schedules. She says that unlimited vacation policies work as long as you have transparency, clear communication, trust and regular performance evaluation. An employee of Squarespace told me that these policies often work to the employer's benefit as, in her experience, many employees took less PTO despite the policy. Generation Z places value on leisure time and flexibility, and so we should expect to see more and more companies adopting PTO policies.

Access to pay every day is a benefit that appeals to Generation Z. Platforms like Instant Financial partner with employers to offer employees part of their forthcoming pay at any point during the month with repayment out of the next pay cheque.

Dropout rates from US universities are increasing as the cost of tuition rises. According to data from Universum Global, a firm specialising in employer branding, 60 per cent of US high schoolers would be willing to go straight into the workforce if their employer offered to provide educational assistance.[19]

Generation Z wants to make a difference, have impact and feel heard, reflecting its view that the world we are leaving it needs to be improved.

MTV conducted a nationwide survey of 1,000 respondents born after 2000 to ask what name they would give to their generation; the group came up with the name 'Founders'.[20] Generation Z clearly has strong entrepreneurial tendencies, and employers will need to think how to accommodate both their keenness to make a difference and their entrepreneurial characteristics.

The League of Intrapreneurs encourages youngsters in organisations and the organisations themselves to embrace intrapreneurship. Myriam Sidibe, one of its members, used her position at Unilever to promote a global handwashing programme aimed at stemming disease which has now become one of the largest public health programmes in the world. Sam McCracken, another member, had an idea at Nike, where he worked, that led to an entirely new category of Nike products – Nike N7 – used to encourage kids to be active, the proceeds of which are invested in aboriginal youth.

Combining Generation Z's search for purpose, their social consciousness and their entrepreneurial skills will, I believe, lead to a movement of social intrapreneurs of this kind. Yunus Social Business, in its report 'Business as unusual', describes a social intrapreneur as an entrepreneurial employee who develops a profitable new product, service or business model that creates value for society and his or her company. Social intrapreneurs help their employers meet sustainability commitments and create value for customers and communities in ways that are built to last. Yunus believes that to fully realise stakeholder capitalism of the kind we defined in the Purpose section, the private sector will need to fully embrace social intrapreneurship. Yunus's research found that successful social intrapreneurship programmes increase employee engagement, job satisfaction, skills, attraction and retention, spur business innovation, help companies to find new markets, improve corporate brand equity and lead to mindset shifts and cultural change.[21]

Surveys show that Generation Z feels in touch with their family's finances and is involved in major household purchase decisions. Stillman and Stillman say that we can expect Generation Z to bring this attitude to the workplace, where they will assume that they should be consulted on major decisions. Generation Z also wants to be nurtured. The idea of supervising junior staff may need to be developed more into a concept of pastoral care.

The traditional corporate command and control structure will need to be completely rethought as Generation Z's independent and execution-minded spirit may not lend itself to producing team players, as has been a hallmark of millennials. Stillman and Stillman's survey found that 75 per cent of Generation Z agreed with the statement 'if you want it done right, then do it yourself'.[22] They also note that Generation Z's collective FOMO results in their being unafraid of failure. Having exposure to a new opportunity, even if the result is unsuccessful, will be more important than missing out on this exposure altogether.

As a result of their exposure to the GFC, Generation Z is focused on the sharing economy. In fact, 41 per cent of Generation Z has participated in the sharing economy to bolster full-time jobs.[23] Generation Z, as a result, expects goods in particular to be used multiple times by multiple users. And they may wish to work in several ways simultaneously, with a part- or full-time anchor job and 'side hustles' separate from the primary employer. Reflecting Generation Z's penchant for multitasking, they will expect to task switch – Stillman and Stillman's survey found that 75 per cent of Generation Z would be interested in a situation in which they could have multiple roles within one place of employment. Forbes reports that 40 per cent of the workforce in the US will be freelancers by 2025. A study by Generational Kinetics found that 77 per cent of 14–21-year-old members of Generation Z make spending money through freelance work, working a part-time job or earning an allowance.[24]

Workplaces are changing rapidly as Generation Z enters the workplace in growing numbers. Concepts like WeWork have taken hold, providing flexible, low-commitment workspaces for businesses and entrepreneurs. In March 2020, WeWork had locations in 77 cities in 23 countries with over 600,000 'members'. Statista estimated there were over 22,400 coworking spaces in the world at the end of 2019.[25] But what is about to happen in the nature of work environments will be a transformation which makes WeWork look tame.

Some of the predicted trends include a blurring of 'city-centre office' and suburb as more campus-style offices emerge, mixing work and leisure more often in the same site. There may also be organisational structure changes from hierarchy to community, more flexible and easily reconfigured offices, open-bench workstations and the use of 3D printers, meaning more gets 'made' in the workspace.

Technology will have a big impact with work-management tools, integrated instant messaging and file sharing taking away the work of some middle management and increasing the efficiency of team working. Personal chat bots may make administrative tasks easier using verbal instructions, and we may see a rise in more automated data-driven decision making.

PwC produced a study with the Oxford University James Martin Institute, surveying 10,000 people in China, India, Germany, the UK and the US, noting that emerging work styles involve humans and machines collaborating to make decisions, leading to uniquely human skills like emotional intelligence, creativity, persuasion and innovation becoming more highly valued. They also noted that by 2030 we will have moved to adaptive continuous intelligent systems that take over a lot of decision making and lead to many humans having to be redeployed.[26]

As for when and how widely organisations decide to provide employees with cognitive and memory performance-enhancing drugs, we will have to wait and see. The James Martin Institute is studying the ethics of this potential development. In the meanwhile, microdosing (usually meaning the practice of taking tiny amounts of psychedelic drugs) is a growing phenomenon, and employers need to be alive to it.

The design of workplaces will require new features that appeal to Generation Z. Unily and Kjaer Global produced a report on the workplace of the future looking out to 2030. They identified four workplaces intended to encapsulate some of the emerging trends which very much build on Generation Z's values.

First, the *emotional* workplace, where employees have a good work–life balance and AI helps with a lot of administrative support. Generation Z is given a voice and leads on positive change. Emotional intelligence, self-regulation and self-awareness are prized attributes, with variable work patterns, benefit wellbeing, inclusivity and productivity at the heart of the culture.

Second, the *physical* workplace, where head office has moved from a statement of corporate power to a social hub for cultural cohesion. Desks are self-cleaning and have textiles designed to change with mood or task. The office is biophilic, bringing nature inside. Walkshops and standing meetings are popular, and AR and VR are the ideation tools. A team brainstorm takes place on VR on Mars. Neurodiversity is recognised with a wide pool of talent. Silent rooms and meeting spaces abound to help employees nurture their creative skills, catch up with family or take a nap.

Third, the *technological* workspace, the smart workplace where humans and tech coexist. Boomerang colleagues become popular, bringing back new skills after periods outside the organisation. Imagination, relationship skills and creativity underlie innovation, fuelled by smart tech. The focus is on learning to learn. Employees are supported by digital assistants mentoring and coaching them and facilitating brain dates between employees.

Fourth, the *purposeful* workplace, where companies fulfil roles traditionally undertaken by policymakers and forge cross-industry alliances.

Betterness is good business, and impact investments, designed to bring measurable societal benefits, are mainstream. Generation Z has ensured organisations 'walk the talk' of purpose.[27]

Cal Newport worries about the effects of open-plan offices on the potential to 'deep work' and has called for the end of the 'tyranny of the open plan office',[28] where interruptions abound and working in a state of unbroken concentration is nigh impossible. He argues for a system of 'hub and spoke' offices, where colleagues can come together for collaboration and stay in their own pods for concentration and deep work. I think that Generation Z will be multitasking in their pods. And as Newport says, 'To make matters worse for depth, there's increasing evidence that this shift toward the shallow is not a choice that can be easily reversed. Spend enough time in a state of frenetic shallowness and you permanently reduce your capacity to perform deep work.'[29] Generation Z will have to fight the temptation to multitask to maximise their value to organisations. As Newport notes, 'Deep work is not … an old fashioned skill falling into irrelevance. It's instead a crucial ability for anyone looking to move ahead in a globally competitive information economy.'[30]

Our new strengths in visual spatial intelligence may weaken our capacity for what Carr calls 'deep processing' that underpins 'mindful knowledge acquisition, inductive analysis, critical thinking, imagination and reflection'. Carr argues that the internet is making us smarter, only if we define intelligence by the internet's own standards. 'If we think about the depth of our thought rather than just its speed, we have to come to a different and considerably darker conclusion.'[31]

In future workplaces, Generation Z will have to find new ways to juggle the distractions of the office environment and technology, the need to build empathy with colleagues – which is important to productivity – and the need to deep work, which Newport says is a process path to deep satisfaction and achieving elite performance.[32]

PART 4

WAKE UP, EVERYONE

15

TIME TO LOG OFF?

The big tech companies use the internet to consume the collective attention of the world's citizens in pursuit of their businesses. In this book, I have sought to highlight the dangers posed by the powerful combination of recent and emerging technology, skilful media designers, technology companies and Generation Z behaviours, which lock Generation Z's attention in a never-ending spiral of addiction to devices and distraction by the content they present.

Prior to Covid-19, I would now have launched straight into an argument about the need for more regulation of technology to make it serve society better. Covid-19 has changed the terms of that debate in many ways. Social media and gaming, which was perceived as a potential threat to some teenagers before Covid, became a crucial support mechanism during lockdown, providing connection, education, information and support. What appeared a convenience to many became absolutely necessary for many more. This in turn threw up other issues – for those who can't afford a device or data access, Covid highlighted the fact that poverty disadvantages some through denying digital access. Generation Z is going through a critical phase of life as the pandemic reverberates. The question is, will big tech companies just take advantage of the bounty which Covid has brought them in terms of extra business or will they refine their business models to help Generation Z recover and prosper?

Global 'thinkfluencer' Yuval Noah Harari, author of *Sapiens*, believes that Covid-19 may have been a tipping point that could result in tech giants 'taking over everything'. He says that alongside China, America is leading the new technological revolution and that 'the big tech companies are securing the future. We are likely to see a second wave of American imperialism, just in a different form – a kind of data imperialism.' He concludes that when people look back at Covid, there is a high chance they will remember that this was the moment when a regime of total surveillance became just part of normal life.[1]

Pilots sometimes experience a condition called spatial disorientation, where the brain starts telling the pilot the plane is doing something it isn't. It was thought to be the cause of the John F. Kennedy plane crash in 1999. I know from personal experience as a private pilot that it is a very unpleasant feeling. But you have to ignore your brain, which wants to believe the visual inputs it is accustomed to relying on, and instead believe the unbiased instruments. Maybe we need to do the same in relation to tech – ignore the distractions we are tempted by and study and believe the evidence about what it is doing to us.

I believe society suffered a form of spatial disorientation in the period leading up to the financial crisis. Market practices changed bit by bit, slowly and gradually over decades, and everything carried on; there was no sudden jolt, and so the boards of banks and regulators, both of whom could have worked it out, were not alive to or were ignoring the growing dangers. Everyone was making money, economies were growing, and everything seemed fine. Until it wasn't. The rest is history, as they say. But the pain and suffering it caused millions in the world is not something we would willingly repeat. I think we are making another similar mistake. The internet has crept up on us in a similar way, and we have been lured by its charms and rewards. It could be infinitely more dangerous when combined with some of the trends in behaviours we see in Generation Z and even more so after Covid-19 has accelerated some of these.

The US started to address the issue of technology regulation after 9/11, but conflicting interests derailed the process. The US is where many of the biggest technology companies are based, and therefore the US government could reasonably have been expected to move first. In the period leading up to 9/11, the technology industry was under scrutiny on a whole range of the fronts reviewed in this book, and the US Federal Trade Commission issued a report in which they recommended legislation to regulate online privacy. Their recommendations would, if implemented, have given consumers rights over how their information was used, access to their own data, including rights to amend or delete it, and rights over the security of their data. After 9/11, the US Congress passed the US Patriot Act, and the administration and its agencies developed much closer relationships with the technology companies in an attempt to overcome their lack of foresight of the attacks of 9/11 and improve counter-terrorism intelligence. Similar moves took place in Europe. These relationships, whilst based on the best of intentions, may have delayed what I believe is the inevitable societal reaction to technology by a decade or more.

'It is my firm conviction, now more than ever, that the degree to which we are able and willing to struggle for ownership of our attention, is the degree to which we are free,' says Williams.[2]

In a recent article in the *Sunday Times Magazine*, 'Outsmarted by our smartphones', John Lanchester explains that the real problem of humanity is that we have palaeolithic emotions, medieval institutions and godlike technology. He describes smartphones as a piece of the fantasy future dropped into our world. 'We are in effect living with magic,' he says. He identifies the combination of deliberate targeting of our cognitive soft spots with the intimacy of the personalised connection which smartphones offer as the 'terrible secret at the heart of social media'. He says this is 'why phones have been such a powerful vector for the derangement that has affected our politics, our societies and our shared sense of truth'. And he says we lack the laws to control the things that pour into our phones and we haven't had time to develop psychological resistance to all the deliberate manipulation taking place. He suggests that the crudest fix would be to give platforms responsibility for their content, which he says would break their models but be a good thing for society. Ultimately, though, 'we will have to learn to resist the magic, to see though it, to get sick of it, to be, in every sense, disenchanted'.[3] And in my words, less distracted.

'We are certainly at an appropriate time to think seriously about what it might mean to reclaim our collective consciousness,' says Wu. 'Ultimately it is not our nation or culture but the very nature of our lives that is at stake. For how we spend the brutally limited resource of our attention will determine those lives to a degree most of us may prefer not to think about.'[4] 'If we desire a future that avoids the enslavement of the propaganda state,' he says, 'we must first acknowledge the preciousness of our attention and resolve not to part with it so cheaply or unthinkingly at all.'[5] In other words, we need to think twice before ticking those Terms and Conditions (Ts and Cs) that give away our data, or opting into constant notifications that detract from our protection from continual interruption. In 2017 Deloitte surveyed 2,000 consumers in the US and found that 91 per cent of people consented to legally binding Ts and Cs without reading them.[6] For those aged eighteen to thirty-four, this proportion rose to 97 per cent. Bradfield notes that the format of terms and conditions explanations and invitations are very carefully designed to ensure users just tick the 'accept' box. He cites an academic study by Bohme and Kopsell which found that 'ubiquitous EULAs [end user licence agreements] have trained even privacy-concerned users to click on "accept" whenever they face an interception that reminds them of a EULA'.[7] As the October 2020 US Committee on the Judiciary's commissioned report 'Investigation of competition in digital markets' noted, 'consumers are forced to either use a service with poor privacy safeguards or forego the service altogether'.[8]

One of the reasons that technology has not been more regulated is that it has all happened so quickly. Visa took about forty-three years from its inception to reach 1 billion cards globally.[9] By my calculation, Facebook took under nine years to reach 1 billion users. Anti-trust authorities traditionally focus on mature, well-established and easily definable and measurable markets, which perhaps explains why the growth and dominance of Google, Amazon, Facebook, Apple and Microsoft has only recently attracted their attention. Looking back, it is incredible to think Microsoft was allowed to buy LinkedIn and Skype, that Facebook could purchase Instagram and WhatsApp, and that Google acquired Waze and DeepMind. Many have argued that this has led to the stifling of innovation from potential new market entrants and these dominant players being allowed to further cement their market positions.

It is perhaps an irony that the same day that TikTok teens catapulted TikTok to the second most used social media platform amongst teens after Snapchat, the US AntiTrust Sub-Committee on the Judiciary concluded in a new report that, 'to put it simply, companies that once were scrappy startups that challenged the status quo have become the kinds of monopolies we last saw in the era of the oil barons and railroad tycoons' and that 'these firms wield their dominance in ways that erode entrepreneurship, degrade Americans' privacy online, and undermine the vibrancy of the free and diverse press. The result is less innovation, fewer choices for consumers and a weakened democracy'. Finally, the report cites Supreme Court Justice Louis Brandeis, who nearly a century ago wrote, 'We must make our choice. We may either have democracy, or we may have wealth concentrated in the hands of the few, but we cannot have both.' The report notes that Google captures about 81 per cent of all general search enquiries in the US, Google's Android and Apple's iOS run on more than 99 per cent of all smartphones in the world, Apple's Siri has an approximate market share of 35 per cent of virtual assistants globally, Amazon and Google have market shares of the voice-activated smart speaker market of around 61 per cent and 24 per cent respectively, and Google Maps and Waze (which Google owns) capture an estimated 80 per cent of the navigation apps market. It also notes that Facebook reaches 74 per cent of US smartphone users, Facebook Messenger 54 per cent, and Instagram (owned by Facebook) 35 per cent.[10] In my opinion, it is difficult to reconcile such substantial and, in some cases, dominant market positions in such crucial world technologies with a properly functioning anti-trust regime. It is therefore clear to me, and it would appear to the Committee on the Judiciary, that the US regime has failed miserably over the last decade. In late October 2020, the US department of Justice filed a lawsuit against Google to stop it from unlawfully maintaining monopolies through anti-competitive and exclusionary practices in the search and search advertising markets and to remedy the competitive harms. The US Attorney General also sent a draft law to Congress that would diminish the immunity shield that frees social media giants of liability for content posted by their users. The election of Joe Biden may yet be a turning point in the power of big tech.

As Miller describes it, 'As the tech giants have grown bigger and bigger, they are swept along by an enormously powerful and new cycle of dominance ... one social network to connect everyone. One website to index the internet. One platform to look for jobs. One messaging service to communicate. One portal to buy everything you need ... the monopolies of today are different from the past, and they generally haven't been challenged by anti-monopoly laws ... This is an example of power sliding outside of its cages – this case monopoly law – that have been built for a former age.'[11]

'Amazon, Google and Facebook all have monopoly power that would not have been allowed to exist for much of the 20th century,' says McNamee, '… the products of Google and Facebook are free, and Amazon has transformed the economics of distribution while keeping consumer prices low, which has allowed all three to argue for freedom to dominate, as well as to consolidate.'[12] The problem with traditional monopoly remedies in the current scenario of a very few dominant companies, however, is that breaking up the existing monopolies would arguably only lead to a slightly larger group of monopolies or an oligopoly which could *increase* the amount of aggregate resource expended on misusing our data and not really address the issues.

In February 2020 the EU issued a new digital strategy, at the centre of which were proposals to force the big tech companies to share their data with smaller companies. This follows the EU's decision to fine Google $2.7 billion in 2017 for anti-trust violations, and its $5 billion fine in 2018 for further anti-trust violations, involving the conditions on which it made proprietary Google apps available on mobile phones.[13]

The EU proposals are bold but not bold enough, and we shall have to see how effective they are in practice once the detail is published. Tristan Harris of the Humane Technology Center in the US (and an ex data ethicist from Google) wrote an article in the *Financial Times* in March 2020 arguing that the EU had 'missed a momentous opportunity'. He proposed that a more aggressive three-point intervention was necessary:

1. The EU should create a new corporate classification for large, dominant, social platform businesses. These 'attention utilities' should be required to operate in the public interest. Rules and licences would guide their business models.

2. These attention utilities should be required to charge a subscription fee like Netflix, not rely on advertising revenue.

The operating licence would include a duty of care to customers. They would be required to produce product impact assessments under which their products would be evaluated for their potential impact on mental health, social isolation, fake news, polarisation and democracy.

3. The EU should create a new directorate to oversee these companies.

In November 2020 Thierry Breton, EU Commissioner for the Internal Market, warned that EU citizens expect to benefit more not less from the full potential of online activities and that the internet cannot remain the 'wild west'. Speaking ahead of the announcement of new rules outlining how tech companies will be expected to share their data with rivals and regulators, he warned the tech giants not to market their products in an anticompetitive way. He said he intended to increase the EU's power to stop unfair behaviour from the gatekeeper platforms with a view to ensuring the benefits flow to SMEs and entrepreneurs, not just a handful of large companies. Also in November, India introduced new measures to cap the volume of payments that could be handled by Google Pay and PhonePe. Facebook-owned WhatsApp was also curbed. The measures were presented as an attempt to avoid the duopoly position that has developed in China (albeit involving domestic companies Alipay and WeChatPay).

McNamee offers two explanations as to why governments and regulators have been so slow to act. First, he says that the popular misconceptions about why regulation is ineffective for technology industries are exactly the arguments that big tech companies have successfully used in the United States: that regulations cannot keep pace with rapidly advancing technology, that regulation tends to stifle innovation, and that regulators don't understand the technicalities to be in a position to provide effective oversight.[14] Moreover, big tech argues that the market, if left to its own devices, will always allocate resources best. But this does not take market failure – like that which we have seen – into consideration. Regulation is meant to address market failures.

I have constantly asked myself whether I am being too negative in this book. Of course, during Covid I could easily argue that I was outdone by the social media in the UK with their constant barrage of negativity on that front! I have tried to reference the many obvious benefits and positives that technology has brought us. I remain positive about the potential for technology to deliver good, but I remain more firmly convinced than ever that society is naive about the downside of the technology which brought so many positives and that more regulation is required. I am not alone. In a March 2019 survey by YouGov of Brits, 40 per cent of respondents said they were somewhat or very pessimistic about the effects of the internet on society, and only 25 per cent said they were somewhat or very optimistic.

OFCOM, the UK media regulator, published 'Online nation' in 2019 and concluded that while 59 per cent of internet users agree that the benefits of going online outweigh the risk, most also have concerns about being online. Fifty-three per cent strongly agreed they are concerned about the internet. Sixty-one per cent of adults and 79 per cent of 12–15-year-olds said they had had a potentially harmful experience online in the previous twelve months. Eighty-three per cent of adults expressed concern about harms to children on the internet including abusive behaviour or threats (55 per cent), exposure to inappropriate content including pornography (49 per cent), violent/disturbing content (46 per cent) and content promoting self-harm (42 per cent). Twenty-eight per cent of 12–15-year-olds said they had had unwelcome friend or follow requests or unwelcome contact; 23 per cent had experienced bullying, abusive behaviour or threats; 20 per cent had been trolled; and 19 per cent had experienced someone pretending to be someone else. Fifteen per cent said they had viewed violent or disturbing content, and Facebook was the most commonly mentioned source of most of the potentially harmful experiences. Only around 25 to 30 per cent of adults trusted Facebook to protect them from offensive content, to weed out misleading information and to use their data responsibly, with only marginally higher percentages for YouTube, Instagram, Twitter and Snapchat.

Seventy per cent of adults said they would support more regulation of social media, 64 per cent said the same for video sharing sites and 61 per cent for messaging services. Support for more regulation had increased substantially since the previous survey. Google and Facebook generated an estimated 61 per cent of UK online advertising revenue in 2018, outsized relative to their viewing share of about 35 per cent. Figures for trust in online services to protect user data, or use it responsibly, however, were only 31 per cent for Facebook and 34 per cent for YouTube compared to the BBC at 67 per cent.

Let's address two big elephants in the room: the ability to be anonymous on the web and the lack of effective age verification by most tech platforms. We don't allow kids into casinos or to buy alcohol or cigarettes without ID in most of the world. Yet we allow children onto the internet, with all the dangers I have outlined, largely unchecked. And we allow adults to pose as children on the internet. If a fifty-year-old man appeared outside a junior school playground dressed as a teenager, he would probably be spotted, questioned and moved on or arrested pretty quickly. On the internet, it's much less likely. If governments and technology firms collaborated to ensure someone was properly identified as themselves on the web and that access to harmful content was limited by age, a very considerable amount of harm could be prevented. I can already hear the web libertarians gasping, but 61 per cent of people want the government to do more to separate what is real and fake on the internet, according to the Reuters Institute. Some UK MPs have recently argued that at least law enforcement should have rights to seek a court order to obtain details of users rapidly from big tech platforms if they have reasonable grounds to suspect users of, for example, hate speech, racism, cyberbullying or CSA.

Generation Z is growing up or has grown up in an era where they could be largely anonymous on the web and gain access to all its content. Despite age-restriction policies set by Facebook, Twitter, Instagram and Snapchat, OFCOM stats also show that 21 per cent of ten-year-olds, 34 per cent of eleven-year-olds and 48 per cent of twelve-year-olds said they had a social media profile, demonstrating that they are either not properly enforced or relatively easily bypassed. The implications for Generation Z are worrying. A quarter of Facebook users between twelve and fifteen said they had recently experienced a potential online harm while on the site (followed by 12 per cent for Instagram and 8 per cent for Snapchat), and the same proportion had taken action to report harmful content they had seen online. Twenty-three per cent of adults did not trust websites and social media sites to remove illegal, offensive or harmful material quickly. And almost all the most recent potential online harms experienced by both children and adults were most likely to be from someone they didn't know personally.

Big tech companies could more rigorously police their own minimum age policies. Many studies have demonstrated widespread underage internet engagement. While some argue that it is difficult to identify underage users, I respectfully disagree. Given the remarkable developments in AI that large tech companies have embraced when it comes to boosting their profits, it seems reasonable to suggest that these same tools could be used in most cases to identify users under a certain age limit. GAP believes that big tech companies must ensure they comply with laws which outlaw targeted advertising to under-thirteens and should turn off behavioural advertising for all children who self-identify as under eighteen, and urges UK regulators to take urgent action to enforce the existing Data Protection

Act and GDPR rules to penalise non-compliance with existing laws. GAP notes the $170 million settlement by YouTube of a complaint by the US Federal Trade Commission in 2019, where it was found to be unlawfully collecting under-thirteens' data and making it available to advertisers, and observes that whilst the settlement amount was nowhere near commensurate with the scale of the problem, it did demonstrate that platforms are capable of acting when forced.

So, what's the answer? Delete all your social media accounts? The first thing Generation Z could do is to go 'on strike' and stop using the services of the existing dominant platforms. Lanier offers up this suggestion in his book *Ten Reasons to Delete All Your Social Media Accounts Right Now*. His argument is that if enough people did this, Facebook and Google would have to redesign their services to be less adversarial to our interests as a society. He is realistic, however. 'Your goal,' he says, 'should not necessarily be to force governments to regulate or even nationalise Facebook before you rejoin, or to force Facebook to change its business model, even though these are achievements that must precede the long-term survival of our species.'[15] Instead, the goal should be to maintain some semblance of autonomy even in the face of encroachment by these gargantuan tech companies. We will never know how many people deleted their accounts after Lanier published his book. But realistically it is difficult to see a scenario where people can strike against the giants like Google and Facebook (and the other platforms they own). They are too embedded in our lives.

'Responsible' or 'sustainable' internet education and device use is a more realistic option. This is sometimes called digital citizenship. An effective approach would need to recognise that different age groups face different risks, and it may be necessary to create age-appropriate dedicated areas of the web. Historically, teenagers have been viewed as one cohort. In fact, to design appropriate safeguards for teenagers, one would need to recognise that there are several phases adolescents go through as they start to use the internet and then become more experienced. In early adolescence, teenagers gain their first exposure to social media. They are by definition naive as to what to expect, and their peers are in discovery too. They may at this stage be particularly vulnerable to emerging mental health issues and may not be prevented from access to adult content by virtue of having bypassed age restriction policies. Later in adolescence, they may be more experienced about what to expect on social media, have developed a more streetwise approach, be more suspicious, resilient and have equally experienced peer groups to support them.

Let's face it, most parents are concerned by what their teens are doing online, but don't use any kind of monitoring or tracking device or service to see what their children are doing. Have you ever really thought about the risks posed to your children by people being anonymous on the web and ineffective age verification? Sleepwalking into the tech traps prepared for them, parents have unwittingly become *under-protective*. He goes insane if I take his PlayStation away from him. He has to go to bed with his iPhone to get to sleep. He says he won't know how to contact his real friends if I delete his Snapchat account.

Nearly half of all eleven-year-olds are routinely tracked and profiled on social media, according to a recent GAP report. It links widespread non-compliance with the UK law outlawing targeted advertising to under-thirteens with parental ignorance as the causes. Emery White suggests that we have a parenting culture today 'that is less protective than at any other time in recent history'.[16] The result may be that childhood innocence evaporates too soon. How can you realistically protect innocence when children are in effect using adult devices? As we have seen, the founders of tech companies understand the risks and have their own restrictive rules for their own children, and this should raise a very large red flag for the rest of us. As Neil Postman put it, 'In having access to the previously hidden fruits of adult information, the child is expelled from the garden of childhood.'[17] A Common Sense Media survey in 2018 found that 54 per cent of teens surveyed said that if parents knew what actually happens on social media, they'd be a lot more worried about it.[18]

While we might not like to admit it, are we, as parents, not hypocrites when it comes to tech? Remember the adage 'Do as I say not as I do'? We have a saying in our house which is coined by whichever of us isn't, for once, on their device, to embarrass the rest of the family: 'Three out of four devices …' Haven't we then created the problem of internet overuse in our children? We bring work home with us, and most of us are not good role models for our children. Psychologist Catherine Steiner-Adair vividly describes how parents' overuse of technology affects kids in *The Big Disconnect*: 'The message we communicate with our preoccupation and responsiveness to calls and email is: Everybody else matters more than you. Everything else matters more than you. Whatever the caller may say is more important than what you are telling me now.'[19] When this happens day after day, kids are likely to 'check out' of their families. They may live at home, but they begin to look elsewhere for entertainment – often in technology. We need to learn our own rules for responsible internet use and apply them equally as we try to guide our children.

Children have always competed for their parents' attention, but this generation has experienced something new – tech, distracting them and their parents. It is our responsibility as parents to ensure that we are not only spatially, but also mindfully, close to our children. It is worth the hard work (or the disconnection from our devices) to get this right. Alter advances that 'if our culture makes space for work-free, game-free, screen-free downtime, we and our children will find it easier to resist the lure of behavioural addiction … we'll communicate with one another directly, rather than through devices, and the glow of these social bonds will leave us richer and happier than the glow of screens ever could'.[20]

Paediatric doctors' professional bodies have long made recommendations about limiting screen time. For example, the American Association of Paediatrics advises against exposing children to *any* screen media before they are two, and to limit screen exposure to 1–2 hours a day for children older than two. There are suggested limits for older children. But a better approach would surely be to focus on educating kids to use technology, which is now central in our lives and here for good whether we like it or not, for positive purposes. We should also aim to understand more about what kids are doing while they are online, not how much time they spend there. Professor in the department of Media and Communications at the LSE Sonia Livingstone and Alice Blum-Ross, Lead for Kids and Families at Google, have undertaken extensive research on family dynamics relating to tech use. In their recent book *Parenting for a Digital Future*, they identify three typical ways in which parents react to technology – either to embrace it (using it to ease family life and future ready their children), to resist it (attempting to limit its use at home), or to attempt to balance its use by encouraging some good digital practices and discouraging others. They contend that it would be too simple to view limiting screen time as a parental success. Rather than 'police and restrict' children's use of digital media, parents need to understand the 'contexts, content and connections' that are involved and so help their children to 'learn, connect and create through, about and beyond digital media'. They also identify that families have become more democratic in their decision making as parental authority has declined, and that 'negotiation', the act of policing and restricting access to kids' devices, has become a central part of family life. This can amplify rather than ease family tensions, as it runs against the trend towards respecting children's right to make decisions as individuals. This makes parenting much harder, since applying judgement about when digital access should be allowed or encouraged requires more effort than simply limiting screen time.[21]

It seems insane to me that we teach sex education to kids in schools, but that in most countries, including ours, teaching responsible internet use is not part of the core curriculum. And this education needs to not only cover the dangers of social media, gaming and device addiction, but also address dating apps, sexting, pornography and the hookup culture. Parents need to talk to their children not just about 'the birds and the bees', but the importance of dating rather than hooking up, the value of loving relationships and the dangers of gaming and porn.

Freddie Pearson, the twenty-one-year-old influencer, says of responsible internet use, 'for something that has become such a central part of the way we live our lives, it is frightening how little education there is on the subject'.

In September 2020 HM Government introduced new relationship education guidance which is now compulsory for primary schools in the UK. It is designed to put in place the building blocks needed for positive and safe relationships. It will start with family and friends, how to treat each other with kindness *and recognise the differences between online and offline relationships.* Whilst UK parents have a right to withdraw their children from sex education, they will have no such right in relation to relationship education.

An expert US panel delivered the following guidelines for parents who want to protect their children:

1. Use technical mediation – parental controls, content filters, PINs and safe search, which restricts searching to age-appropriate sites.
2. Talk regularly to your children about managing online risks.
3. Set rules or restrictions around online access and use.
4. Supervise your children when they are online.

These incredibly simple rules, which are common sense, could be most valuable if we all had the willpower to implement them.

Alberto, twenty-one, says, 'For those who have thought it OK to place their children in front of a screen in order not to dedicate so much needed attention, it is time to recognise that effective parenting requires sacrifice. A good example must be set from above. If parents do not help us with this battle, the war against technology addiction is lost.'

For older children, Aiken offers this practical advice for parents:

1. Ask them about their real-world day, and don't forget to ask them about what's happening in their cyber life.
2. Tell them about risks in the real world, accompanied by real stories – then tell them about evolving risks online, and how to not show vulnerability.
3. Talk about identity formation and what it means – distinguishing between the real-world self and the cyber self.
4. Talk about body dysmorphia, eating disorders, body image and self-esteem – and the ways their technology use may not be constructive.[22]

When Gen Z leaves home and begins negotiating relationships at university, all sorts of behaviours commonplace on the internet, but which are *not* acceptable on campus, have led to a substantial rise in sexual assault charges. In 2018 there were 626 alleged cases of sexual assault at British universities, up from 65 in 2014.[23]

I am not so deluded as to believe that even the most diligent and disciplined parents and youngsters will succeed in perfectly responsible internet use on a sustained basis without help from device designers and some regulation. As Freed says, it's 'illogical to believe that children can protect themselves from rooms filled with neuroscientists who use lab tested techniques to keep kids staring at screens'.[24]

It certainly seems naive to expect companies to 'self-regulate, or voluntarily refrain from producing the full effects they're organisationally structured and financially incentivised to produce'.[25] As such, our objective instead must be to move big tech away from capturing our *at*tention towards supporting our *in*tentions. 'We have an obligation to rewire this system of intelligent persuasion before it rewires us,' Williams suggests.[26] 'Doing so requires hacking together new ways of talking and thinking about the problem as well as summoning the courage necessary for advancing on it in inconvenient and unpopular ways.'[27] He is right, because the harms which technology creates are not capable of being categorised with well-known harms, like monopoly or invasion of privacy, and cannot therefore be remedied with existing forms of remedy. 'The new harms we face entail challenges to the sanctity of the individual, and chief among these challenges I count the elemental rights that bear on individual sovereignty, including the right to the future tense and the right to sanctuary,' says Zuboff.[28]

So, what else might the big tech companies and product and service designers do to be more responsible? Bill Davidow says in his *Atlantic* article entitled 'Exploiting the neuroscience of internet addiction' that tech executives are presently faced with 'an interesting, if also morally questionable, imperative; either they hijack neuroscience to gain market share and make large profits, or they let their competitors do that and run away with the market'.[29] While this may be valid in the short term, I believe that if the businesses of these companies are to be sustainable, they will need to examine their own backyards very carefully and modify some of their behaviours.

I am on the phone to Paulo, talking about the book. He works for a leading gaming manufacturer as a designer, and I want his take on my concerns. As I talk about the risks of gaming, he confides in me that he is thinking of leaving his employer. He says, 'I am just not comfortable any more taking a bonus which is dependent on achieving higher levels of addiction to our products in children.'

The key corporate responsibility business coalitions should be pursuing a responsible technology agenda. Business for Social Responsibility

(BSR) and the World Business Council for Sustainable Development could both usefully take leadership positions to put pressure on technology businesses to behave more responsibly.

In the institutional investment world, there is an organisation called the UN PRI. PRI stands for Principles for Responsible Investing. Asset managers around the world sign up voluntarily to only invest their customers' funds in line with the PRI, which broadly support the UN's sustainable development goals. Interestingly, there is no principle relating to the sustainable development goal surrounding health and wellbeing. I argue that the PRI should be amended to include a requirement on companies to commission independent impact assessments on their products and services in order to demonstrate how they measure and address any negative effects on their customers, or society more generally. This could establish once and for all whether compulsive attraction to social media or video gaming is as damaging as addiction to alcohol or cigarettes.

Some technology products and services are addictive by design. If the boards of the companies who commission these designs decline to reform their approach, then it falls to the design industry itself to take a stand. There is a growing interest in the academic field of design ethics, which would add a useful perspective to the creation of a global internet code of design conduct. Indeed the EU Ethics Advisory Group says it is important to begin regulation at the design stage, as digital ethics that come after the fact have wasted an opportunity to inform and shape the world. The Group notes that a design perspective in digital ethics would help overcome the problem because it would insert moral considerations, at the point in which they can make a significant difference, with lower costs and risks. While technology companies often justify their design decisions by purporting that they are giving customers what they want, Williams posits that they are more often than not giving customers what they '*want their customers to want*'.[30]

Creating a code of conduct for ethical design is Wu's suggestion, as well as the implementation of an oath that individual designers might make on qualification. The oath could include an undertaking to consider potential negative effects on consumers, or even go as far as to rule out designing products to be addictive. This is not as far flung as it may seem; in fact, the Dutch have a similar idea in the banking industry. Every new banker swears a personal oath that requires them to act ethically and with care at all times, to carefully balance the interests of all stakeholders (including shareholders, customers, employees and society), to keep client information confidential and not abuse it and to always act to promote trust in the banking industry. The oath is supervised by an independent authority; breach of the oath is a criminal offence. Professional design bodies globally could work with their local governments to implement similar schemes. Livingstone and Blum-Ross argue strongly that whilst it's time to implement and ensure compliance for children-appropriate and family-friendly design, parents need to be centrally involved in the policy development to help ensure the right conclusions are reached about which design features can promote opportunities and which impede or detract from them, and that such policy development needs to be based on the evidence available already about parenting, parental mediation and family dynamics.

The organisation Computer Professionals for Social Responsibility (CPSR) produced an interesting paper on the potential for producing socially responsible video games. It asks explicitly what 'socially responsible video games' might be able to achieve and concludes that they could improve cognitive skills, including memorisation of spelling and multiplication tables, as well as deeper skills such as analysis, interpretation or evaluation. Another possibility is leveraging virtual reality within video games to develop empathy, for example, giving users the opportunity to 'experience' delivering supplies to refugees in a war zone. Interestingly, during Covid-19, the UK games industry, led by Xbox, teamed up with the UK government to get critical public health messages into more UK households by placing them in games. The global games industry supported the World Health Organisation by promoting awareness measures and practices, including social distancing, in a similar way. In clinical research, AI and machine learning, developed initially for use by the games industry, has been used in the mobile game Sea Hero Quest to advance understanding of dementia. And UKIE has led a Digital Schoolhouse Programme to support teachers in their delivery of the computer science curriculum. All important, given that a recent government report found that 21 per cent of people in the UK lack full basic digital skills, part of the widely reported tech skills gap.

Ultimately, however, more and better technology regulation may be the only comprehensive solution. Though big tech companies have been granted ample opportunities to self-regulate, many feel they have failed repeatedly to pick up on public and political reaction to harms caused by their services. As McNamee says of Facebook, 'Facebook owes a duty to its users – and the whole world – to optimise itself for the public good, not just for profits. If Facebook can't do that – and the evidence at this point is not promising – then government intervention to reduce its market power and introduce competition will be required.'[31]

'Surveillance capitalist leaders assume that we will succumb to the naturalistic fallacy,' Zuboff argues.[32] And because surveillance capital has succeeded, the assumption is that 'its rules must obviously be right and good'.[33] But whereas men and women made the rules and can control them, they have chosen not to do so. Wu concurs with this assessment, positing that 'if the attention economy is to work to our benefit (and not just exploit us), we need to be vigilant about its operation and active in expressing our displeasure about its degrading tendencies ... its worst excesses may have no remedy but law'.[34]

The growing prospect of internationally coordinated regulation has spurred reactions from big tech companies, some of which may be designed to seek to make new regulation appear to be less necessary, whilst not comprehensively addressing the issues. In 2006 the Technology Coalition was formed to seek to eradicate child abuse through platforms. In 2008 the Global Network Initiative was formed and includes Facebook, Google and Microsoft, who, along with leading civic society organisations, have developed a number of high-level principles based on international human rights for each organisation to implement. In 2019 Google announced a proposal to 'give users more transparency, choice and control over how their data is used in digital advertising'. Facebook is in the process of setting up its own social media council, or Oversight Board. According to Zuckerberg, this board will serve as Facebook's Supreme Court, an analogy that doesn't hold up to scrutiny, since it will only issue recommendations to Facebook on content policy, which Facebook can ignore, subject to an explanation as to why it decided not to comply. Decisions on individual users' content appeals, however, will be binding. The board will be funded by a foundation, albeit funded from Facebook, and will choose its own subjects to investigate. Board members can only be fired for breach of a code of conduct, not for making decisions Facebook doesn't like. It looks like a good step forward, but the members of the first board will define its likely success or failure. Alan Rusbridger, former editor of the UK's *Guardian*, told *Metro UK* that it had taken too long to create such a system for moderating content but that he was pleased such a body was now in place. 'We are living in a world of information chaos and standing on the precipice of darkness. Societies can't function unless their citizens can agree on what constitutes evidence, fact and truth,' he said. 'The Oversight Board seems to be the first imaginative and bold step by one of the major players to find a way of reconciling the need to start imposing some kind of judgement and standards on what is published.'

Media manipulation experts remain critical. Joan Davison of the Harvard Shorenstein Centre said in the *Guardian* that the Oversight Board is ultimately a distraction from 'what really needs to happen, which is to design technology that doesn't allow for the expansive amplification of disinformation'.[35] As Carole Cadwalladr, the author who investigated the involvement of Cambridge Analytica in posting campaigns on Facebook during the Brexit referendum, said, 'democracy is not guaranteed, and it is not inevitable ... and we cannot let these tech companies have this unchecked power. It's up to us; you; me and all of us. We are the ones who have to take back control.'[36]

Siva Vaidhyanthanan, University of Virginia Professor of Media Studies, says, 'I wish I could say that the Facebook review board was cosmetic, but I am not sure it's even that deep ... this is greenwashing.'[37] She also notes that the real power of Facebook is to amplify some content over other content, and points out that the Oversight Board's remit will not extend to retuning Facebook's algorithms which drive this process. In October 2020, the Citizens, a US charity, decided that since Facebook's Oversight Board would not be fully operational for the November US presidential election, they would form an alternative Oversight Board. They have dubbed it the *Real* Facebook Oversight Board: it comprises some of Facebook's most vocal critics and it analysed and criticised Facebook's role in that election. In December 2020, Jason Kint, CEO of Digital Content Next, tweeted 'Seriously, Facebook couldn't be a bigger embarrassment to our industry. Imagine issuing a 20 page self-assessment of the 2020 US election that mentions fraud twice, Trump once, micro-targeting in all forms zero times... What's the point? Propaganda'.

Social media councils and content moderation processes need more public scrutiny. Experts have largely maligned the opacity of the processes by which most social media companies moderate the content on their sites. In effect, there is a corporate 'censorship' process which is run by the site operators; the question, of course, is whether these censorship guidelines privilege the good of society or the bottom line of the companies. Armies of content moderators the world over, in what is now a substantial unregulated global industry, take minute-by-minute decisions on whether to allow individual user-generated posts. Much has been written about the negative effects on the mental wellbeing of those who do this difficult job. The decisions which content moderators take affect what the site users and ultimately society see and form the basis of public discourse. Roberts observes that this gives the platforms and the content moderators who work for them an outsized role in affecting discourse on politics and global conflicts.[38] I can't help but think that if governments were doing the censoring, it would be immediately condemned. Why, then, are we happy for individuals we don't know, operating under guidance we haven't seen, to be taking decisions of such potential consequence? In my opinion, we shouldn't be. Nor can we safely assume that platforms will consistently enforce their own community guidelines.

Encourage users to insist on responsible technology, particularly given that self-regulation by companies rarely cures the problem comprehensively. 'As we live longer and longer in the digital world and learn more, there will be a growing number who see past the obfuscation ... this is where the voice of Responsible Tech makes itself naggingly insistent,' writes Bradfield.[39] PwC defines responsible technology as that which maximises the positive impacts whilst minimising the negative ones and says it emanates from purpose – to build trust in society and solve important problems, align with our values and intent to act with integrity whilst reimagining the possible. Bradfield says, 'Responsible Tech is not only respect for our customers, but respect for the world at large, respect for previous traditions and modes of interacting with others, respect for the beauty of privacy, of sanctuary, of core human values that can never be disrupted, trampled and scorned … it's an acknowledgment that self-regulation often only helps the self-regulators.'[40] PwC has developed a comprehensive responsible technology policy which incorporates a recognition of human rights, privacy and security and has regard for mental and physical wellbeing.

'The liberation of human attention may be the defining moral and political struggle of our time,' argues Williams.[41] At the end of the day, the ongoing struggle is one that revolves around trust. As McNamee notes, 'Technology platforms like Facebook and Google are the beneficiaries of trust and goodwill accumulated over 50 years by earlier generations of technology companies. They have taken advantage of our trust, using sophisticated techniques to prey on the weakest aspects of human psychology, to gather and exploit private data, and to craft business models that do not protect users from harm.'[42] As a result, we must now remain vigilant and indeed sceptical about the products we use, taking the initiative to change our online behaviour and force platforms to act responsibly when faced with the potential impact of their actions.

Part of the challenge of recognising the problems of technology is the high value we place on the benefits derived from it. It is the addiction we develop to our devices that pits our wish for an easy life against what we know to be an incursion into our privacy in a losing battle. We are back to the words convenience and efficiency, which underlie Generation Z's approach to life and which have led to them expecting life to be on demand with one click. 'This conflict produces a psychic numbing that inures us to the realities of being tracked, parsed, minded and modified,'[43] says Zuboff. We rationalise it away with excuses like 'I have nothing to hide,' or 'It just makes life more convenient, so it's worth it.'[44] In this way, Zuboff argues, 'Surveillance capitalism imposes a fundamentally illegitimate choice that twenty first century individuals should not have to make, and its normalization leaves us singing in chains.'[45]

China comprehensively regulates how its internet platforms may operate. While the original intention may have been to censor material deemed unhelpful to the ruling regime, there are other aspects to the regulation which are interesting. Online platforms must verify the identities of users, meaning in theory there can be no fakes or anonymity. Content producers must employ measures to prevent and resist the making, reproduction or publication of what the government believes to be negative information. This includes anything with sexual innuendo, gore or horror. Platforms are made responsible for policing these restrictions and must create mechanisms for reviewing content and real-time inspections. Those who host public social media accounts or host chat rooms are liable for their content. Failure to comply can lead to fines or revocation of operating licences. Managers must be designated for these activities and have personal responsibility. China also has a shutdown law for online gaming which applies between midnight and 6 a.m.

Critics of China's approach focus on the censorship angle and the opaque nature of the content which is forbidden. While I do not seek to defend China's authoritarian control over mass media, there are three aspects of this approach that stand out and may warrant further investigation:

1. No right to anonymity.
2. Clearly outlawed types of content.
3. Corporate and personal accountability for execution of the publisher's responsibilities.

South Korea also has strict internet regulation with interesting features. The authorities reserve the right to block content which is subversive of or harmful to the public order, including pornography, nudity, materials harmful to minors, cyber defamation and sexual violence. They also have a system of real name verification, where so-called netizens are required to prove their identities before contributing to online social media. However, this system has been criticised for certain failures, including anti-pornography measures as well as politicians' abuse of cyber-defamation rules.

Japan's internet is characterised by self-regulation organised principally by non-governmental, non-profit organisations that are supported financially by the internet industry. The ISPs are required to create and operate a self-regulatory framework for take-down requests of illegal or objectionable content. The Content Evaluation and Monitoring Association focuses on mobile content, and the internet Content Safety Association focuses on blocking child pornography. The use of the internet for child pornography or for the solicitation of sex with minors is specifically illegal. Revenge porn take-down requests must be complied with in two days.

In Taiwan, parents can be fined for allowing their children more than reasonable use of the internet.

The bold ambition of the February 2020 UK government white paper was that the UK should aim to be the safest place to go online. The white paper set out plans for a new system of accountability and oversight for tech companies. It also proposed an independent regulator to set clear safety standards, bolstered by reporting requirements and effective enforcement powers. The paper claims that whilst 'other countries have introduced regulations to address specific forms of harm, this is the first attempt globally to address a comprehensive spectrum of online harms in a single and coherent way'.[46]

Critical to the law proposed in the white paper is a new statutory duty of care to make companies responsible for the safety of their users, and to tackle harm caused by content or activity within their services. Companies will be required to demonstrate compliance, and an independent regulator will have powers to enforce action, issue fines and impose liability on individual members of senior management, akin to the Senior Managers Regime now used by the Financial Conduct Authority in financial services. The regulator will require annual transparency reports, in which the companies will have to outline the prevalence of harmful content on their platforms and explain what steps they have taken to address it. The regulator will also have powers to require companies to explain the impact of their algorithms in selecting content for users and to ensure companies proactively report on emerging risks. This will include AI. It will be crucial that data and evidence is collected from the platforms by the regulator to establish exactly what harms are being caused by platforms so that regulation is seen as proportional and necessary. As the NSPCC observes in its report 'Taming the Wild West Web', 'Given their inherent reluctance to share data, social media companies arguably frustrate the development of evidence-based understandings of the impact of children using their sites. As a result, it is likely to prove impossible to fully understand the scale and extent of online harms until and unless a regulator exists and has the information disclosure powers to compel firms to disclose data to it.'[47]

The UK's proposals go well beyond anything implemented almost anywhere in the world and for this the government and in particular Jeremy Wright MP, Secretary of State for DCMS at the time much of the preparation was done, deserves credit. My hope is that the white paper is implemented without being rendered toothless by tech lobbyists, and that its success can then be assessed to determine the degree to which other countries can create similar measures.

Despite its triumphs, the white paper lacks a number of features that would have made its impact even more likely to be a resounding success. It does not include the need to identify yourself and therefore it will not prevent anonymity; we have seen how fakes play an outsized role in many of the worse harms – including child sexual abuse, harassment, intimidation, bullying and fake news. It is important to note that having to identify yourself would not mean you would have to publicly disclose your identity online – something which runs counter to privacy lobby views and would be highly problematic to achieve. What it would mean is that you would have to identify yourself accurately to the platform with which you had the accounts making the posts. This would still be enough, however, to deter much of the worst behaviours, and I struggle to see how any reasonable person could justifiably object. Neither does the white paper impose a minimum age on the right to access services, in stark contrast to law and regulation of other dangerous activities. Contrast this with the banking industry, which requires 'Know Your Client' (KYC) procedures to regulate users. Typically, users are required to produce a passport and two recent utility bills from their home address. This means the bank knows with reasonable certainty a customer's identity, age and home address. KYC protocols would stop both fakes and children opening accounts at too young an age, and might make some people think twice before they post hate speech, bully someone, post sexually explicit material or commit child sex abuse. Finally, the bill does not include online fraud in the list of harms for which the platforms will have responsibility. We know that many of the drivers of fraud sit outside the financial system in e-commerce platforms, for example. Whilst the financial sector pays big tech to carry adverts to inform the public about how to avoid fraud, those same companies benefit from revenue from adverts placed by fraudsters to attract money mules and promote fake investment companies.

Producing an age-appropriate design code was a key provision of the UK Data Protection Act of 2018. Specifically aimed at services likely to be used by children, it is meant to ensure 'information society services' put child user interests at the heart of their design process. At the time of writing, this code has been drafted and laid before Parliament for debate and approval. It is bold in its approach and will require providers to consider how, in their use of children's personal data, they can:

1. keep children safe from exploitation (including commercial or sexual);
2. protect and support children's health and wellbeing;
3. protect and support children's physical, psychological and emotional development;
4. protect and support children's need to develop their own views and identity;
5. protect children's right to freedom of association and play;
6. support the needs of children with disabilities;
7. recognise the role of parents in promoting the best interests of children;
8. recognise the evolving capacity of children to form their own views.

The code will cover search engines, apps, video games, internet-connected toys and home devices and as a result includes devices which could be watching or listening to the child.

At its heart, the code requires providers to perform Data Protection Impact Assessments of their products. Default settings need to be on the highest level of privacy, and the repercussions of any attempted movement from this default must be carefully explained to the child. The process of achieving age-appropriate design, of course, requires the provider to know the child's age. Since KYC type processes are not mandatory, the provider is allowed to use self-declaration practices, AI-deduced age, third-party verification, account holder confirmation of the child's age or hard identifiers (e.g. passport); while the choice of source is up to the provider, it must be justified against the risk assessment.

Breach of the code can lead to fines which are potentially very meaningful, depending on the ICO's assessment of the risks which were found not to be appropriately mitigated. This will be a massive exercise for the providers and should lead to some very substantive new protections. Early indications are that the first drafts need improving to take more account of the different protections needed for children of different ages rather than assuming they can be grouped into large age group categories.

Big tech platforms have done the bare minimum to comply with GDPR, according to McNamee, and the ICO will therefore need to be proactive in supervision and enforcement of these new measures.[48] Some early interventions and large fines may be required to ensure that the providers smell the coffee. The code may provide a useful template for other governments to roll out similar protections – and it has the useful imprimatur of being based on the UN's Convention on the Rights of Children (UNCRC).

In 2019 UNICEF produced a definitive report on children's rights in relation to the global video gaming industry, in which it makes a series of excellent recommendations. There are individual recommendations for game developers, game publishers, game distributors and users addressing the most egregious dangers.[49] They centre on recognising that those under eighteen and those who supervise them need more protection and support. In summary, they would attack inappropriate behaviours, toxic environments, loot boxes, explicit content and reduce the risk of kids using games which are not healthy or which could be harmful.

I believe national governments should enshrine measures based on these recommendations into law where possible. The new UK government's bill's scope could usefully incorporate UNICEF's guidelines as the basis for the regulator's guidelines on responsible industry behaviour. As it is, many countries don't even have age ratings for entertainment technology that are independently assigned and legally binding. In the US, the ratings of the Entertainment Software Rating Board are not enforced under federal law; within the EU, the Pan European Game Information (PEGI) guidelines are not law in many countries, and it remains opaque as to how the system is actually applied online.

Aiken has argued that we should have a kind of Magna Carta for the web; in particular, she focuses on children's rights. At the Hague in 2015 she formally proposed a new amendment to the UN Convention that would protect children's rights specifically in the cyberspace context. She asks, 'When a child sees pornography, violence, decapitation, suicide, cutting, or bulimia, who is responsbile?' Whether the answer is the platform, the software designer or the ISP, Aiken believes that all complicit should be held accountable legally, morally and ethically.

In 2020, Aiken and her colleague, Professor Julia Davidson, were expert advisors for the UK government's Department of Digital, Culture, Media and Sport report on online safety technologies.[50] I interviewed her as I was completing this book, and she explained to me that whilst traditional cyber security focuses on protecting data and information, cyber safety focuses on protecting people online – the 'internet of humans', as she calls it. 'Your data does not suffer from low self-esteem, self-harm or suicidial ideation; your data does not become depressed or seek revenge,' she says. This is where online safety technology solutions or "Safety Tech" can excel, bringing responsible safety-by-design to software platforms and putting the users' interests ahead of the profits of the platform. She is quite clear: it's not that technology is good or bad; it is designed and then used, well or poorly, by humans. Aiken is one of the pioneers of the emerging Safety Tech sector, which has the potential to provide tech solutions to tech-facilitated problems and criminal behaviours at scale. Her vision and latest mission are to promote global expertise in online safety technologies and in doing so 'help to create a safer and more secure cyberspace, and in doing so, a better cybersociety.'

Sir Tim Berners-Lee, who was heavily involved in the invention and development of the internet, has created an organisation called Contract for the Web. While his initial hope for the web was that it would be used primarily to serve humanity, Berners-Lee believes that this has not exactly come to fruition. Instead, disinformation is peddled online, stalkers harass and intimidate victims, and bad actors subvert democracy. 'We're at a tipping point,' he notes. 'How we respond to this abuse will determine whether the web lives up to its potential as a global force for good or leads us into a digital dystopia.'[51] Berners-Lee argues that we need to overcome the stalemate that has blocked previous attempts to solve the problems facing the web, including governments blaming platforms for inaction, and companies not being constructive about shaping future regulation. A number of governments, including France, Germany and Ghana, have signed up to the core tenets of the contract, which include: *governments* to ensure everyone can connect to the internet, keep all of the internet available all of the time and respect and protect people's fundamental online privacy and data rights; *companies* to make the internet affordable and accessible to everyone, respect and protect people's privacy and personal data to build online trust and develop technologies that support the best in humanity and challenge the worst; *citizens* to be creators and collaborators on the web, build strong communities that respect civil discourse and human dignity and fight for the web. The World Wide Web Foundation will monitor progress and call out inaction.

Some have suggested that anyone using our data should pay us for it. Apps like Digime have been designed to prevent consumers giving away their data without explicit consent. Data is encrypted with a set of keys and ciphers equivalent to those of banks and the military. Your data can only be viewed and shared when you are logged into the app and give explicit consent.

Is data the new oil? Data was famously described by customer data expert Clive Humby (inventor of the Tesco Club Card) as the next precious natural resource. Dataeconomy believes that as blockchain and decentralised marketplaces develop, people will be able to take more control of and monetise their data. Wibson, a blockchain-based decentralised marketplace, has estimated that the average US consumer could earn at least $240 a year by monetising their data and potentially very much more.[52] Lanier says, 'even if moral automation could be implemented, it might still be necessary to appeal to the old demigod of economic incentives'.[53] We could also move to a model where, instead of free access, we could pay big tech companies for a premium service that prevents our data from being harvested.

Data as labour is the notion Lanier floats in his book *Who Owns the Future?* He and others worry that giving our data away free will both exacerbate unemployment in a world of AI and lead to some data not being available, hindering the potential productivity growth available from AI. Data labour unions need to be established to restore some power to citizens by representing their collective interests against the monopsonies, he posits. Posner and Weyl point out that the share of both value and income paid to employees of big tech companies is a fraction of what it is in most other businesses. That, of course, they point out, is because these companies are getting a lot of 'free work' from us – their customers – in the form of our data. In fact, the authors note, 'the share of income going to labor in the largest tech companies is roughly 5 to 15 per cent lower than in any industry other than extractive ones such as oil, and dramatically lower than service-sector companies like Walmart, where labor's share is roughly 80 per cent'.[54] As a further illustration, they observe that YouTube says it uploads 300 hours of video from user content creators every minute, but 'a typical content creator receives $2 for every 1,000 views of a video'.[55] Conversely, Netflix makes about half a cent per minute, or ten times as much as these content creators.[56]

Tim Berners-Lee has teamed up with a twenty-four-person startup in Boston called Inrupt to 'right ways up' the web. Based around a new open-source engine called Solid, users will be given control over their own data. They will decide who accesses their data, for what purposes, and have the option to charge for its use. Inrupt is already working with the NHS in the UK and has pilots with several other major enterprises involving tens of millions of users.

Perhaps we should have a right not to have our attention distracted, just as we have a right not to have our property trespassed upon. Perhaps if we do, the 'interrupter' should have to buy 'attention offsets' like plastic packaging manufacturers have to buy Plastic Recycling Notes in the UK. Receipts from the offsets could be used to fund research on the mental health and wellbeing effects of technology or to fund behavioural addiction rehab clinics. Williams argues that today we have, in effect, an attentional tax imposed on us by big tech companies, but we have no collective representation about how it is spent.

A parallel may be drawn with the world's oceans. Following moves by individual countries to claim territorial waters, in 1982, an international treaty set out principles whereby countries would own 12 nautical miles immediately offshore and up to 200 miles offshore for economic purposes. Perhaps a new global internet treaty could establish guidelines for the notional use of our attention, including a mechanism to charge for it, and rules under which it could be used. I would argue that the sum of human attention is worth every bit as much as territorial waters. Today it has been hijacked by pirates, and we need to return it to its rightful owners – us.

A simpler and blunter instrument that has been proposed is a tax on big tech companies. In the UK, after the GFC, the government imposed a bank levy on UK banks as a means to ensure they contributed to the rebuilding of the economy after the crisis. In the UK, the government has imposed a digital tax of 2 per cent on the revenues of certain big tech companies, including search engines, social media services and online marketplaces. The tax is intended as a stopgap until the OECD agrees new international arrangements to ensure big tech companies pay appropriate taxes globally, and cannot hide profits in low-tax jurisdictions. Fair Tax Mark, a US watchdog, said in 2020, 'Our analysis of the long run effective tax rate of the Silicon Valley six over the decade to date has found there is a significant difference between the cash taxes paid and both the headline rate of tax and, more significantly, the reported current tax provisions. We conclude that the corporation tax paid has been much lower than is commonly understood.'[57] The companies concerned dispute the findings. The CEO of the Tax Justice Network explains that when multinational corporations abuse their tax responsibilities to society, they weaken the supports that our economies need to work well and create wealth. Imposing additional taxes on big techs might lead to changes in practices at the companies concerned and could provide hypothecated funds to repair damage caused by online harms, but it would not prevent their occurrence, nor would it restore attention to its owners.

So where are we now? Many of the issues I have written about could be resolved by the big tech companies themselves. I believe that the boards of large tech companies must reform their business models. This could usefully start by them enhancing the diversity of their boards of directors. The board of Google, for example, comprises very wealthy business people, including venture capitalists, ex-senior executives and one academic (but in microbiology, not an obviously useful discipline, given the issues raised in this book). Where is the psychologist, where is the digital ethicist, where is the ex-leader of a national child protection charity, where is the mental wellbeing specialist? Not even an ex-media regulator anywhere to be seen. And where is Generation Z? Surely a company with an average employee age of twenty-nine to thirty and whose products play to Generation Z's new value system should have someone on the board younger than forty-seven. By my calculation, the average age of the board is around fifty-nine! I would say this is a company not seeking diversity of challenge at the board. A similar board scenario can be found at Facebook.

When I joined the board of UK Finance as its Founder Chairman, I made it a condition that the board be more than a collection of member representatives. I insisted that we have independent representatives of the values that were important to our members' customers and also included a representative of the consumer, as well as the SME. This, I hoped, would prevent the board from becoming an echo chamber and further ensure that there were qualified people present to challenge the banking and finance industry on its practices and plans. Google and Facebook would do well to consider bringing onto their main boards some independent-minded, non-business people who represent the users that their products and services may harm including some Generation Zers. I hereby offer my services free, though I rather doubt my offer will be taken up.

Eric Schmidt, the former CEO of Google, has predicted that the global internet will split into two within ten years. At last year's World Economic Forum, all the talk was of the internet splitting on the back of US–China tensions. China and surrounding countries would adopt Chinese principles and apps, whereas the Western world would follow the United States. This is of crucial importance because China and the US are locked in a new arms race over AI, which could be the most potent weapon in the developing China–US cold war. China is rapidly developing an alternative to the Global Positioning System (GPS), which locates phones based on their signals and is used for many apps including those for car navigation. China is close to completing its own satellite system for this purpose. Huawei has argued that the Transmission Control Protocol (TCP) and Internet Protocol (IP), on which today's global internet infrastructure is based, are not future-proof and are developing their own, which will be tested in early 2021. China has, of course, banned Google, YouTube, Facebook, Reddit, Instagram and Twitter and according to Hampson and Jardine has 30,000 internet police and 300,000 active internet monitors. It is interesting to note that China has developed a more 'responsible' approach and regulatory regime when it comes to curbing online harms, whilst the US is relatively laissez-faire in its approach to the Web. Must the world really be faced with choosing the lesser of two evils: free speech and full information accompanied by relatively uncurbed exposure to harmful online content, or superior protections accompanied by stringent censorship?

The potential for internet fragmentation does not stop with US–Chinese tensions. Russia and India, two other huge nations, have also opposed the idea of internet governance moving into a UN-based body. Hampson and Jardine observe that this is a response to the real and perceived dominance of current internet governance bodies by the West and the US in particular.

Covid-19 has accelerated both the adoption of digital technology by consumers – home shopping, food delivery and videoconference software – and investment by the big tech companies to fund these technologies. Whilst the traditional business world is in trauma, the big techs continue their relentless path towards unchallengeable scale; the five giants now represent more than 20 per cent of the S&P 500 US stock market index. They are amongst the few companies to have substantially gained from Covid in terms of profit and market capitalisation.

Every anti-trust review and intervention starts with a definition of the market over which a company might or might not be exerting monopolistic influence. The big tech companies will be arguing for the largest possible market definitions to make their market shares look smaller, but hopefully the regulators will be diligent. As Carl Bildt, Chairman of the CIGI, puts it, 'The internet has already become the world's most important infrastructure. But this is only the beginning; soon it will be the infrastructure of all other infrastructures.'

'As we stand on the edge of the IoT revolution, a status quo, steady-as-she-goes public policy approach to these issues is simply not adequate,' say Hampson and Jardine in their book about internet governance, *Look Who's Watching*.[58] Whilst I applaud the UK government's introduction of domestic legislation to address online harms for at least minors, I don't hold out much hope for the US legislature holding big techs to account. And given their bases, the US is where it needs to start to be really effective. Recent US parliamentary hearings have demonstrated that US leaders either don't understand the risks big tech pose, or can't enunciate their understanding in a way which achieves cut-through. Higher salaries in industry than in the public sector will help the private sector stay one step ahead. The enormous power of lobbying in the US will likely ensure the Office of Technology Assessment (OTA), which was put in place between 1972 and 1975 to advise the US government on the complex technology issues of the late twentieth century, will not be reinstated. Interestingly, Hilary Clinton pledged to reinstate it, and Andrew Yang, an early 2020 US presidential candidate, made it an explicit commitment that he would never sign a budget that didn't have funding in it for a replacement of the OTA. Hopefully, Joe Biden will make something similar an early priority for his presidency.

As the power of social media grows ever larger, Zuboff asks, 'Who will stand for freedom now?' She argues that today's digital denizens must 'dare to be the friction that disrupts economies of action that have been carefully, elaborately, and expensively constructed to exploit our natural empathy, elude our awareness, and circumvent our prospects for self-determination'.[59]

In this book, I have sought to pull together the themes which I think reflect the way Generation Z lives. I have looked at the way their behaviours have been impacted by technology, for better or worse. In particular, I have focused on how technology reduces the opportunities to build empathy and have argued that we need to wrest back control of our attention to give us time and space to rebuild empathy at all stages of our lives. This requires us to recognise that our attention has been hijacked by a very small number of powerful companies and that we freely acquiesce to this hijacking. We now need to change our behaviours and demand better: teachers and educators need to provide us with leadership and guidance, corporations need to change their business models, and governments need to act urgently and radically to effect regulatory and anti-trust improvements. The status quo should not be acceptable to anyone. Generation Z, with its new value system, focus on purpose and technology-aided modes of political activism, could act quickly to restore control of attention. Technology can indeed be harnessed to build a better world, one in which empathy flourishes to the benefit of all. But this won't happen unless Generation Z refuses to stand for the world it is being bequeathed, recognises the dangers and acts boldly. In *The Social Dilemma*, Tristan Harris identifies a point in the development of social media, which we have arguably already reached, where big tech *overpowers human weakness*, just before we reach the point where it *overpowers humans themselves*. Going beyond this point, he says, represents 'checkmate on humanity'.

I am sitting with my sons having a drink on holiday. 'So, what have you learned from your research for the book,' one asks.

'I guess I have learned that I was oversimplifying things when I assumed technology *causes* mental health issues, as opposed to making those who are vulnerable potentially more vulnerable, and that there are worrying links between mental wellbeing and particular aspects of technology use. I have learned that technology is central to your lives and has many good purposes. And it's not *how much time* you spend on screen, but *what you are doing* that matters. I am afraid I haven't changed my view that the big tech companies have a lot more to do to create a better balance between societal responsibility, sustainability and profit and to take action to prevent or mitigate the harmful impacts of some of their products. I also don't buy any of the objections to age and identity verification on the internet. I think you should have to identity yourself to the platform you are using even if you use a different name for your profile online. It would cut out a lot of the worst behaviours.'

'And your view on my gaming "addiction"?'

'I guess I don't think you are addicted; I buy the benefits of being able to talk to your mates while you play during lockdown. But I still think it lures you into more and more screen time and it does make you aggressive, though I would admit it may not make you any more aggressive than when Chelsea loses a football match! And arguing with me about limiting your screen time may cause as much conflict as the game does you harm! I have also learned that you can't lump teenagers into one group, that we need to better understand the effects of technology on the different stages of childhood and adolescence, and for that we need the big tech companies to work with academia, regulators and supply data. Ultimately, we all need to learn or to be taught responsible internet use, and big tech companies need to moderate content so that it is health-promoting, not the opposite. Finally that I am going to see what I can do to persuade global investing institutions to put pressure on the big techs to adopt responsible design and Safety Tech, and to persuade the UK government to introduce compulsory identity or hard age verification and include fraud in the list of online harms that are regulated.'

My son says with a broad grin on his face, 'Well, Dad, I will leave it to you to tell the Home Secretary and the Culture Secretary how to fix all that, but in the meantime, why don't we write up and agree a Wigley family social media plan for responsible internet use? One condition: it has to apply to all of us, including you!'

APPENDIX 1

PERSONAL TIPS FOR CONTROLLING EXCESSIVE INTERNET USE

These are just the ways I *try* to control my own technology use.

- Reduce the number of apps and platforms you are on. Do you really need Facebook, Instagram, Facebook Messenger, WhatsApp, Snapchat, Twitter and TikTok in addition to your traditional SMS or MMS messaging app?
- Turn off your notifications for anything that isn't genuinely time-critical. Moreover, disable sound notifications for social media. Every time you look at your screen, you have notifications which you find you simply 'can't' ignore, and more often than not you're lured to your screen by pings or buzzes. If someone really needs your urgent attention, they will text or in extremis call you. I always send my children a text if I want their urgent attention – otherwise my message goes into a never-ending queue of instant messages.
- Organise your home screen to minimise the risk of distraction. Most smartphones give you the option to organise your apps by page. Limit your front page to text and email, or other critical communication platforms. Make it such that you will have to make a conscious decision to go to the second page during your allocated social media times.

- Download and use an app that makes you aware of the time you spend on your phone. Apple, for example, has tools that produce activity reports on your screen time, allows you to set limits for particular apps and have 'do not disturb' features (useful for when you are trying to do something focused like study, work or have a meal with others). Apps like Checky will monitor how often you look at your phone, and BreakFree will help you monitor your phone use and give you an addiction score. The Moment app will train you in healthy phone use.

- Do not take your phone into the bedroom. In fact, do not look at it for the hour before you go to sleep. Consider setting controls that stop you from using it during bedtime hours. Use a device that has a near-sleep or night-time screen setting that doesn't emit blue light.

- Keep your phone physically beyond reach. When you are having a conversation or communal meal, put your phone somewhere you literally cannot access it, or at the very least out of sight, to help you be more present in your in-person interactions.

- Take a digital time-management course. Essentially, there are only three things you should ever do with an email, for example. One, read and delete it. Two, read, reply to it and delete it. Three, read it and forward it to someone else with an instruction or request for action and delete it. There should never be more than a few emails in your inbox on this basis. Be ruthless with unsubscribing from any organisation which sends you emails you don't really need.

- Use a service which answers your calls and turns any message left into an email or text which is immediately sent to your phone. It also allows you to deal with the message by returning the call if a conversation is justified, or simply ignore it or deal with it by text or email.

- If you can't be disciplined and resources allow, get a second phone. Have work on one phone and social media on another; only access your social phone during allocated times. Keep it turned off and out of sight the rest of the time.

APPENDIX 2

ADVICE FOR PARENTS

Delay purchasing a phone for your child and attempt to make their first phone something simpler than a smartphone. Limit their data package and use child protection software. For example, BBC's free to download and use Own It app monitors a phone's keyboard, camera and incoming and outgoing messages, and if it gauges that a child is on the verge of engaging in imprudent behaviour, presents a pause message and explains why sending an explicit image or abusive language is not a good idea. What's so good about this is that it doesn't require the parent to have access to the child's activities and empowers the child to control their own behaviours with education pitched in a way that's attractive to them and doesn't put them into conflict with their parents. I am an investor in the company which built it.

Microsoft's Launcher app for Android has new family facilities that allow parents to set up location trackers, app use trackers and site blockers.

Beware of seemingly harmless 'education' apps and games which kids use to learn. They can become 'gateway' games to entertainment games that will later displace reading and homework. As such, it is important to research the actuality of education games before buying them for children.

Gaming and e-sports deserve, in my view, particular consideration in relation to their potential for risk. Two leading US psychologists, Dave

Grossman and Gloria DeGaetano, have recommended not allowing kids to access video games until they are at least twelve and preferably fourteen.[1] Once games are allowed, it is recommended that screen time be strictly limited to avoid addiction. Xbox, which manufactures some of the bestselling gaming systems of all time, has numerous features designed to enable diligent parents to keep their children's use responsible and prevent harms. These include the ability to set device, app and screen time limits; produce activity reports showing what they have been doing; control the child's purchases; keep track of purchases; limit the ability to join group games; and facilitate muting and blocking of other parties and report bullies. I could find no data on what proportion of parents avail themselves of these controls, however.

In relation to moderation and self-regulation, parents need to wise up. Freed suggests that parents 'instinctively know moderation isn't a good way to protect kids from drug and alcohol addictions. Responsible parents don't consider giving children – especially when they are young – moderate amounts of alcohol, tobacco or recreational drugs, because we know that young brains struggle mightily with self-control'.[2] As such, moderation isn't the answer. Instead, insist on phone downtime (particularly during family meals or homework), limit data packages and forbid the phone immediately before sleep and during the night. You may have to choose between being your child's friend and their parent.

When it comes to homework and the use of laptops, make sure the laptop doesn't have any other apps on it, particularly gaming or messaging apps, and take the mobile phone away. You need to avoid the potential for your child to be distracted during study time to the extent possible.

APPENDIX 3

INTERNET GOVERNANCE

In the course of researching this book, I have learned a lot about the opaque world of internet governance. What follows is a summary of some of the many initiatives, one of which will hopefully result in a way forward.

Regulation of the internet, given its expansive reach, is no easy task. The internet is global, recognises no national boundaries and is based on some principles that may conflict with regulation – for example, free access, transparency, privacy and freedom of speech.

In an attempt to build a framework for governance of the internet, digital ethicists ask and seek to answer some important questions. They observe that many tech platforms have one role as 'information gatekeepers' to us all. This gives rise to issues like the intentional or unintentional skewing of information. The algorithms which drive this bias are not accessible to the end user, and therefore the bias is often hidden. This is a problem. As users, we have a right to understand what and how we are being shown, and why it is being shown.

Internet platforms also have a role to play as the 'stewards' of our data. What exactly should platforms be allowed to do with our data, either with or without our explicit permission? Do we have a right to be forgotten? There are also a great many questions about what AI should be allowed to be used for and how. These are all important but not easy questions to address, with a wide range of answers. We shall examine what civic society has said on these issues.

In 2015 Professor Luciano Floridi of Oxford University, who also serves as Director of its Data Ethics Lab, authored a report called 'The Online Manifesto'. It suggested that an online bill of rights be created based on the following principles:

1. Everyone has a right to privacy.
2. Individuals own their own data.
3. Everyone has a right to a personal life.
4. No one should have to switch off completely to protect him or herself.
5. Switching off should sometimes be encouraged and cultivated.
6. There should be third spaces that should be owned/regulated by the European public.

Interestingly, the UK, which has a number of proposals to address online harms, does not have a modern written constitution; instead, many of its underlying constitutional principles date back to a bill of rights passed in 1689. In light of recent political events, it seems that now is the time not only to create a bill of rights, but to include rights which would address the issues of the digital age, including perhaps rights over our own attention, the right to a childhood and the protection of innocence. No one should underestimate, of course, the difficulty of finding appropriate legal definitions for such concepts.

If there is a body with the potential to create a global framework to govern the internet, it is the United Nations' Internet Governance Forum. The IGF was formed by the UN in 2006 and is a multi-stakeholder group for policy dialogue on issues of internet governance. Its main organ is its multi-stakeholder advisory group, which is almost sixty strong and comprises international representatives from the governmental, private, technical, academic and NGO sectors. Some of the key takeaways from its 2019 annual meeting were:

1. The internet will only achieve its potential as a channel for free speech and economic growth if it remains a safe place where people feel secure.
2. Tackling hate speech is a shared responsibility of stakeholders.
3. Children's rights are no different in the online or offline world – in particular, their rights to be protected from inappropriate, illegal and bullying behaviours as well as their right to be protected from sexual abuse and commercial exploitation.
4. The international multi-stakeholder community needs to accurately define scope and terminology issues on disinformation and interference in electoral processes.
5. The current trend to tackle illicit or abusive content is to cancel, transfer, delete or suspend domain names; this does not provide an effective or sustainable way to remove malicious content.
6. Strengthening digital and media literacy is key to combating the harms of distribution of misinformation and strengthening people's resilience to minimise impacts of cyberbullying.
7. Taxing social media use creates barriers to people's communication and is not an effective way for states to gain revenue.
8. Bias and exclusion continue to be deeply embedded in digital spaces.
9. Working collaboratively in a global context on developing commonly agreed values and principles for data frameworks could assist in building confidence in cross-border data flows.
10. AI and algorithms, if not governed effectively, can be used

to monitor and manipulate behaviour, to besiege us with ever more targeted and intrusive advertising, to manipulate voters and stifle freedom of expression. Algorithmic discrimination affects labour markets, the criminal justice system and access to public services.

11. Use of AI on anonymised big data sets can de-anonymise and identify specific individuals within the data sets.

12. When developing algorithms there should be a policy balance between being able to extract knowledge that can be used for good and knowledge that can be used to infringe on the fundamental right of people whose data has been collected.

I have picked the most relevant outputs from a much longer list. But my overall observation is that while these sound laudable principles and objectives, and most of the IGF's members are no doubt well-meaning, some of them have very major conflicts of interest given their employment by, or funding from, big tech companies. Given the technology companies' extensive lobbying efforts, particularly in the US, we should not expect it to urgently address what I believe are pressing issues any time soon.

In 2018 the UN Secretary-General established a High-Level Panel on Digital Cooperation (HLPDC) to consider how better global digital cooperation could support delivery of the UN's Sustainable Delivery Goals. It reported in 2019 that in our digitally interdependent world improved cooperation is urgently required in order to maximise the benefits of, and minimise the harm from, digital technologies. It suggested that any cooperation should be based on the core values of inclusiveness, respect, human-centredness, human rights, international law, transparency and sustainability. It observed that the need for strengthened cooperation mechanisms has been raised many times in recent years by broad initiatives such as the NetMundial Conference, the Global Commission on

Internet Governance and the Web Foundation's Contract for the Web, but that none had yet succeeded. It identified six main gaps in the existing multilateral arrangements:

1. Internet governance is too low on many national government agendas.
2. Existing technical and standard-setting bodies are not inclusive enough.
3. The existing architecture for internet governance is highly complex but not effective.
4. Digital technologies increasingly cut across issues where policies are shaped by separate institutions.
5. There is a lack of reliable data on which to base practical policy interventions.
6. There is a lack of trust among governments, civil society and the private sector.

It also found broad agreement that 'governments, civil society and the private sector would need to find new ways to work together to steer an effective path between extremes of over regulation and complete laissez faire'. It examined three potential models for such cooperation, one of which was to build on the Internet Governance Forum, addressing its lack of actionable outcomes, limited government and business engagement and particularly smaller country representation. A new overarching Advisory Group would oversee this body, and there would be a Cooperation Accelerator, a Policy Incubator and an observatory and help desk. It would be funded by governments and business.

In June 2020 the UN published its report of the Secretary-General, 'Roadmap for digital cooperation'. This identified that discussions over the three potential governance models continued with no conclusion. The UN said it stood ready to serve as the platform for multi-stakeholder dialogue on emerging technologies and that the Secretary-General would appoint an Envoy on Technology in 2021. The Envoy will serve as an advocate and focal point for digital cooperation. It also outlined that the United Nations High Commission for Human Rights will develop system-wide guidance on human rights, due diligence and impact assessments in the use of new technologies. The Secretary-General called on member states to put human rights at the centre of regulatory frameworks and legislation on the development and use of digital technologies. It also included new proposals to make the Internet Governance Forum more responsive and ensure actionable outcomes. In relation to AI, the report identified that there remains a gap in international coordination, collaboration and governance. Current global discussions on the subject were identified as not inclusive, particularly of developing nations. Whilst there are 160 sets of artificial intelligence ethics and governance principles worldwide, there is no platform to bring them together. The report concluded that in relation to AI, public sectors around the world needed more resources and expertise to bring oversight and governance to the use of AI. The report concluded, 'In this unprecedented moment, the power, promise and peril of digital technology cannot be underestimated. Coming together will allow the international community to ensure that technology is harnessed for good, seek the opportunity to manage its impact and ensure that it presents a level playing field for all. Future generations will judge whether the present generation seized the opportunities presented by the age of digital interdependence. The time to act is now.'[1]

The Centre for International Governance Innovation has been established to examine how international governance can innovate, especially for technology. In 2019 it published a series of articles on potential models for platform governance. Taylor Owen, one of its contributors, noted that after two decades of 'techno-optimism', where everyone assumed that digital technology generally and social media in particular were aligned with social good, and a laissez-faire environment of governance had been allowed to develop, we are now facing 'techlash'. He notes that during this period the big tech companies including Facebook (WhatsApp and Instagram's parent), Amazon, Apple, Netflix and Alphabet (Google's parent), collectively known as the FAANGS, have become some of the most profitable companies in the world, while the social, economic and democratic costs of this 'unfettered' system have been borne by the public. 'The social costs of the platform economy are manifesting themselves in the increasingly toxic nature of the digital public sphere, the amplification of misinformation and disinformation, the declining reliability of information, heightened polarisation and the broad mental health repercussions of technologies designed around addictive models,' Owen argues.[2] He notes that potential policy responses are riddled with difficulties, not least the huge power of the FAANGS, the complexity of the challenges and the level of international coordination and collaboration required. He suggests that one promising place for progress is the International Grand Committee on Big Data, Privacy and Democracy (IGC).

High-level overall governance of the internet is one idea. At a lower and more specific level, Social Media Councils (SMCs) are another. Article 19, a leading free speech global organisation, has proposed that these voluntary multi-stakeholder accountability mechanisms could be set up by the big tech companies to address content-moderation issues on social media platforms. The developing consensus is that these councils would operate within a legal framework created by international standards on human rights. Debate is ongoing as to whether they should just be advisory or have adjudicatory powers. A global SMC might provide a universal code on human-rights-based principles on content moderation, within which national SMCs could deal with local cultural and legal divergence. Heidi Tworek, CIGI contributor, says SMCs will not solve the structural problems of the big techs' business models, but could offer an interim solution, pending more comprehensive global internet governance. Many questions remain, though, about the memberships and precise roles and powers of potential SMCs. Article 19 and Stanford's Digital Policy Incubator are working on proposals. A High Level Transatlantic Working Group on Content Moderation and Freedom of Expression Online is also examining how transatlantic cooperation on dispute resolution might help. Tworek says SMCs 'could put the societal back into social media. They could establish fair, reliable, transparent and non-arbitrary standards for content moderation ... creating a democratic, equitable and accountable system of platform governance will take time. Councils can be part of the solution.'[3]

Robert Fay, another CIGI contributor, has suggested that in much the same way that the GFC led to the establishment of the Financial Stability Board, so too should the attention crisis lead to the establishment of a Digital Stability Board (DSB). Led by a board of international officials, its functions would be to coordinate standards, regulations and policies for platforms, including big data and AI, and assess vulnerabilities to society from technological developments and create policy actions necessary to address them promptly. Fay also suggests the IGC could create the DSB.[4]

Another area of focus for CIGI is the need to synchronise anti-trust and regulatory policy to boost competition in the digital market. Gene Kimmelman, CIGI contributor, observes that consumers' preferences towards easy, simple and one-stop shopping on digital platforms create more barriers to competition and favour the dominant monopsonies. He believes a new expert platform regulator equipped with the tools to promote entry and expansion in digital markets could actually expand competition to benefit consumers, entrepreneurship and innovation in a way which existing national regulators have failed to achieve. One key idea would be to introduce the idea of interoperability, whereby a regulator could require dominant platforms to allow others to access their networks when using their services.[5] In the UK, the Open Banking initiative has introduced similar measures to allow fintech startups to use the account data of the largest banks' customers with a view to promoting competition in banking.

Another area of thinking is that of information consumer protection. Jonathon Penney, a CIGI contributor, suggests national information consumer protection agencies be established to focus on the quality, safety and transparency of information, anti-deception, consumer choice and accountability. One of his specific ideas is to require account labelling: each social media account's label would show whether the identity of the owner has been verified, its location, whether the account is real or automated and whether the content is sponsored or promoted. This should allow users to better judge the quality and integrity of the information. Another idea is a requirement on platforms, in law and on notice, to remove or reduce the visibility of false information. Platforms could also be required to issue standardised disinformation corrections, recalls or warnings. Platforms could be subjected to information and content-moderation audits. Users could be given warnings that their post content violates terms of service before they post it, and new users could be given cooling-off periods, during which they are required to create a track record of reliable information posting before allowing their posts to be made public.[6]

APPENDIX 4

A WORD ON AI

Many observers have concerns over the potential misuse of AI. Wu sums up the risk as the combination of the scale of big tech companies, their almost infinite resources and, most importantly, their ownership of 2.2 billion profiles of users, including a deep understanding of emotional triggers. The combination of these assets gives big tech a 'complete picture of each user's location, relationships and activities, and an economic incentive to manipulate user attention without regard to the consequences'.[1]

When it comes to AI and machine learning, similar ideas to design ethics have been mooted under the banner of Responsible Innovation. 'Partnership on AI', an international NGO, has been established to bring industry, academia and civil society together to realise the promise of artificial intelligence. It aims to formulate best practice on AI technologies, to advance the public's understanding of AI and to serve as an open platform for discussion and engagement about AI and its influences on society and people. This is a good start, but the body is voluntary and has no power. I believe there needs to be a global body, perhaps under the auspices of the UN, which studies ethical use of AI and sets standards for what is acceptable and what is not. Over time, proscribed uses could be incorporated into international law, a bit like the aviation and maritime industries, and policed by a Security Council equivalent.

In April 2020 the EU published a white paper on AI governance. It envisages a programme of work between the public and private sectors to identify high-risk AI activities and considers how they might be controlled within two overarching principles of trust and excellence. Trust incorporates the idea that as AI develops citizens' rights must be protected by law and law enforcement. A risk-based approach to identifying high-risk activities must include proportionate regulation. In terms of excellence, rules are envisaged for training relating to AI, for record keeping of datasets and for the existence and performance of AI activities. Monitoring and testing by relevant authorities would follow, and a labelling scheme could be introduced categorising the safety of processes. Finally, the use of remote biometric identification is to be controlled.

RESOURCES FOR THOSE INTERESTED IN LEARNING MORE OR GETTING INVOLVED

Center for Humane Technology
www.humanetech.com
US-based publisher of *The Social Dilemma* in partnership with Netflix. Resources for campaigning and education on humane technology design.

Center for International Governance Innovation
www.cigionline.org
Think tank supporting research that forms networks, advances policy debate and generates ideas for multilateral governance improvements.

The Children's Society
www.childrenssociety.org.uk
Aims to improve the lives of children and young people and create a positive shift in social attitudes to improve the situation facing children and all young people. Their Good Childhood Report is a major survey of child wellbeing and the reasons for issues children have, including social media.

Common Sense Media
www.commonsensemedia.org
US-based, leading source of entertainment and technology recommendations for families.

Digital Futures Commission

www.digitalfuturescommission.org.uk

The DFC is an exciting research collaboration of organisations that invites innovators, policymakers, regulators, academics and civil society to unlock digital innovation in the interests of children and young people. It will initially focus on three areas: play in a digital world, beneficial use of education data and guidance for innovators.

5Rights Foundation

www.5rightsfoundation.com

5Rights Foundation exists to make systemic changes to the digital world that will ensure it caters for children and young people, by design and default, so that they can thrive.

Global Action Plan (GAP)

www.globalactionplan.org.uk

GAP's early focus was on climate change but it has now started researching and writing reports on the digital wellbeing of children and the dangers of technology. It has recently highlighted the issue of tech companies targeting children with advertising in the UK in breach of regulation and supported the litigation against Google re YouTube currently in the courts.

Mind

www.mind.org.uk

Mind offers information and advice to people with mental-health issues and lobbies government and local authorities on their behalf. It also seeks to raise public awareness and understanding of issues related to mental health.

Next Generation Internet Initiative

www.ngi.eu

A diverse array of researchers and activists who describe themselves as building the internet of tomorrow.

NSPCC

www.nspcc.org.uk

The largest children's charity in the UK, preventing abuse and helping those affected to recover. Produces excellent research and resources and campaigns on all aspects of technology's effects on children.

Oxford Internet Institute

www.oii.ox.ac.uk

Advances our understanding of life online with world-leading research. Leads the subject of Internet Governance and Data Ethics.

UK Safer Internet Centre

www.saferinternet.org.uk

Brings together news and events from three organisations: Childnet International, The Internet Watch Foundation and South West Grid for Learning.

World Wide Web Foundation

www.webfoundation.org

Founded by Tim Berners-Lee, empowers people to bring about positive change. Primary focus is advocating for a free and open web for everyone.

www.parentzone.org.uk

Parent Zone are the experts in digital family life providing support and advice to parents, children and schools to help families navigate the internet safely and confidently'

www.childnet.com

Childnet's mission is to work in partnership to help make the internet a great and safe place for children'

www.youngminds.org.uk

The UK's leading charity fighting for children and young people's mental health'

www.theyouthgroup.com

The Youth Group aims to improve the odds for young people to reach their full potential in work'.

www.ownyourdata.foundation

The Own Your Data Foundation is implementing programs that democratise digital intelligence education and create measurable social impact.

NOTES

Introduction

1   Donna Freitas, *The Happiness Effect*, Oxford: Oxford University Press, 2017, 251.
2   Ibid.
3   Sherry Turkle, *Reclaiming Conversation: The Power of Talk in a Digital Age*, New York: Penguin Press, 2015, 9.
4   Ibid.
5   Winifred Gallagher, *Rapt: Attention and the Focused Life*, New York: Penguin Press, 2010.
6   'Young people fear for their future and feel ignored by politicians according to new report', Barnado's, 8 July 2019, https://www.barnardos.org.uk/news/young-people-fear-their-future-and-feel-ignored-politicians-according-new-report.

Chapter 1

1   Lee Miller and Wei Lu, 'Gen Z is set to outnumber millennials within a year', Bloomberg, 20 August 2018, https://www.bloomberg.com/news/articles/2018-08-20/gen-z-to-outnumber-millennials-within-a-year-demographic-trends.
2   James Emery White, *Meet Generation Z: Understanding and Reaching the New Post*, Michigan: Baker Books, 2017, 24.
3   David Pakman, 'May I have your attention please?' 10 August 2015, https://pakman.com/may-i-have-your-attention-please-19ef6395b2c3.
4   Miller and Lu.
5   Simon Denyer and Annie Gowen, 'Too many men', *Washington Post*, 18 April 2018.
6   Jason Dorsey and Denise Villa, *Zconomy: How Gen Z Will Change the Future of Business – and What to Do About It*, HarperCollins and The Center for Generational Kinetics, LLC, USA, 2020.

7   'Why Generation Z has a totally different approach to money', World Economic Forum, 30 November 2018, https://www.weforum.org/agenda/2018/11/why-gen-z-is-approaching-money-differently-than-other-generations-95032cb6-6046-4269-a38a-0763bd7909ff?fbclid=IwAR11eNMcHvsXiluUR34hy7_OyZ1hn7VXl0XCo5JSSKVuENwy05wiMnD7Ylk.

8   '"Generation Z" is entrepreneurial, wants to chart its own future', News @ Northeastern, 18 November 2014, https://news.northeastern.edu/2014/11/18/generation-z-survey/.

9   Adam Alter, *Irresistible: The Rise of Addictive Technology and the Business of Keeping Us Hooked*, New York: Penguin Press, 2017, 252.

10 Ibid, 252.

11 Ibid, 253.

12 Meg Aldrich, 'Too much screen time is raising rate of childhood myopia', Keck School News, 22 January 2016, https://keck.usc.edu/too-much-screen-time-is-raising-rate-of-childhood-myopia/.

13 Nikita Coulombe and Philip Zimbardo, *Man, Interrupted: Why Young Men Are Struggling and What We Can Do About It*, Michigan: Brilliance Publishing, 2017.

14 'Generation Z is stressed, depressed and exam-obsessed', *The Economist*, 27 February 2019.

15 O. Miron, K. Yu, R. Wilf-Miron and I. S. Kohane, 'Suicide rates among adolescents and young adults in the United States, 2000–2017', JAMA, 18 June 2019, https://jamanetwork.com/journals/jama/fullarticle/2735809.

16 The Children's Society, *The Good Childhood Report*, 2020.

17 Gabriella Swerling, 'Non-stop social media blamed for rise in young women with depression', *The Telegraph*, 3 October 2020

18 E. Broadbent, J. Gougoulis, N. Lui, V. Pota and J. Simons (2017), 'Generation Z: global citizenship survey,' in *What the World's Young People Think and Feel*, London: Varkey Foundation, 26–44.

19 White, 42.

20 Corey Seemiller and Meghan Grace, *Generation Z: A Century in the Making*, Abingdon: Routledge, 2019, 125.

Chapter 2

1   'Audience report on millennials', GlobalWebIndex, 2019, https://www.globalwebindex.com/reports/millennials.

2   https://go.cheetahdigital.com/e/427422/2020-11-17/.

3   Ibid.

4   'Asia's Generation Z comes of age', McKinsey Global Institute, 17 March 2020, https://www.mckinsey.com/industries/retail/our-insights/asias-generation-z-comes-of-age#. A survey by Snapchat and GlobalWebIndex of 79,000 16–22-year-olds across 45 markets found that mobile phones were used by 97

per cent of those surveyed. Seventy-eight per cent of Generation Z said mobile was their most important means of access to the internet by comparison with 74 per cent of millennials. They spent an average of 4 hours 15 minutes a day on their devices. 'The youth of the nations: global trends among Gen Z', GlobalWebIndex and Snap Inc., 13 June 2019, https://forbusiness.snapchat.com/blog/the-youth-of-the-nations-global-trends-among-gen-z.

5   Sandra Henshaw, 'Mobile phone usage statistics in the UK: how many smartphone users are there?' Tiger Mobiles, 27 December 2018, https://www.tigermobiles.com/blog/mobile-phone-usage-statistics/.

6   eMarketer.com reported in September 2019 that 98 per cent of 13–16-year-olds used YouTube; 79 per cent Instagram, 68 per cent Snapchat, 40 per cent Twitter, 42 per cent TikTok, and 41 per cent Facebook. 'Social media platforms used by US Gen Z and millennial internet users, by demographic, Sep 2019 (% of respondents in each group)', eMarketer, 5 November 2019, https://www.emarketer.com/chart/231814/social-media-platforms-used-by-us-gen-z-millennial-internet-users-by-demographic-sep-2019-of-respondents-each-group. Amongst 17–21-year-olds, Facebook's penetration was higher at 68 per cent, rising to 85 per cent for 22–26-year-olds. Eighty-four per cent of 17–21-year-olds use Instagram, and 74 per cent Snapchat.

7   'Taking stock with teens', Piper Sandler, Spring 2019, www.pipersandler.com/3col.aspx?id=5956.

8   Yuan Ren, 'Know your Chinese social media', *New York Times*, 19 November 2018.

9   Ibid.

10 Ibid.

11 Ibid.

12 Ibid.

13 Dorsey and Villa, 98.

14 http://fortune.com/2015/08/18/facebook-google/.

15 'Teenagers are rewriting the rules of the news', *The Economist*, 18 December 2019.

16 'Ofcom: BBC must do "much more" for young audiences', *BBC News*, 24 October 2019.

17 www.air.org/project/program-international-student-assessment-pisa.

18 Mal Nashed, 'Distrusting the press, Arab youth turn to social media', Ozy, 10 June 2019, https://www.ozy.com/news-and-politics/distrusting-the-press-arab-youth-turn-to-social-media/94805/.

19 The figure for usage of Naver is 97. Jaya Halepete Iyer and Shubhapriya Bennur, *Retailing in Emerging Markets*. London: Bloomsbury Press, 2017.

20 'How young people consume news and the implications for mainstream media', Report commissioned by the Reuters Institute, authored by Flamingo, August 2019, https://reutersinstitute.politics.ox.ac.uk/our-research/how-young-people-consume-news-and-implications-mainstream-media.

21 Toni Fitzgerald, 'Wow: millennials watch more online video than traditional television', *Forbes*, 28 November 2018. Netflix dominates SVOD in the Americas and Europe, with 79 per cent of North Americans, 48 per cent of Europeans and 84 per cent of Latin Americans reported using devices to watch Netflix in the previous month. Mansoor Iqbal, 'Netflix revenue and usage statistics (2020)', Business of Apps, 24 April 2020, https://www.businessofapps.com/data/netflix-statistics/. Total Netflix subscribers at the end of 2019 were 167 million, with 61 million of those in the US and the remainder spread around the globe. Edmund Lee, 'Netflix reports a subscriber bump as Disney poses a new threat', *New York Times*, 21 January 2020. In China, iQiyi and Tencent Video have 100 million and 94 million users, respectively. Pei Li and Brenda Goh, 'China's iQiyi looks abroad after hitting 100 million paying subscribers', Reuters, 24 June 2019, https://www.reuters.com/article/us-china-iqiyi-idUSKCN1TP13Q.

22 Matt Binder, 'Netflix and YouTube are taking over your TV set', Mashable, 11 February 2020, https://mashable.com/article/streaming-services-television-netflix-nielsen-report/?europe=true.

23 'The youth of the nations'.

24 Mansoor Iqbal, 'Twitch revenue and usage statistics (2020)', Business of Apps, 24 April 2020, https://www.businessofapps.com/data/twitch-statistics/.

25 'The state of online gaming 2019', Limelight Networks, 2019, https://www.limelight.com/resources/white-paper/state-of-online-gaming-2019/.

26 Ofcom recently surveyed the online gaming activities of 3–15-year-olds in the UK. Thirty-nine per cent of 3–4-year-old boys play games for 4 hours 42 mins a week, rising to 81 per cent of 12–15-year-olds watching for 11 hours 36 minutes. Gaming involves a strong social element: 38 per cent of 8–11-year-olds and 58 per cent of 12–15-year-olds said they regularly use the online chat facilities offered by gaming apps. Boys aged 12–15 are twice as likely as girls to chat to people they know solely via the gaming platform, including therefore people they don't know as true friends and potentially not even the person they think they are talking to (30 per cent vs 16 per cent). 'Children and parents: media use and attitudes report: 2018', Ofcom, 29 January 2019, https://www.ofcom.org.uk/research-and-data/media-literacy-research/childrens/children-and-parents-media-use-and-attitudes-report-2018.

27 '2020 shopping outlook: 82 percent of consumers more inclined to purchase after seeing, holding or demoing products in-store', Shopkick, 2 January 2020, https://www.businesswire.com/news/home/20200102005030/en/2020-Shopping-Outlook-82-Percent-Consumers-Inclined.

28 'Taking stock with teens'.

29 Sonia Livingstone and Alice Blum-Ross, *Parenting for a Digital Future: How Hopes and Fears about Technology Shape Children's Lives*, New York: OUP USA, 2020.

30 'The Common Sense census: media use by kids age zero to eight', Common Sense Media, 2017, https://www.commonsensemedia.org/research/the-common-sense-census-media-use-by-kids-age-zero-to-eight-2017.

31 'The Common Sense census: media use by tweens and teens', Common Sense Media, 2019, https://www.commonsensemedia.org/research/the-common-sense-census-media-use-by-tweens-and-teens-2019.

32 Ibid.

33 'Apple investors urge action on "smartphone addiction"', *BBC News*, 8 January 2018.

34 Sean Coughlan, 'Most children sleep with mobile phone beside bed', *BBC News*, 30 January 2020.

35 'Childhood 2019 – new independent report', Childwise, 2019, www.childwise.co.uk/uploads/3/1/6/5/31656353/childwise_press_release_-_monitor_2025.pdf. The average time spent on mobiles by 7–16-year-olds is 3 hours and 20 minutes per day. There are 57 per cent who always have the phone beside their bed, and 44 per cent feel 'uncomfortable' if they are ever without a phone signal. There are 42 per cent who say they keep their phone on them at all times and never turn it off.

36 'Taming the Wild West Web', NSPCC, 2019, https://www.nspcc.org.uk/globalassets/documents/news/taming-the-wild-west-web-regulate-social-networks.pdf.

37 Ibid.

38 'How to protect your child from the top 7 dangers of online gaming', Kaspersky, https://www.kaspersky.co.uk/resource-center/threats/top-7-online-gaming-dangers-facing-kids.

39 Ibid.

40 White, 137.

41 'Media use by children younger than 2 years', *Pediatrics*, 128(5), November 2011.

42 Seemiller and Grace, 191.

43 Matthew Walker, *Why We Sleep*, New York: Penguin Random House, 2017.

44 Madlen Davies, 'Average person now spends more time on their phone and laptop than sleeping, study claims', *Daily Mail*, 11 March 2015.

45 Alter, 69.

46 'Why electronics may stimulate you before bed', National Sleep Foundation, https://www.sleepfoundation.org/articles/why-electronics-may-stimulate-you-bed.

47 'The state of online gaming 2019', Limelight Networks, 2019, https://de.limelight.com/resources/white-paper/state-of-online-gaming-2019/.

48 Yoram Wurmser, 'Wearables 2019: advanced wearables pick up pace as fitness trackers slow', eMarketer, 3 January 2019, https://www.emarketer.com/content/wearables-2019.

Chapter 3

1   Alter, 7.
2   Ibid, 15.
3   Tim Wu, *The Attention Merchants: The Epic Struggle to Get Inside Our Heads*, London: Atlantic Books, 2017, 6.
4   Ibid, 6.
5   Shoshana Zuboff, *The Age of Surveillance Capitalism: The Fight for a Human Future at the New Frontier of Power*, New York: PublicAffairs, 2019, 36.
6   'The future of fixed telephone services', Ofcom, 22 February 2019, https://www.ofcom.org.uk/phones-telecoms-and-internet/information-for-industry/telecoms-competition-regulation/future-fixed-telephone-services.
7   Seemiller and Grace, 64.
8   Ibid, 117.
9   Sherry Turkle, *Alone Together: Why We Expect More from Technology and Less from Each Other*, New York: Basic Books, 2011.
10 Ibid, 15.
11 Ibid, 10.
12 Turkle, *Reclaiming Conversation*, 34.
13 James Williams, *Stand out of Our Light: Freedom and Resistance in the Attention Economy*, Cambridge: Cambridge University Press, 2018, 9.
14 Nicholas Carr, *The Shallows*, New York: W. W. Norton & Company, 2010, 133.
15 Ibid.
16 Turkle, *Reclaiming Conversation*, 346.
17 Ibid, 35.
18 Alter, 232.
19 'Common Sense research reveals everything you need to know about teens' use of social media in 2018', Common Sense Media, 10 September 2018, https://www.commonsensemedia.org/about-us/news/press-releases/common-sense-research-reveals-everything-you-need-to-know-about-teens.
20 Amanda Lenhart, 'Social media and friendships' from 'Teens, technology and friendships', Pew Research Center, 6 August 2015. https://www.pewresearch.org/internet/2015/08/06/teens-technology-and-friendships/.
21 'New Girl Scout study shows what girls are doing to gain traction as digital leaders', Girl Scouts of America, 11 February 2019, https://www.girlscouts.org/en/press-room/press-room/news-releases/2019/new-girl-scout-study-shows-what-girls-are-doing-to-gain-traction-as-digital-leaders.html.
22 Wu, 293.
23 Ibid, 295.
24 Alter, 28.
25 Ibid, 28.
26 Ibid, 118.

27 Freitas, XV.
28 Wu, 301.
29 Turkle, *Alone Together*, 280.
30 Freitas, 91.
31 Ibid, 86.
32 Ibid, 103.
33 Ibid, 262.
34 Mary Aiken, *The Cyber Effect – A pioneering Cyberpsychologist Explains How Human Behaviour Changes Online*, London: John Murray, 2016, 184.
35 Freitas, 15.
36 Turkle, *Reclaiming Conversation*, 3.
37 Freitas, 14.
38 Wu, 301.
39 Freitas, 251.
40 Red Vogelstein, 'The Wired Interview: Facebook's Mark Zuckerberg', *Wired*, 29 June 2009.
41 Rex Sorgatz, 'The microfame game', *New York Magazine*, 17 June 2008.
42 Wu, 307.
43 Williams, 59.
44 Jean Twenge and Keith Campbell, *The Narcissism Epidemic*, New York: Simon and Schuster, 2009.
45 Freed, 166.
46 Wu, 24.
47 Williams, 72.
48 Ibid, 70.
49 Jaron Lanier, *Ten Arguments for Deleting Your Social Media Accounts Right Now*, New York: Henry Holt & Co., 2018, 18.
50 Matt Haig, *Notes on a Nervous Planet*, Edinburgh: Canongate Books, 2018, 10.
51 Ibid, 33.
52 Alter, 42.
53 Lanier, 88.
54 Alter, 41.
55 Haig, 61.
56 Freitas, 4.
57 Ibid, 39.
58 'Goals for good, values to transform our world', Global Action Plan, https://www.transform-our-world.org/files/values_to_transform_our_world_white_paper.pdf.
59 Richard Freed, 'Why smartphone dependence is ravaging a generation', *Huffington Post*, 21 August 2017.
60 Cyberbullying Research Center, multiple annual surveys, https://cyberbullying.org.facts.
61 Freed, 154.
62 Freitas, 10.

63 Ibid, 261.
64 Ibid, 256.
65 Stella Bugbee, 'In the 2010's, Instagram became the world's filter', *The Cut*, 27 November 2019.
66 Tumblr is used by 20 per cent of 18–29-year-olds, and 29 per cent of Generation Z, according to GlobalWeb Index. Reddit is used by 58 per cent of 18–29-year-olds, and 16 per cent of Generation Z have used it according to Seemiller and Grace.
67 Freitas, 258.
68 White, 99.
69 Greg Lukianoff and Jonathan Haidt, 'The Coddling of the American Mind', *The Atlantic*, September 2016.

Chapter 4

1 Seemiller and Grace, 45.
2 Williams, 90.
3 Viaccess-Orca Blog, https://www.viaccess-orca.com/blog/tv-viewing-habits-binge-watch-addiction.
4 Chris Stokel-Walker, *YouTubers: How YouTube Shook Up TV and Created a New Generation of Stars*, Kingston-upon-Thames: Canbury Press, 2019.
5 Ibid, 71.
6 Freed, 38.
7 Leonard Sax, *Boys Adrift: The Five Factors Driving the Growth Epidemic of Unemotional Boys*, New York, Basic Books, 2016, 63.
8 Alter, 189.
9 Nir Eyal, 'Kids gaming obsession isn't really about the games', *Psychology Today*, 19 August 2018.
10 Oliver Burkeman, 'Want to succeed? You need systems not goals', *Guardian*, 7 November 2014.
11 Ibid.
12 Alter, 233.
13 Susan Greenfield, *Mind Change: How Digital Technologies Are Leaving Their Mark on Our Brains*. New York: Random House, 2015, 198.
14 Freed, 21.
15 Bruce Perry and Maia Szalavitz, *Born for Love: Why Empathy Is Essential – and Endangered*, New York: William Morrow, 2010, 42.
16 Freed, 77.
17 Ibid, 76.
18 Greenfield, 177.
19 Ibid, 186.
20 Dorsey and Villa, 112.
21 Freed, 99.
22 Ibid, 100.

23 The Computer Professionals for Social Responsibility, 'Socially responsible video games', http://www.publicsphereproject.org/node/325.

24 Carr, 71.

25 Ibid, 102.

26 Ibid, 103.

27 Seemiller and Grace, 208.

28 Carr, 108.

29 Ibid, 108.

30 Freed, 39.

31 Carr, 87.

32 'Eric Schmidt', *The Charlie Rose Show*, 6 March 2009.

33 Greenfield, 232.

34 Ibid, 256.

35 Anne Tervainen-Goff, 'Annual Literacy Survey', National Literacy Trust, 2019, https://cdn.literacytrust.org.uk/media/documents/Junior_Annual_Literacy_Survey_2019_-_Baseline_trends_FINAL.pdf.

36 Wu, 330.

37 www.addictionhelper.com/addiction/internet/the-binge-watch-generation-understanding-netflix-addiction-and-youtube-addiction/.

38 https://about.netflix.com/en/news/ready-set-binge-more-than-8-million-viewers-binge-race-their-favorite-series.

39 Aatif Sulleyman, 'Mark Zuckerberg says virtual reality is better than the "limited" real world', *Independent*, 11 October 2017.

40 Jaron Lanier, *Dawn of the New Everything: Encounters with Reality and Virtual Reality*. New York: Holt Publishing, 2017, 150.

41 Ibid, 2.

42 Damien Bradfield, *The Trust Manifesto*, London: Penguin, 2019, 264.

43 Ibid, 265.

44 https://www.commonsensemedia.org/about-us/news/press-releases/common-sense-media-report-highlight-potential-impact-of-virtual-reality-on.

45 Lanier, *Dawn of the New Everything*, 153.

46 Alter, 142.

47 Lanier, *Dawn of the New Everything*, i.

48 Alter, 142.

49 Lanier, *Dawn of the New Everything*, 139.

50 Wu, 339.

51 'What's that you say? Smart speakers and voice assistants', Common Sense Media, 2019, https://www.commonsensemedia.org/smart-speakers-and-voice-assistants.

52 Zuboff, 259.

53 Ibid, 292.

54 Ibid, 240.

55 Williams, 88.

56 Fen Osler Hampson and Eric Jardine, *Look Who's Watching: Surveillance, Treachery and Trust*, Waterloo, CIGI, 2016, p. 255.

57   James Manyika et al., 'The internet of things: mapping the value beyond the hype', McKinsey Global Institute, June 2015, https://www.mckinsey.com/~/media/McKinsey/Industries/Technology%20Media%20and%20Telecommunications/High%20Tech/Our%20Insights/The%20Internet%20of%20Things%20The%20value%20of%20digitizing%20the%20physical%20world/Unlocking_the_potential_of_the_Internet_of_Things_Executive_summary.ashx.

58   Turkle, *Reclaiming Conversation*, 295.

59   Victoria Waldersee, 'Is there a place for humans after the robot revolution?', YouGov, 1 November 2018, https://yougov.co.uk/topics/technology/articles-reports/2018/11/01/there-place-humans-after-robot-revolution.

60   Turkle, *Alone Together*, 17.

61   Turkle, *Reclaiming Conversation*, 52

62   Turkle, *Alone Together*, 11.

63   Andrea Morris, 'Prediction: sex robots are the most disruptive technology we didn't see coming', *Forbes*, 25 September 2018.

Chapter 5

1   'Cigna U.S. loneliness index', Cigna, 2018, https://www.cigna.com/assets/docs/newsroom/loneliness-survey-2018-full-report.pdf.

2   Marissa King, *Social Chemistry*, New York: Dutton Publishing, 2021, 60.

3   Ibid.

4   Maia Szalavitz and Bruce D. Perry, *Born for Love: Why Empathy is Essential and Endangered*, HarperCollins e-books, 2010, 292.

5   Julia Hobsbawm, *Fully Connected: Surviving and Thriving in an Age of Overload*. London: Bloomsbury Business, 2017, 18.

6   King, 158.

7   Ibid, 159.

8   Ibid, 159.

9   Szalavitz and Perry, 3.

10   Simon Baron-Cohen, *Zero Degrees of Empathy: A New Theory of Human Cruelty*. London: Allen Lane, 2011, 127.

11   Turkle, *Alone Together*, 172.

12   Alan Collins (Nottingham Trent University) and Adam Cox (University of Portsmouth), 'Coronavirus: why lockdown may cost young lives over time', The Conversation, 26 March 2020, https://theconversation.com/coronavirus-why-lockdown-may-cost-young-lives-over-time-134580.

13   Szalavitz and Perry, 19.

14   Adam Smith, *An Enquiry in the Nature and Causes of the Wealth of Nations*, New York: Bantam Books, [1776] 2003, 572.

15   Szalavitz and Perry, 42.

16   Lanier, *Dawn of the New Everything*, Appendix 3.

17 Roman Krznaric, 'Six habits of highly empathic people', *Greater Good Magazine*, 27 November 2012.

18 Cary Cherniss, *The Business Case for Emotional Intelligence*, Graduate School of Applied and Professional Psychology, Rutgers University, 1999.

19 Jon Kabat-Zinn, *Wherever You Go, There You Are: Mindfulness Meditation in Everyday Life*, New York: Hyperion, 1994, 4.

20 Richard Layard, *Happiness: Lessons from a New Science*. London: Allen Lane, 2005, 42.

21 Zuboff, 468.

22 Michael Lieberman, *Social: Why Our Brains Are Wired to Connect*. New York: Penguin, 2013, 241.

23 Jeff Fromm and Angie Read, *Marketing to Generation Z: The Rules for Reaching This Vast – and Very Different – Generation of Influencers*, New York: AMACOM, 2018, 175.

24 Williams, 127.

25 Ibid.

26 Haig, 76.

Chapter 6

1 Olivia Solon, 'Ex-Facebook president Sean Parker; site made to exploit human "vulnerability"', *Guardian*, 9 November 2017.

2 King, 197.

3 Don Tapscott, *Growing Up Digital: The Rise of the Net Generation*. New York: McGraw-Hill, 1997, 93.

4 Zuboff, 453.

5 Haig, 224.

6 Greenfield, 123.

7 Ibid.

8 Nicholas Kardaras, *Glow Kids: How Screen Addiction Is Hijacking Our Kids – And How to Break the Trance*, New York: St Martin's Press, 2016.

9 Gallagher, 8.

10 Ibid, 84.

11 Greenfield, 24.

12 Aiken, 153.

13 Greenfield, 107.

14 Ibid, 113.

15 Alter, 3.

16 Ibid, 5.

17 Ibid, 6.

18 Matt Richtel, *A Deadly Wandering: A Mystery, a Landmark Investigation, and the Astonishing Science of Attention in the Digital Age*, New York: William Morrow, 2014, 108.

19 Ibid.
20 Ibid, 146.
21 Ibid, 3.
22 Turkle, *Always On*, 174.
23 Zuboff, 466.
24 Matt Richtel, 'Silicon Valley says step away from the device', *New York Times*, 24 July 2012.
25 Freed, 84.
26 Alter, 9.
27 Ibid, 114.
28 Richtel, *A Deadly Wandering*, 194.
29 Ibid, 198.
30 Alter, 78.
31 Ibid, 5.
32 Ibid, 8.
33 Richtel, *A Deadly Wandering*, 105.
34 Ibid, 220.
35 Freed, 162.
36 Frank Scoblete, AZQuotes.com, Wind and Fly Ltd, 2020: https:/www.azquotes.com/quote/842542
37 Wu, 315.
38 Richtel, *A Deadly Wandering*, 215.
39 Alter, 186.
40 Carr, 48.
41 Ibid, 34.
42 Ibid, 35.
43 Ibid.
44 Ibid, 45.
45 Szalavitz and Perry, 230.
46 Seemiller and Grace, 72.
47 Carr, 114.
48 Haig, 161.
49 Turkle, *Reclaiming Conversation*, 219.
50 Turkle, *Alone Together*, 162.
51 Carr, 115.
52 Ibid, 140.
53 Ibid, 117.
54 Turkle, *Alone Together*, 163.
55 Alter, 40.
56 Cal Newport, *Deep Work, Rules For Focused Success in a Distracted World*, US: Grand Central Publishing, 2016.
57 Carr, 141.
58 Lanier, *Ten Arguments*, 5.

59 Williams, 29.

60 Lanier, *Ten Arguments*, 10.

61 Ibid, 23.

62 Carl Miller, *The Death of the Gods: The New Global Power Grab*, London: Penguin Random House, 2018, 306.

63 Ibid, 26.

64 Ibid, 91.

65 Zuboff, 300.

66 Ibid, 301.

67 Ibid, 304.

68 Ibid, 292.

69 Eric A. Posner and E. Glen Weyl, *Radical Markets: Uprooting Capitalism and Democracy For a Just Society*, Princeton University Press, 2018.

70 Ibid, 293.

71 'Kids for sale, online advertising and the manipulation of children', Global Action Plan, 2020., https://www.globalactionplan.org.uk/files/kids_for_sale. pdf.

72 Seemiller and Grace, 149.

73 Ibid, 150.

74 Ibid, 147.

75 Ibid, 146.

76 Wu, 352.

77 Ibid.

78 Dennis Stevenson and Stephen Farmer, 'Thriving at work: the Stevenson/ Farmer review of mental health and employers, 2017', https://assets.publishing. service.gov.uk/government/uploads/system/uploads/attachment_data/ file/658145/thriving-at-work-stevenson-farmer-review.pdf.

79 Seemiller and Grace, 139.

Chapter 7

1 Seemiller and Grace, 263.

2 Ibid, 266.

3 Ibid, 92.

4 Ibid, 87.

5 Ibid, 93.

6 Fromm and Read, xvii.

7 Alter, 19.

8 Fromm and Read, 9.

9 Lux Alptraum, 'Silicon Valley's obsession with efficiency is fundamentally rooted in sexism', Quartz, 10 February 2017, https://qz.com/906115/silicon-valleys-obsession-with-efficiency-is-fundamentally-rooted-in-sexism/.

10 Seemiller and Grace, 92.

11 Ibid, 237.

12 Jane Margolies, 'Speed dating your sofa', *New York Times*, 6 May 2019.

13 Dorsey and Villa, 99.

14 Ibid, 127.

15 'Reality bytes: second annual generational study reveals how Gen Z behaves, buys and builds online', WP Engine, 30 January 2019, https://wpengine. co.uk/blog/reality-bytes-second-annual-generational-study-reveals-how-gen-z-behaves-buys-builds-online/.

16 Fromm and Read, 101.

17 Dorsey and Villa, 152.

18 Ibid, 124.

19 '"True Gen": Generation Z and its implications for companies', McKinsey & Company, 12 November 2018, https://www.mckinsey.com/industries/consumer-packaged-goods/our-insights/true-gen-generation-z-and-its-implications-for-companies.

20 Ibid.

21 Zuboff, 30.

22 Ibid.

23 Ibid.

24 DoSomethingStrategic, 'Cause is working, your marketing isn't – a report on brand taking stands and a guide to getting it right', 2019, https://dosomethingstrategic.org/2019-report-download-page.

25 PwC, Retail Briefing 2020, https://www.pwc.co.uk/industries/retail-consumer/golden-quarter/retail-briefing-highlights.html.

26 Ibid.

27 '2020 resale report', ThredUp, https://www.thredup.com/resale/.

28 Dorsey and Villa, 95.

29 'The influencer report, engaging Gen Z and millennials', Morning Consult, https://morningconsult.com/form/influencer-report-engaging-gen-z-and-millennials-download/, November 2019.

30 'Influencer marketing 2019 industry benchmarks', Mediakix, https://mediakix.com/influencer-marketing-resources/influencer-marketing-industry-statistics-survey-benchmarks/.

31 Fromm and Read, 78.

32 'Millennials on steroids: is your brand ready for Generation Z?', Knowledge@ Wharton, 29 September 2015, https://knowledge.wharton.upenn.edu/article/millennials-on-steroids-is-your-brand-ready-for-generation-z.//.

33 Russell Feldman, 'Unreal life: just 21% of Brits believe internet personalities portray life honestly', YouGov, 31 October 2019, https://yougov.co.uk/topics/technology/articles-reports/2019/10/31/unreal-life-just-21-brits-believe-internet-persona.

34 Leslie Hook, 'Airbnb moves beyond accommodation into tours and immersive trips', *Financial Times*, 17 November 2016.

35 'Millennials, fueling the experience economy', Harris Group for Eventbrite,

https://www.eventbrite.com/blog/academy/millennials-fueling-experience-economy/, 2014.

36   Anne Gherini, 'Millennials ignited the experience economy, here is how to cash in', Inc., 31 October 2018, https://www.inc.com/anne-gherini/cash-in-on-experience-economy.html.

37   'Millennials, fueling the experience economy'.

38   Hillary Hoffower, 'Millennials would rather spend money on experiences than on things. There are 4 reasons why that's a smart money move, according to a financial expert', Business Insider, 31 March 2019, https://www.businessinsider.com/money-advice-spending-tips-experiences-boost-happiness-jean-chatzky-2019-3?r=US&IR=T.

39   Elizabeth Dunn and Michael Norton, *Happy Money, The New Science of Smarter Spending*, London: Oneworld Publications, 2014.

40   'True Gen'.

Chapter 8

1   'The future of dating', eharmony and Imperial College Business School, November 2019, https://www.eharmony.co.uk/dating-advice/wp-content/uploads/2015/11/eHarmony.co_.uk-Imperial-College-Future-of-Dating-Report-20401.pdf.

2   Michael Rosenfeld, Reuben J. Thomas and Sonia Hausen, 'Disintermediating your friends: how online dating in the United States displaces other ways of meeting', PNAS, 3 September 2019, https://www.pnas.org/content/116/36/17753.

3   Turkle, *Reclaiming Conversation*, 181.

4   Ibid.

5   Isabel Thottam, '10 online dating statistics you should know', 2018, www.eharmony.com/online-dating-statistics/.

6   Suzanne Woolley, 'Your credit score could make or break your love life', Bloomberg, 21 August 2017, https:www.bloomberg.com/news/articles/2017-08-21/a-high-credit-score-can-make-you-look-sexy-on-dating-apps.

7   Freitas, 5.

8   Lisa Wade, 'Sex on campus isn't what you think: what 101 student journals taught me', *Guardian*, 23 August 2016.

9   La Trobe University Research Centre in Sex, Health and Society, as summarised by Miranda Prynne, '"Sexting is the New Courtship" parents are told', *Telegraph*, 5 May 2014.

10 Ibid.

11 Catherine Hamilton-Giachritsis et al. (2017), '"Everyone deserves to be happy and safe": a mixed methods study exploring how online and offline child sexual abuse impact young people and how professionals respond to it', NSPCC, https://learning.nspcc.org.uk/media/1123/impact-online-offline-child-sexual-abuse.pdf.

12 Nick Newman, 'Cybercrime tipping point', PA Consulting, 23 April 2015, https://www.criticaleye.com/inspiring/insights-servfile.cfm?id=4359&view=1.

13 Turkle, *Reclaiming Conversation*, 24.

14 Freitas, 37.

15 Turkle, *Reclaiming Conversation*, 56.

16 Freitas, 12.

17 Ibid, 11.

18 Ibid, 16.

19 Turkle, *Alone Together*, 16.

20 Freitas, 13.

21 Seemiller and Grace, 123.

22 Freitas, 2.

23 Freed, 232.

24 Ibid, 123.

25 Ibid, 165.

26 Ibid. 49.

27 Seemiller and Grace, 162.

28 Aiken, 212.

29 White, 58.

30 'The pornification of Generation Z', https://understandingteenagers.com.au/the-pornification-of-generation-z/#:~:text=The%20Pornification%20of%20Generation%20Z%20Are%20today%E2%80%99s%20teenagers,is%20a%20natural%20curiosity%20associated%20with%20growing%20up.

31 Ross O'Hara, 'Exposure to sexual content in popular movies predicts sexual behaviour in adolescence', *Psychological Science*, 17 July 2012.

32 White, 59.

33 Ibid, 58.

34 Ibid, 60.

35 Rod Dreher, 'The porn catastrophe', *American Conservative*, 5 April 2016.

36 'The pornification of Generation Z'.

37 Philip Zimbardo and Nikita Coulombe, *Man (Dis)connected: How Technology Has Sabotaged What It Means to Be Male*, London: Ebury Publishing, 2016.

38 Hannah Rosin, 'Boys on the side', *The Atlantic*, September 2012.

Chapter 9

1 Turkle, *Alone Together*, 152.

2 Beth Sherouse, 'More youth are identifying as "pansexual". Here's what the term means', ThinkProgress, 12 June 2018, https://archive.thinkprogress.org/youth-identifying-pansexual-lgbtq-3b010841159c/.

3 White, 46.

4 Ibid, 47.

5   Ibid, 46.
6   Gaby Hinsliff, 'The pansexual revolution: how sexual fluidity became mainstream', *Guardian*, 14 February 2019.
7   Sherouse.
8   Ibid.
9   Hinsliff.
10   Ben Dowell, 'David Walliams – a schoolboy misfit who was nicknamed Cuthbert', *Radio Times*, 5 August 2013.
11   Seemiller and Grace, 30.
12   Ibid, 114.
13   Ibid, 162.

Chapter 10

1   White, ii.
2   Ibid.
3   'Religious landscape survey', Pew Research, 2014, https://www.pewforum.org/religious-landscape-study/.
4   White, 24.
5   National Centre for Social Research, 'British Social Attitudes Survey, 2009' [data collection], UK Data Service, 2011. SN: 6695, http://doi.org/10.5255/UKDA-SN-6695-1.
6   NSD, 'European Social Survey data', Bergen: Norwegian Social Science Data Services, 2006.
7   Stephen Bullivant, 'Europe's young adults and religion', St Mary's University Twickenham, 2018, https://www.stmarys.ac.uk/research/centres/benedict-xvi/docs/2018-mar-europe-young-people-report-eng.pdf.
8   White, 39.
9   Freed, 4.
10   Angie Thurston and Casper Ter Kuile, 'How we gather', 2015, https://caspertk.files.wordpress.com/2015/04/how-we-gather.pdf.
11   Wu, 222.
12   Ibid, 307.
13   Williams, 87.
14   Freitas, 140.
15   Gretchen Livingston, 'About one-third of U.S. children are living with an unmarried parent', Pew Research Center, 27 April 2018, www.pewresearch.org/fact-tank/2018/04/27/about-one-third-of-u-s-children-are-living-with-an-unmarried-parent/.
16   D'Vera Cohn and Jeffrey S. Passel, 'A record 64 million Americans live in multigenerational households', Pew Research Center, 5 April 2018, www.pewresearch.org/fact-tank2018/04/05/a-record-64-million-americans-live-in-multigenerational-households/.
17   Ibid.

18 Gary J. Gates, 'LGBT parenting in United States', Williams Institute School of Law, February 2013, https://williamsinstitute.law.ucla.edu/publications/lgbt-parenting-us.

19 White, 19.

20 Seemiller and Grace, 104.

21 Ibid, 107.

22 Szalavitz and Perry, 179.

23 Freed, 7.

24 Ibid, 17.

25 Raffi Cavoukian, *Lightweb, Darkweb: Three Reasons to Reform Social Media Be4 It Re-forms Us*, Homeland Press, 2013.

26 Freed,11.

27 Szalavitz and Perry, 221.

28 Freed, 7.

29 Ibid, 19.

30 Ibid, 20.

31 Ibid, 154.

32 Szalavitz and Perry, 195.

33 Ibid, 216.

Chapter 11

1   Cushman and Wakefield, 'Food Halls 3.0: The Evolution Continues', 2019, https://cushwake.cld.bz/Food-Halls-3-0-The-Evolution-Continues/4.

2   Zimbardo and Coulombe, 41.

3   Bradfield, 281.

4   OECD PISA report on students' wellbeing, April 2017, www.oecd.org/…/first-oecd-pisa-report-on-students-well-being…2017.htm.

5   Robin Dunbar, 'Breaking bread: the functions of social eating', *The Journal of Adaptive Human Behaviour and Physiology*, March 2017.

6   Freed, 26.

7   Kim John Payne and Lisa M. Ross, *Simplicity Parenting: Using the Extraordinary Power of Less to Raise Calmer, Happier, and More Secure Kids*, Kindle edition, New York: Ballantine, 2009.

8   Robin Dunbar, 'Social eating connects communities', *University of Oxford News*, 16 March 2017.

9   Ibid.

10 Ibid.

11 'Delivering growth: the impact of third-party platform ordering on restaurants', Deloitte, November 2019, https://www2.deloitte.com/uk/en/pages/financial-advisory/articles/delivering-growth.html.

12 'Restaurants 2017: food for thought', PwC, https://www.pwc.co.uk/services/business-restructuring/insights/restructuring-trends/restaurants-2017-food-for-thought.html.

13 Vision Critical, (2016). 'The everything guide to Generation Z'. www.vision-critical.com/wp/content/uploads/2016/10GenZ_Final.pdf .

14 Ibid, 137.

15 Szalavitz and Perry, 116.

Chapter 12

1   Turkle, *Reclaiming Conversation*, 50.

2   Miller, 191.

3   Williams, 79.

4   Lanier, *Ten Arguments*, 110.

5   Williams, 50.

6   Ibid, 52.

7   Ibid.

8   Ibid, 36.

9   Samantha Bradshaw and Philip Howard, 'The global disinformation order: 2019 global inventory of organised social media manipulation', Oxford University, September 2019, https://comprop.oii.ox.ac.uk/wp-content/uploads/sites/93/2019/09/CyberTroop-Report19.pdf.

10 Peter Pomerantsev, 'Inside the Kremlin's hall of mirrors', *Guardian*, 9 April 2015.

11 McNamee, 245.

12 Ibid, 230.

13 Ibid, 218.

14 Zoe Corbyn, 'Facebook experiment boosts US voter turnout', *Nature*, 12 September 2012.

15 'How social networks can be used to bias votes', *Nature*, 4 September 2019.

16 Craig Silverman, 'This story shows how viral fake election news stories outperformed real news stories on Facebook', BuzzFeed News, 16 November 2016, https://www.buzzfeednews.com/article/craigsilverman/viral-fake-election-news-outperformed-real-news-on-facebook.

17 'People, power and technology: the 2018 digital attitudes report', Doteveryone, http://attitudes.doteveryone.org.uk/files/People%20Power%20and%20Technology%20Doteveryone%20Digital%20Attitudes%20Report%202018.pdf#:~:text=People%2C%20Power%20and%20Technology%3A%20The%202018%20Digital%20Attitudes,like%2C%20and%20builds%20active%20communities%20to%20create%20change.

18 Lanier, *Dawn of the New Everything*, 328.

19 McNamee, 117.

20 Bradfield, 148.

21 Lanier, *Ten Arguments*, 36.

22 Ibid, 55.

23 Emily Steward, 'Facebook has taken down billions of fake accounts, but the problem is still getting worse', Recode, 23 May 2019, https://www.vox.com/recode/2019/5/23/18637596/facebook-fake-accounts-transparency-mark-zuckerberg-report.

24 McNamee, 102.

25 Lanier, *Ten Arguments,* 79.

26 Ibid, 80.

27 McNamee, 255.

28 Seemiller and Grace, 276.

29 Williams, 65.

30 Ibid, 73.

31 Ibid, 76.

32 Ibid, 73.

33 Ibid, 95.

34 Zuboff, 110.

35 Ibid, 508.

36 Sarah Roberts, *Behind the Screen: Content Moderation in the Shadows of Social Media*, New Haven: Yale University Press, 2019, 25.

37 Joan Donovan, 'Navigating the tech stack: when, where and how should we moderate content?', Centre for International Governance Innovation, 28 October 2019, https://www.cigionline.org/articles/navigating-tech-stack-when-where-and-how-should-we-moderate-content.

38 Cathy O'Neil, *Weapons of Math Destruction: How Big Data Increases Inequality and Threatens Democracy*, London: Penguin Random House, 2016, 3.

39 Ibid, 7.

40 Ibid, 199.

41 Carr, 45.

42 https://www.gov.uk/government/news/stellar-new-board-appointed-to-lead-world-first-centre-for-data-ethics-and-innovation.

43 Seemiller and Grace, 220.

44 Zuboff, 470.

45 Williams, 89.

46 Ibid, 36.

47 Danny Fortson, 'The breakaways who brand Big Tech too soft', *Sunday Times*, 30 August 2020.

48 Miller, 221.

49 Ibid, 268.

50 Victor Pickard, 'Public investments for global good', in 'Models for platform governance', Centre for International Governance Innovation, 2019, https://www.cigionline.org/sites/default/files/documents/Platform-gov-WEB_VERSION.pdf.

51 Ibid.

Chapter 13

1   David Grayson, *All In: The Future of Business Leadership*, London: Routledge, 2018.
2   Seemiller and Grace, 217.
3   Ibid, 216.
4   Ibid, 288.
5   See 'Survey: Gen Z counting on brands to deliver a "radically better future"', Sustainable Brands, 2020, https://sustainablebrands.com/read/marketing-and-comms/survey-gen-z-counting-on-brands-to-help-create-a-radically-better-future.
6   'Our Business' from Visa corporate website, www.visa.co.uk/legal/privacy-policy.html.

Chapter 14

1   Turkle, *Reclaiming Conversation*, 49.
2   David Stillman and Jonah Stillman, *Gen Z @ Work: How the Next Generation Is Transforming the Workplace*, New York: HarperCollins, 2017, 88.
3   Ibid, 220.
4   Seemiller and Grace, 84.
5   C. Steele Flippin, *Generation Z in the Workplace*, 2017, n.p.
6   Higher Education Research Institute, 'College senior survey', 2017, https://heri.ucla.edu/college-senior-survey/.
7   Seemiller and Grace, 31.
8   Stilllman and Stillman, 108.
9   Guy Berger, 'Data reveals the most in demand soft skills among candidates', 30 August 2015, https://business.linkedin.com/talent-solutions/blog/trends-and-research/2016/most-indemand-soft-skills.
10 Blair Heitmann, 'The job-hopping generation: young professionals are on the move', LinkedIn Official Blog, 11 October 2018, https://blog.linkedin.com/2018/october/11/the-job-hopping-generation-young-professionals-are-on-the-move.
11 Stillman and Stillman, 70.
12 Dorsey and Villa, 171.
13 Seemiller and Grace, 234.
14 Ibid, 216.
15 Ibid, 219.
16 Dorsey and Villa, 206.
17 Randall Forsyth, 'Millennials prefer perks over salary increases', Barron's, 29 March 2018, https://www.barrons.com/articles/blame-millennials-its-their-fault-wages-arent-rising-more-1522333213.

18   Monster Worldwide, Inc. (2016). 'Move over Millennials: Gen Z is about to hit the workforce', https://www.prnewswire.com/news-releases/move-over-millennials-gen-z-is-about-to-hit-the-workforce-300319567.html.

19   Bailey, A. (2017) 'Generation Z: Understanding your youngest hires', https//Irivet.com/pdf/IRivet_Insight_Gen%20Z_Andrew_B_Templated.pdf

20   White, 41.

21   'Business as unusual: how social intrapreneurs can turn companies into a force for good', Yunus Social Business, 2019, https://www.yunussb.com/business-as-unusual.

22   Stillman and Stillman, 227.

23   'Generation Z and millennials lead the way as more than a third turn to gig economy to supplement primary income', AlixPartners, 3 December 2018, https://www.alixpartners.com/media-center/press-releases/generation-z-and-millennials-lead-the-way/#:~:text=Generation%20Z%20and%20Millennials%20lead%20the%20way%20as,1%2C000%20UK%20consumers%20by%20global%20consulting%20firm%20AlixPartners.

24   'The state of Gen Z 2017: meet the throwback generation', Generational Kinetics, April 2017, https://genhq.com/wp-content/uploads/2017/04/The-State-of-Gen-Z-2017-White-Paper-c-2017-The-Center-for-Generational-Kinetics.pdf.

25   E. Mazareanu, 'Coworking spaces – statistics and facts', Statista, 9 July 2019, https://www.statista.com/topics/2999/coworking-spaces/.

26   'Workforce of the future, the competing forces shaping 2030', PwC, 2018, https://www.pwc.com/gx/en/services/people-organisation/publications/workforce-of-the-future.html.

27   'Future of the workplace 2030+', Unily, July 2019, https://www.unily.com/insights/guides/future-of-the-workplace.

28   Newport, 126.

29   Ibid, 7.

30   Ibid, 14.

31   Carr, 141.

32   Newport, 31.

Chapter 15

1   Josh Glancy, 'This crisis will be the making of one person – Big Brother', *Sunday Times*, 1 November 2020.

2   Williams, 128.

3   John Lanchester, 'How smartphones are taking control of our minds', *Sunday Times Magazine*, 27 September 2020.

4   Wu, 7.

5   Ibid, 352.

6   Bradfield, 36.

7   Ibid, 39.

8   Subcommittee on Antitrust, Commercial and Administrative Law of the Committee of the Judiciary, 'Investigation of competition in digital markets, majority staff report and recommendations', 6 October 2020.

9   'Our history', Visa corporate website, https://www.visa.co.uk/about-visa/our_business/history-of-visa.html#:~:text=Visa%E2%80%99s%20journey%20begins%20in%201958%2C%20the%20year%20that,1974%2C%20and%20introduced%20the%20debit%20card%20in%201975.

10 'Investigation of competition in digital markets'.

11 Miller, 119.

12 McNamee, 136.

13 McNamee, 138.

14 Ibid, 112.

15 Lanier, *Ten Reasons*, 143.

16 White, 53.

17 Neil Postman, *The Disappearance of Childhood*, New York, Delacotte Press, 1982.

18 'Social media, social life', Common Sense Media, 2018, https://www.commonsensemedia.org/research/social-media-social-life-2018.

19 Catherine Steiner-Adair, *The Big Disconnect: Protecting Childhood and Family Relationships in the Digital Age*, London: Harper, 2013.

20 Alter, 320.

21 Livingstone and Blum-Ross.

22 Aiken, 204.

23 Tim Stickings, 'Rape and sex assaults at British universities rocket: tenfold increase in reported attacks with Cambridge students among the most-accused amid "blackout drinking culture"', *Daily Mail*, 18 July 2019.

24 Freed, 88.

25 Williams, xii.

26 Ibid.

27 Ibid.

28 Zuboff, 54.

29 Bill Davidow, 'Exploiting the neuroscience of internet addiction', *The Atlantic*, 18 July 2012.

30 Williams, 122.

31 McNamee, 10.

32 Zuboff, 225.

33 Ibid.

34 Wu, 349.

35 Julie Carrie Wong, 'Will Facebook's new oversight board be a radical shift or a reputational shield?', *Guardian*, 7 May 2020,

36 Carole Cadwalladr, 'Social media is a threat to democracy', TEDBlog, 16 April 2019, https://blog.ted.com/social-media-is-a-threat-to-our-democracy-carole-cadwalladr-speaks-at-ted2019/.

37 Wong.
38 Roberts, 200.
39 Bradfield, 212.
40 Ibid, 214.
41 Williams, xii.
42 McNamee, 2.
43 Zuboff, 10.
44 Ibid.
45 Ibid.
46 Department for Digital, Culture, Media and Sport. 'Online harms white paper – initial consultation response', 12 February 2020, https://www.gov.uk/government/consultations/online-harms-white-paper/public-feedback/online-harms-white-paper-initial-consultation-response.
47 'Taming the Wild West Web: how to regulate social networks and keep children safe from abuse', NSPCC, https://www.nspcc.org.uk/globalassets/documents/news/taming-the-wild-west-web-regulate-social-networks.pdf.
48 McNamee, 221.
49 'Child rights and online gaming: opportunities and challenges for children and the industry', UNICEF, 9 September 2019, https://www.unicef-irc.org/files/upload/documents/UNICEF_CRBDigitalWorldSeriesOnline_Gaming.pdf.
50 'Safer technology, safer users: the UK as a world leader in Safety Tech', HM Government, DCMS, 27 May 2020.
51 Tim Berners-Lee, 'I invented the World Wide Web. Here's how we can fix it', *New York Times*, 24 November 2019.
52 'How much is your data worth? At least $240 per year. Likely much more', Wibson, 19 January 2018, https://medium.com/wibson/how-much-is-your-data-worth-at-least-240-per-year-likely-much-more-984e250c2ffa.
53 Lanier, *Dawn of the New Everything*, 323.
54 Posner and Weyl, 209.
55 Ibid.
56 Ibid.
57 'The Silicon Six and their $100 billion global tax gap', Fair Tax Mark, December 2019, https://fairtaxmark.net/wp-content/uploads/2019/12/Silicon-Six-Report-5-12-19.pdf.
58 Fen Osler Hampson and Eric Jardine, *Look Who's Watching: Surveillance, Treachery and Trust Online*, CIGI Press, 2017.
59 Ibid, 326.

Appendix 2

1 Freed, 96.
2 Ibid, 95.

Appendix 3

1   'Report of the Secretary-General: roadmap for digital cooperation', UN, June 2020, https://www.un.org/en/content/digital-cooperation-roadmap/assets/pdf/ Roadmap_for_Digital_Cooperation_EN.pdf.

2   Taylor Owen, 'Models for platform governance, introduction: why platform governance?', Centre for International Governance Innovation, 28 October 2019, https://www.cigionline.org/articles/introduction-why-platform-governance.

3   Heidi Tworek, 'Models for platform governance: social media councils', Centre for International Governance Innovation, 28 October 2019, https://www. cigionline.org/articles/social-media-councils.

4   Robert Fay, 'Models for platform governance: digital platforms require a global governance framework', Centre for International Governance Innovation, 28 October 2019, https://www.cigionline.org/articles/digital-platforms-require-global-governance-framework.

5   Gene Kimmelman, 'Models for platform governance: syncing antitrust and regulatory policies to boost competition in the digital market', Centre for International Governance Innovation, 28 October 2019, https://www. cigionline.org/articles/syncing-antitrust-and-regulatory-policies-boost-competition-digital-market.

6   Jonathon Penney, 'Models for platform governance: protecting information consumers', Centre for International Governance Innovation, 28 October 2019, https://www.cigionline.org/articles/protecting-information-consumers.

Appendix 4

1   Wu, 219.

Acknowledgements

First a massive thanks to Lulu Chang, my researcher, whose diligent referencing and editorial challenges have been crucial. And to Jemima Hunt for her editorial support and encouragement. And of course to John Bond and George Edgeller at whitefox.

Thanks to all those who endured early drafts or contributed personal observations, including Professor Mary Aiken, Professor Rauridh Battleday, Charles Benet, Rob Bennett-Baggs, Professor Steve Brammer, Andy Burrows, Alberto Busnelli, Marco Calabrese, Giulio Capodimonti, Matteo Colledan, H. Ashton Crosby, Pier Luigi Culazzo, Jack Dyrhauge, Jack Ferrari, Lorne Forsyth, Katie Fulford, Baptiste Gamblin, Professor David Grayson, Oliver Hayes, Eddy Jones, Martha Kendall, Hannah Kirley, Fritz Lensch, James McDowall, Jimmy McLoughlin, Nigel Meek, Henry Nicholls, Professor Dan Nicolau, Christian Nourry, Stephen O'Reilly, Roger Parry, Jack Parsons, William Pearson, Steve Perry, Astrid Persson, Sam Peters, Molly Pickance, Giovanni Raiteri, Ludolf von Schoning, Chris Schumacher, Eduardo Simoes, Marco Staal, Alex Storer, Davide Taliente, Kees T'Hooft, Sam Tidswell-Norrish, Sam Turpin, Dan Uusilato, James Wheeler, Baux Wigley, George Wiltshire, Jeremy Wright MP and Professor Daniel Zizzo.

Thanks to the 200+ Generation Z entrepreneurs I have met in the last two years for their enthusiasm, positivity, inspiration and contributions.

Thanks to my wife and three sons, who lost me during Covid-19 to the dining room, where I bunkered down to write, and for putting up with 'it's all in the book' every time they said something at a family meal table.

About the Author

Robert Wigley backs young entrepreneurs in cutting-edge technology businesses and is the Chairman of UK Finance. He sits on the UK's Economic Crime Strategic Board, co-chaired by the Chancellor of the Exchequer and the Home Secretary. He spent a career in finance rising to be EMEA Chairman of Merrill Lynch and a member of the board of the Bank of England during the 2008 financial crisis. He was Chairman of the Green Investment Bank Commission and wrote the seminal report *Winning in the Decade Ahead* on the future of London as a Global Financial Centre for Boris Johnson when he was Mayor of London.

He is a Fellow of the Institute of Chartered Accountants and Companion of the Chartered Management Institute, an Adjunct Professor at the University of Queensland, a Visiting Fellow of Oxford University's Saïd Business School and an Honorary Fellow of Cambridge University's Judge Business School. He is also an Officer of the Order of St John. *Born Digital* is his first book.

INDEX

addiction: dating apps and 150–1; depression and 119; device 24, 28, 29, 30, 42, 119, 166, 184, 243, 258, 286; e-books and 68–9; gaming 19, 62, 64, 66, 67, 105, 106, 283, 288; internet 13–14, 32, 39, 106, 260; sex/pornography 159–61, 166; social media 42, 48, 52, 60, 87, 92, 96, 103
ADHD 66
adolescence 88, 98–9, 104–5, 107–8, 120, 160, 162, 164, 175, 180, 255–6, 283
advertising, behavioural 115–19, 253
age-appropriate design code 271–3
age verification policies 24, 252–5, 258, 272, 283
AI (artificial intelligence) xv, 80, 118, 195, 204, 205, 206–7, 239, 253, 263, 270, 272, 276, 279, 289, 291–2, 294, 296, 298–9
Aiken, Mary iii, 100, 102, 159, 259, 274
Airbnb 35, 131, 139–40
Alexa (digital assistant) 9, 76–7, 79, 117, 133
algorithms 4, 51, 59, 60, 72, 115, 116, 154, 192, 201, 205–6, 207, 208, 209, 211, 212, 265, 270, 289, 291–2

Alibaba 5, 20, 148
Alter, Adam 13, 32, 42, 47, 52, 62, 63, 75, 103–4, 106, 107, 108, 114, 129, 256
Amazon 5, 22, 23, 72, 76, 129, 130, 207, 247, 248, 249, 295
anonymity, internet 25, 56–7, 103, 200, 252–3, 255, 268, 270
anxiety 3, 10, 14, 29, 32, 42, 51, 66, 79, 86, 87, 89, 91, 120, 122, 158
Apple 24, 76, 136, 247, 248, 286, 295
apps 17, 20, 24, 30, 34, 51, 77, 139, 146–7, 150, 154, 155, 184, 185, 209, 218, 219, 275, 285, 286, 287, 288
attention: arbitrage 48; crisis 3, 32–3, 91, 103, 296; deep 68, 72, 102, 110, 112, 115, 123, 157; democracy and 211; economy 170, 192, 203, 210, 240, 263; fractured 112; happiness and 100; hijacked v, xiii; liberation of 267; management, centralised system of 194; monetising of 49; multi-tasking and *see* multi-tasking; offsets 277; right not to have our attention distracted 277, 290; spans 93, 114, 138; top down and bottom up 107; utilities, regulation of 249

330